COMPLETENESS
IN
SCIENCE

COMPLETENESS
IN
SCIENCE

Richard Schlegel

Professor of Physics
Michigan State University

New York

Appleton-Century-Crofts

Division of Meredith Publishing Company

6126-1

Library of Congress Card Number: 67-11919

PRINTED IN THE UNITED STATES OF AMERICA
E 78265

PREFACE

To what extent can science describe and explain the natural world—including ourselves? Are there intrinsic limits to the methods of science that make an adequate scientific description impossible, or can we expect that science will eventually give us a complete account of the universe?

The limitations, or the scope, of science have been discussed before, usually either in the terms of philosophical studies of method, or in specialized, relatively brief comments by scientists. In writing this book-length study, I have tried to bring together both those considerations that arise from logic and philosophical analysis, and those that come from the content of science itself. Considering the magnitude of the question, I can indeed say that I would have known that I had failed, if I had come to a final answer. Rather, I shall be happily satisfied with any partial further elucidation of the completeness problem that may be found in this book.

What we find Nature to be is itself part of the solution to the problem of how well we can give an account of her in our science. For this reason, any assessment of the completeness of science cannot be independent of the state of our science. And also, for the same reason, a considerable part of this book is taken up with presenting results of science. Specifically, Chapters 6 through 12 are presentations of certain aspects of present-day mathematics and physics (chiefly the latter).

The book is written, then, for those who are interested in the achievements of science in furthering our understanding of the natural universe, and in the possible extent and limitations of those achievements. Broadly speaking, I would expect readers to have some background education in science and an interest in the philosophy of science. In a few sections a fair degree of sophistication with respect to current physical theory is presumed for full understanding, but the reader will not suffer seriously by not being able to follow those sections in detail. Mathematical argument is used rather sparingly, and when it is used I have tried also to give parallel statements that are purely discursive.

My first notebook of material for the book was started in 1958. A large share of the preliminary work, and some of the writing, was done during an academic year, 1961–1962, spent in Cambridge, England. This period of freedom from customary academic duties was made possible by a sabbatical leave from Michigan State University and a research grant from the National Science Foundation. I am grateful to Professor Sir Nevill Mott, Professor John M. Ziman, and Professor E. R. Dobbs for the hospitality they showed me at the Cavendish Laboratory, Cambridge University, and to the Cambridge History and Philosophy of Science Group for the cordial welcome they gave me at their colloquia and informal discussions. Also, at Cambridge, I am deeply indebted to Professor R. B. Braithwaite for his kind sponsorship, and for many hours spent with me in critically discussing my mathematical, logical, and philosophical studies relating to the completeness problem.

In my home university and department, my colleagues have been a source of stimulation and encouragement, and I am deeply appreciative of the generous research time that has been given to me. A grant from the all-University research fund has provided useful clerical assistance. Professors Henry S. Leonard and Gerald J. Massey of the Philosophy Department at Michigan State University have read a first draft of Chapter 5; the detailed comments and corrections which each prepared were of invaluable assistance to me, and I want to express my warm thanks. The manuscript has been read and criticized throughout by my colleague, Professor Donald J. Montgomery. His many helpful suggestions, with respect both to content and to clarity of language, have been generously given. I feel it is good fortune indeed for me to have such a friend and critic.

Over a period of several decades, I have deeply benefited from the philosophic insight and unfailing friendship of the late Lawrence K. Townsend.

It is a pleasure to acknowledge the competent stenographic assistance of Meredith Thompson. A large share of the routine work associated with the manuscript and the task of preparation of the index has been carried out by my wife, Sally McKee Schlegel. But this contribution, substantial as it is, has been small compared with her help and encouragement in many, many discussions.

R. S.

CONTENTS

4

COMPLETENESS AND EXPLANATION

5

THE GÖDEL INCOMPLETENESS THEOREM

6

CONCEPTS OF INFINITY

7

COSMOLOGY

8

DECISIONS IN COSMOLOGY

9

THE NATURAL LIMITS OF DESCRIPTION

10

THE OBSERVER IN QUANTUM PHYSICS

COMPLETENESS
IN
SCIENCE

They had found the boundary to our knowledge; some things would remain unknown forever; one of the results of this new representation of matter was to tell what we could not know as well as what we could. . . . We were in sight of the end.

C. P. Snow, *The Search*

1

The Problem of Completeness in Science

1   INTRODUCTION

SCIENCE in the past few centuries has carried our knowledge of the natural world far beyond that which is gained through the perceptions of ordinary experience. The life processes of man and the other living organisms, the elemental domain of atoms and particles of atoms, and the realm of stars and galaxies, have been opened to mankind. Further, we seem always to learn more about nature, and to gain new demonstrations of its vastness, richness, and complexity. The question naturally arises, can we expect that science, now firmly established, will forever go on disclosing new aspects of nature? Or, is there a possible limit? Those who work as scientists know that the further details to be investigated in any one subject of study seem in-exhaustible, and yet, it is also the case that the attentions of scientists do shift, almost in fads, from one topic to another. Are these changes because completeness has been achieved at least in a given subdomain of nature? And what of the larger problem, of science generally? Will science ever exhaustively describe all nature, giving us a complete science of our universe, and of our own behavior; or can such a possibility even be meaningfully considered? It is with questions such as these that this book is concerned. In a sentence, our problem is, What do we mean by completeness in science, and to what degree is this completeness achieved or achievable?

Many brief statements about completeness in science may be found, and in order to give further content to the completeness problem, we will present a few of these.

Horace Lamb, in his *Dynamics*, first published in 1914, wrote[1]:

"The object of all science, it is held, is to give an account of the way things go on in the world . . . it is to be remembered that we do not aim at anything so hopeless, or indeed so useless, as a complete description of any phenomenon. Some features are naturally more important or more

[1] Horace Lamb, *Dynamics* (New York, Cambridge University Press, 1914), p. 346.

interesting to us than others; by their relative simplicity and evident constancy they have the first claim on our attention. . . ."

Yet, from another writer we learn that in a sense there is at least some
kind of completion in mechanics. Robert B. Lindsay writes[2]:

". . . theoretical mechanics forms a highly successful theory. We shall
see that its principles are comparatively simple in form yet all-embracing
in generality, for from them can be deduced all the observed large-scale
features of the universe."

Likewise, the study of atomic structure by means of emitted radiation
has been described as a subject that is in its main outlines complete. Thus,
from a standard treatise and reference work, Condon and Shortley's *The
Theory of Atomic Spectra*, we have[3]: "In this monograph we have undertaken
a survey of the present status of the problem of interpreting the line spectra
due to atoms. This interpretation seems to us to be in a fairly closed and
highly satisfactory state. All known features of atomic spectra are now at
least semi-quantitatively explained in terms of the quantum-mechanical treatment of the nuclear-atom model." A few pages later the authors present
the reservation that "there may well be lurking somewhere important residual
effects" which will require essential alterations in the theory, but then they
again state, "At present the theory exists in a somewhat closed and complete
form . . ."

Or, even for the wider problem of the atomic structure of matter, we
have the following statement by an active research worker in this field,
J. C. Slater, writing in the Preface to his *Quantum Theory of Matter*.[4]

"It is here [in quantum theory] that we have found how inclusive is
the theoretical tool. It becomes clear that we have the fundamental basis
on which all the structure of matter in its ordinary form is constructed.
Molecules, solids, liquids, gases, electricity, magnetism, light, all such things
follow by straightforward mathematical deduction, so that we have the theory
of chemistry and metallurgy and many other things besides physics . . . un-
fortunately the theory is enormously complicated, though mathematically
beautiful. . . . But whenever the mathematics has been overcome, and an
exact answer has been computed, it has agreed with experiment to a great
accuracy; so well that we have no hesitation about believing the correctness
of the quantum mechanics."

In a review, however, of a later book by Slater, William F. Meggers[5]
finds lack of completeness in quantum theory. With reference to the Pauli

[2] R. B. Lindsay, *Physical Mechanics* (Princeton, New Jersey, Van Nostrand, 1933), p. 2.
[3] E. U. Condon and G. H. Shortley, *The Theory of Atomic Spectra* (New York, Cambridge
University Press, 1957), pp. 1, 9.
[4] John C. Slater, *Quantum Theory of Matter* (New York, McGraw-Hill, 1951), pp. vi–vii.
[5] Review of J. C. Slater's *Quantum Theory of Atomic Structure*, vols. I and II (New
York, McGraw-Hill, 1960), in *Physics Today*, 21, 48 (May 1961).

exclusion principle and its derivation from a postulate of antisymmetry for wave functions, he quotes from Slater's book: "As for the explanation of that postulate, however, we must realize that it does not follow from any principle of quantum mechanics but must be accepted as an additional assumption justified because it leads to results in agreement with experiment" (Vol. I, p. 285). Meggers then writes: "In this respect, the quantum theory of atomic structure after 35 years of development is still inadequate or incomplete."

Views similar to those expressed by Lindsay, Condon and Shortley, and by Slater are given in a succinct statement by G. P. Harnwell and W. E. Stephens[6]: "A description or theory is considered adequate to the extent that it provides a universal, precise, and simple account of observation."

A quite different statement of completeness of any one field of physics is given by Karl K. Darrow[7]:

"Physics therefore is far from being a complete description of the phenomena of even a restricted field of nature. It is rather a collection of observations made because they were practicable and seemed important to various people, at various times for various reasons. Among these, however, there are some which possess one or the other of two qualities of the first importance. . . . Some phenomena can be imitated by imagining abstract models of extreme simplicity; and some are themselves simple in a way which suggests that theirs is in a sense an ultimate simplicity, not to be simulated by models but suited to serve itself for the construction of models."

Although Darrow's statement disclaims any completeness in physics, it hints at a correspondence between science and nature which in yet another view is taken as a necessary element for completeness. In a technical paper, A. Einstein, B. Podolsky, and N. Rosen wrote[8]:

"Whatever the meaning assigned to the term *complete*, the following requirement for a complete theory seems to be a necessary one: *every element of physical reality must have a counterpart in the physical theory*. We shall call this the condition of completeness."

Finally, to exhibit still another aspect—and point of view—with respect to the completeness of science we quote from a letter in *Science*, written by the biologist Florence Moog.[9]

[6] G. P. Harnwell and W. E. Stephens, *Atomic Physics* (New York, McGraw-Hill, 1955), p. 1.
[7] Karl K. Darrow, *Introduction to Contemporary Physics* (Princeton, New Jersey, Van Nostrand, 1926), p. xvi.
[8] A. Einstein, B. Podolsky, and N. Rosen, "Can Quantum Mechanical Description of Physical Reality Be Considered Complete," *Physical Review*, **47**, 777 (1935).
[9] Florence Moog, *Science*, **134**, 797 (1961).

"That science is an essential activity in our modern world cannot be doubted; nor need it be doubted that science is in itself a fascinating, enlightening, and rewarding pursuit. Yet it is a planet that has been circumnavigated. Its limits are known. It is not through science that men will come to live in peace and dignity. . . ."

We see in these quotations a wide spectrum of conflicting opinions: Complete description of any phenomenon is hopeless and useless, but atomic spectra and structure are today virtually united in a closed, explanatory system. Physics is far from being a complete description of even a restricted field of nature, yet molecules, solids, liquids, gases, electricity, magnetism, light are to be explained by straightforward deduction from quantum theory. The content of science is determined by reasons of convenience or simplicity without regard to completeness, but it is found necessary to formulate a working definition of completeness in carrying out a theoretical physics investigation. Where one scientist sees science as inevitably removed from completeness, another describes it as a circumnavigated domain whose limits are known. I do not point out these contradictions in order to discredit the statements quoted; indeed, I believe that each quotation is at least partially defensible in the context in which it was written. Rather, the point to be made is that completeness of science is a many-sided concept that can be used in various and even apparently conflicting ways.

We must therefore distinguish between several different meanings, or applications, of the completeness concept that are relevant to science. We shall then be able to discuss the state of science with respect to each of these meanings. It will not be possible (and this would hardly be expected) to come to a definite answer for the great question of whether or not science can completely describe our universe; but we can perhaps gain some partial indication of where there may be limits and where there may be completion.

2   LOGICAL, PHYSICAL, AND PRAGMATIC ASPECTS

Science is expressed in language, and to a considerable extent science is a deductive system; or, more accurately, science includes various deductive systems within its language. A deductive system, however, clearly has certain limitations as an explanatory system; the nature of these limitations may well give insight into bounds on the explanatory power of science. Furthermore, logicians and mathematicians have devoted much attention to the questions of the structure of deductive systems and, in particular, to the problem of what constitutes a complete axiom set for a deductive system. Also it has been found, notably in the celebrated theorem of Gödel, that there are certain defects in the completeness of all logical systems that have at least a certain specified degree of complexity. Is this finding relevant for natural science? These logical aspects of completeness clearly suggest that one approach to our problem should be through the study of the purely logical aspects of science.

Science, however, is much more than a deductive system. It uses logical and mathematical methods, but its content comes from the natural world, and its ultimate reference is to that world. So, whether or not a science may be complete will have strong dependence on the kind of world the science is describing. If the universe were finite and relatively simple in its structure and number of basic elements it would clearly be a much easier one to describe than if it were infinite and highly complex in structure. The very findings of science about the universe are, then, a major element in the study of the completeness of science. Also, we need not consider the entire universe; we can look to the complexity of a given domain of nature as being a determining factor—in general, *the* determining factor—with respect to the possible completeness of the science of that domain.

I will also speak, then, of what I call the physical aspects of the completeness problem, by which I mean the problems that are to be answered in terms of what is discovered by science about the natural world. One might ask, Since the nature of living organisms must certainly determine the extent of possible completeness of biological science, why not use the term "biological" as well as "physical"? The answer, for this book, lies in part in limitations in the competence of the author; hence the emphasis in our discussions will very much be on the physical sciences. It may also be argued that the basic natural domain is the physical world, in which living things are particular kinds of developed structures; questions of ultimate completeness of science must first, then, be answered for the physical world. This is to argue that in discussing the physical world we are also talking about the biological world. I would not want to imply, however, that what is customarily treated in physics is necessarily adequate for a complete science of biology; there may well be basic properties of nature that become apparent only in the realm of biology.

Besides its logical and physical aspects, the completeness-of-science problem has an aspect that relates to the desires of the people who do science. How much do we wish to know about a given part of nature? Shall we describe every square foot of a given piece of land, or is a characterization of each square mile sufficient? Do we stop when we have learned the co-efficient of thermal conductivity of gold, at a given temperature and pressure, to one part in a hundred, or do we want to work to find it to one part in a thousand? We may refer to the factors in the completeness of science that seem to be chiefly dependent on the interests of scientists as the pragmatic aspect of the completeness problem. This aspect determines a limit on completeness that arises not out of the kind of language we use, or the nature of the world we study in science, but out of how much we *want* to know.

There are, then, three aspects of completeness in science: logical, physical, and pragmatic. As our discussions proceed in this book we shall see illustrative examples in contemporary science of each of the three. Taken together, the analyses in terms of the three aspects will carry us to the conclusions that we can reach about the possibilities for complete knowledge and philosophy through science.

2

A Philosophy of Science

IT IS DESIRABLE that as we discuss completeness in science we have
before us a fairly explicit concept of the structure of science. The statements
of science involve many different kinds of constituents: direct description,
measurements, equations, hypotheses, theories, logical and mathematical deductions, and hypothetical natural entities. We want to know something about
the place of these various elements in science. Also, we can hardly talk about
the extent of completeness of science without having a prior notion of the
relation between science and the natural world it describes. The nature of
this relation is a part of the epistemological question of philosophy, and it
is one that has associations generally with philosophy. I shall do little more,
however, than present a point of view, without attempting an extensive
philosophical argument. Likewise, our discussion of the structure of science—
a topic that has been the subject of long treatises—will be limited to what
I regard as some salient features.

In brief, a treatment of the completeness problem requires that we have a
working philosophy of science, and it is that which I shall try to present in
this chapter.

1 REFERENCE TO OBSERVATION

The doing of science involves many very different kinds of activities. A
mathematically expert theorist, who may not care even to attempt the washing
out of a test tube, and a data-gathering laboratory worker, who perhaps
feels uneasy with common fractions, are both scientists, and both may be
making significant contributions. In spite of wide differences in the materials
that are studied, in the techniques that are used, or in the kind of scientific
description that results, scientists have a common commitment to an empirical philosophy. The ultimate test of any scientific statement must be
whether or not it is in accord with observation of the natural world. This

7

test may not be applied directly, and in some instances it may be years, or even hundreds of years, before the test is applied. Nonetheless, in the long run, no brilliant argumentation, or aesthetic appeal, or high authority can save a scientific assertion or theory which is in established disagreement with laboratory experiment or observation of nature.

It is not to be denied that considerations other than those of agreement with experience may often have an important secondary role in the formation of science. Questions of experimental method are obviously of great relevance in the acceptance of a piece of scientific information. If the canons that have been developed for proper experimentation in a given field are violated, any results obtained will be of little value. For example, a spectroscopic measurement of the absorption of radiation by acetic acid, obtained in the possible presence of water vapor, with perhaps resulting interference, is to be suspected as invalid on grounds of the experimental procedure alone. The simplicity of a result is also a factor in its acceptance as part of science. Elementary mechanics problems, for example, are usually simpler if solved by the method of Newton's laws rather than by the mechanics based on these laws as modified by the theory of relativity. There would be no denial of the greater adequacy of the relativistic laws as a description of nature; but, still, if the "nonrelativistic" description were sufficiently accurate it would generally be the one given, just because of its greater simplicity.

The logical consistency of a scientific argument is, of course, also of crucial importance in determining its acceptance. And, in sciences that have been developed to the point where they have a considerable amount of mathematical structure, some workers may devote their scientific activity entirely to developments in the ramifications and consequences of the mathematical aspects of the science. Here too, though, there is always a final reference to observation. The matter was succinctly put by Albert Einstein. In Einstein's research, particularly in his later work, a regard for questions of mathematics often seemed to be predominant. Yet he could write, late in life: "A logical conceptual system is physics insofar as its concepts and assertions are necessarily brought into relationship with the world of experience." [1]

2   DESCRIPTION AND THEORY

There is a common notion that science consists of statements of facts, gained by observation, and the theories that are constructed from these statements. The factual statements, on this point of view, are secure and firm, untainted by speculation. They, however, must be organized into a coherent pattern, and it is the role of theory to provide such organization. Moreover, a theory must, first of all, agree with the known facts. Predictions that can

---

[1] *Albert Einstein: Philosopher-Scientist*, edited by P. A. Schilpp (Evanston, Illinois, Library of Living Philosophers, Inc., 1949), p. 680.

be made from the theory for phenomena not yet observed are compared with subsequent observations of the phenomena in order to provide further tests of the theory.

A conception of fact and theory as just described is in some ways correct: statements of fact do rest on observation; we do want theory for the sake of organizing and understanding facts; and confirmation (or negation) of a theoretical prediction is persuasive evidence for (or against) a theory. In an important and profound way, however, this conception is seriously misleading, for it presupposes that in science we have theory, on the one hand, and, on the other, facts that are true or false independently of any theory. Actually, an independence does not generally obtain, as I shall now try to show. Science is rarely simple description, with a complete absence of theoretical content; rather it is description and interpretation in terms of a set of concepts.

First, consider the example of an astronomical description of the planets. It is clear from the very name, derived from the Greek word for "wanderer," that early observers viewed a planet in the terms of a theoretical construction (probably an anthropomorphic myth) which required it, as well as the sun and the moon, to have in some way an irregular motion in contrast to the motions of the "fixed" stars. The Ptolemaic cosmology gave each planet an appropriate set of cycles and epicycles, carried out by heavenly spheres, so that when one who accepted the Ptolemaic system observed a planet, he believed he was viewing the motions about the central earth of the great globes of the heavens. Today, with our established model of the solar system, these same observations are of course quite changed in significance: to us they mean the appearance by reflected solar light of a great sphere of material, held to its orbital motion by the gravitational influence of the sun. And, we can expect that with further developments in our knowledge of the origin and development of the solar system, and also of the nature of the individual planets, the observation of a given planet will connote something considerably different from what it does today.

Clearly, then, our knowledge of the planets is not a simple consequence of direct observation of facts. Rather, we observe in the framework of a theoretical model, and fit our facts into that model. Now, it might be said that pure observations still are the root ingredients of our knowledge. The concept of a model could be divorced entirely from the facts, so that we have, for example, a series of statements of the following kind about a certain point of light: at 8 PM, Greenwich mean time, on 2 July 1963, the point was measured to be in the sky at right ascension 5^h 14^m 2^s and declination $+10°$ $27'$ $1.5''$. Even in these statements some theory would be involved, in that a coordinate system for the location of points on the celestial sphere must first be established. Aside from that system, it is true, however, that the mere statement of the appearance of the spot of light does come fairly close to being pure description. But for even the most rudimentary kind of astronomical science we want something more: at the least, say, the interpretation that the spot of light indicates the presence of an object that is outside the earth, and in some certain direction from the earth. To make this statement at once involves us in physical theory. We require conceptions of appropriately empty space in which the earth is located and of the kind of path that light takes in moving through space. For, only to the extent that space is free of interfering material can light come through it from a source; and, the propagation of light must be in a straight line if we are to conclude from apparent position of a point of light anything about the location of the source (or, alternatively, we must know for the light the deviations, if any, from straight-line propagation).

The concept of an empty space surrounding the earth is a fairly sophisticated one, and certainly, for most of us, is a theoretical construct far removed from direct experience. The straight-line propagation of light is something that we learn in everyday life, probably as a result of a synthesis of visual and tactual experiences. The extrapolation to astronomical distances is, however, a rather considerable theoretical assumption, and is in fact subject both to important practical corrections as a result of refraction of light by the earth's atmosphere and to possible spatial corrections resulting from the presence of gravitational fields in the path of the light. Eddington, in his *The Expanding Universe*, gave a convincing discussion of the role of theory in the astromoner's statement of the location of a star:[2]

"When an observer reports that he has discovered a new star in a certain position, he is probably unaware that he is going beyond the simple facts of observation. But he does not intend his announcement to be taken as a description of certain phenomena that have occurred in his observatory; he means that he has located a celestial body in a definite direction in interstellar space. He looks on the location as an observational fact. . . . We must break it to him that his supposed 'fact'. far from being purely observational, is actually an inference based on Einstein's theory—unless, indeed, he has based it on some earlier theory which is even more divorced from observational facts. The observer has given a theoretical interpretation to his measurements by assuming for theoretical reasons that light travels through interstellar space approximately in a straight line. Perhaps he will reply that, in assuming the rectilinear propagation of light, he is not concerned with any theory but is using a fact established by direct experiment. . . . But indeed the observer is utterly mistaken in supposing that the straightness of rays of light assumed in astronomy has been verified by terrestrial experiment. . . . Our warrant for concluding that the celestial body is nearly in the direction in which it is seen, is Einstein's theory, which determines the deviation of light from a straight line. Coupled with other theoretical deductions as to

[2] Sir Arthur Eddington, *The Expanding Universe* (New York, Cambridge University Press, 1933), pp. 18–19.

the density of matter in interstellar space, it allows us to conclude that the deviation in this case is inappreciable. So if we are willing to use both fact and theory as a basis for belief, we can accept the observer's announcement; but it is not a 'hard fact of observation'."

It is by no means only in a science which reaches as far from our immediate surroundings as does astronomy, that we find a pervasive theoretical component in "statements of fact." We might consider the concept of mass as used in elementary physics. The definition of this concept is, indeed, a subtle and complicated one, as teachers of physics well know. Whether it is done in terms of ratios of applied forces and resulting acceleration, in effect making use of Newton's second law, or in terms of numbers of constituent atoms in a sample of matter, the theoretical constructs of Newtonian dynamics or the sophisticated concepts of atomic theory are involved. Even the notion of matter itself as that which is in contrast to nothing or not-matter requires some concepts of physics, or metaphysics, about extension, space, and perhaps existence and reality. The concept of velocity, to take yet another "simple" descriptive term that we apply to the physical world, is highly theoretical in content. We can probably compare speeds of movement of two bodies on the basis of fairly direct observation, but the physical concept of velocity implies the elaborate theoretical apparatus of a time scale with defined units, and also a length scale with its units.

Even the observation and description of simple objects of ordinary experience cannot be said to be lacking in elements of theoretical construction. If I point out, say, that a rock lies on the ground before me I assume an idea of a lump of matter with the collection of properties of hardness, irregularity, and heaviness that we associate with the term "rock." Or similarly, if we speak of a flower we involve a concept of a living (or recently living) part of a plant with petals of characteristic fragility and design. To pick out objects like rocks and flowers as distinct entities, with which we associate a name and a set of defining properties, is to form concepts out of our sense experience. The process seems an obvious one for entities—as, for example, a flower—which in their nature are fairly distinct from their surroundings. Still, it is certainly a process that requires considerable cerebral complexity, and it may be done to only a relatively slight extent by animals other than man.

Many of the entities discovered by science are far removed from the objects of everyday life, in that they have very little content that is directly given in sense experience. The electron, for example, is in no way directly observed, and the properties found for it are themselves theoretical constructs. The neutrino is even farther removed from what is directly observed. The very concept of an atom is, of course, a devised construct. Gravitational and electrical or magnetic fields, photons, momentum, energy, entropy: these and many other entities are supplied by the physicist in order to form a coherent science of the natural world. Einstein has emphasized how much "free invention" plays a role in theory construction; the scientist must create the terms (or entities) which will enter into a theory that does explain nature in an orderly and coherent fashion. Thus, Einstein wrote[3]: "The system of concepts is a creation of man together with the rules of syntax, which constitute the structure of the conceptual systems." Or, in a similar vein, "All concepts, even those which are closest to experience, are from the point of view of logic freely chosen conventions. . . ."

It is not to be thought that in emphasizing the theoretical content of the terms of science we are impugning the validity of science as an account of the natural world. The invention of scientific concepts is *free*, but the acceptance of them into the body of science is inexorably determined by their adequacy in the face of experience. If it has been a part of our concept of a rock that it will always sink in a liquid, we change the concept after we learn that rocks float on mercury. The concept of the electron as a "pointlike" particle, permanently coalesced into a tiny volume, had to be changed after observation of electron diffraction displayed the wavelike properties of the particle.

3   CONSTRUCTS

The presence in science of both that which is supplied by the scientist and that which comes directly in experience is nicely shown in an analysis given by Henry Margenau.[4] He introduces the term "construct" for "rational elements to which datal experience is made to correspond." These are the "invented" constructions that we form in the world of our experience. They are not, Margenau emphasizes, ideas or hypotheses, in contrast to entities of the natural world; rather, constructs are what we find to make up the natural world. The construct, flower, is that grouping of plant tissues which we designate by the word; it is altogether a part of nature, but it is we who have distinguished it as something apart from the grasses among which it grows. Similarly, the electron exists in matter, not among the ideas of physicists; nonetheless, it is a construct that was devised (discovered if one prefers) as the result of observations on the behavior of other aspects (constructs) of nature. We cannot say that our construct of a flower presents every natural property of a flower, because we do not know everything that there is to be known about flowers. But any new information that we gain about a flower becomes part of the construct that is the flower.

We clearly are coming into epistemological questions when we discuss the construct, which is partially determined by the human being, as part of

[3] *Albert Einstein: Philosopher-Scientist*, edited by P. A. Schilpp (Evanston, Illinois, Library of Living Philosophers, Inc., 1949), p. 13.
[4] Henry Margenau, *The Nature of Physical Reality* (New York, McGraw-Hill, 1950), Chaps. 4 and 5. Also, the discussion by John L. McKnight, *Philosophy of Science*, **25**, 209 (1958).

the natural world. These questions will be considered in some detail in Section 7; but at this point we shall state that we consider constructs as being a kind of organization, by use of ideas, of existing things. We can have an idea (or concept or image) of a flower, and that clearly is not the flower of the natural world (the idea of a flower does not need water, for example, for its continued existence!). The construct is meant to be the flower of nature, and yet it may happen not to be so in essential respects. The living flower, for example, is part of a natural environment, and has many interactions with its surroundings. Some of these we know, and can specify as part of the flower: thus, the process of drawing liquid from the earth, up through its stem, is part of our construct, flower. But almost certainly there are relations which a flower has with other plants, or with insects, or with the ground or atmosphere, that botanists have not yet associated with the construct. It would seem, then, that the construct is not properly to be referred to as identical with the flower of nature, even though we cannot specify how it differs.[5] We easily see how the same distinction applies to the electron; here the inadequacies of present-day knowledge of elementary particles are so obvious that we can expect that our construct, the electron, is still very much awry with respect to the basic structure and processes of matter.

Margenau uses diagrams to indicate symbolically the relations of the construct both to the natural world and to other constructs. One of these is shown in Figure 2-1. The vertical line N on the right indicates the natural world that is the source of all of our experience. The constructs, C, are built

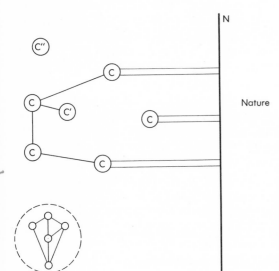

Figure 2-1. Constructs are represented by the encircled C's. Double lines relate constructs to the vertical line, N, which indicates the natural world that is the source of our experience. Formal relations between constructs are indicated by single lines.

[5] I am here implying a philosophical realism that Professor Margenau did not intend, I believe, in his introduction of the term "construct."

in accordance with the sensations (the sense data of our experience) which Nature presents to us. The double line between N and a construct is an "epistemic connection," or a rule of correspondence, which links the construct with sense data.

There are also relations among the constructs, formal relations, which we impose in building a science. These relations include the formal structure of the science: the definitions and deductive relations which enable us to pass from the existence of one situation to the necessary existence (insofar as our science is correct) of another. Also, it is this formal structure which gives us a sense of understanding or explanation in science: a certain phenomenon occurs because we know that a certain "natural law" (an appropriate formal relation) applies.

In the diagram, formal relations between constructs are indicated by single lines. Thus, the fact that a flower requires water might be indicated by a single line between two C's, one for water and one for flower, each of which is directly connected to N by a double line. The need of a flower for water, although first learned as an empirical fact, might also be derived from a network of relations among constructs; these relations would express the physiological processes of plants, of which it is a consequence that a flower needs water. In general, the formal, deductive relations arise in terms of a set of hypotheses, or axioms, about the constructs of a natural domain.

In proper science the constructs are "multiply connected," as Margenau puts it, with relations to other constructs which allow us to confirm (or disprove) a construct in terms of its relations to other constructs. Thus, kinetic energy is ascribed to gas molecules; we then have a relation between the constructs "molecule" and "kinetic energy." But kinetic energy in turn implies velocity, momentum, and mass; the world of experience may be questioned for each of these with respect to gas molecules. A single connection to a construct does not allow any further test of the construct, and is therefore without significance. The property of being "hard to the touch," for example, might be suggested for each individual molecule. This has, however, no implication for human sensation since we do not feel an individual gas molecule—and also no implications either for the theoretical relations of the kinetic theory of gases or for the structure of molecules. It is, therefore, a construct relation of no significance.

Constructs do, of course, have varying degrees of theoretical content. Some, as flower, or spatial extension, are in very direct relation to sense data. Others are defined only in terms of relations to other constructs, which may in themselves also have no direct epistemic relations to the world of experience. The physics concept of nuclear force, for example, is far removed from direct experience. But any construct that is part of science must eventually be related, however indirectly, with the world of experience. An "insular construct," C″ in the diagram, has no relation to experience or other constructs, and hence is without scientific meaning. A completely indiscernible fluid, permeating all space but absolutely without interaction with any physical entity, is an example of such a construct. Again, some constructs (indicated within the broken-line circle in the figure) may be set up with elaborate formal relations among themselves but with no connections to experience. Such a system of constructs also, of course, cannot be part of science. The theory of relativity was (incorrectly) charged by some of its opponents, in its early days, as being this kind of system. Some have attacked psychoanalytic systems, built on such constructs as subconscious, id, ego, and superego, as being systems that are isolated from experience. But such attacks on a scientific construction that has had some confirmation are usually extreme; it may rather be that the formal relations, and the correspondence between constructs and experience, are only partially correct.

4 CONSTRUCTS AND LANGUAGE

Constructs are in the natural world; and yet, even though they are entities of that nature which is around us and of which we are a part, they are not independent of our world of ideas. The construct, then, is a bridge between the natural world of events and things, which occur with no relation to our consciousness, and our human world of awareness and ideas. Sensory experiences are the raw material, we can say, that allow this bridge to be formed.

It is one of the supreme facts of our universe that there can be intermediaries between the realm of existent natural structures and processes on the one hand and the realm of ideas on the other; for it is by these intermediaries that nature (as in human beings) can become aware of itself. Further, the natural world of "that which is" has the inflexibility of necessity about it: "brute fact" can only be the way things are. In contrast, in the realm of ideas there is flexibility and imagination. Hence, when nature's creatures are sufficiently complex in structure to be able to think and imagine, as are we human beings, they can then try various possibilities for order and pattern in nature, discarding all except those ideas that seem to fit the natural world. One might expect that nature could only impress its aspects upon an organism, so that the organism would attain to no more awareness than what we term raw sense impression. The remarkable fact, however, is that we can form patterns in nature, as in constructs, and then, further, set up appropriate relations between the constructs. We can both have the firmness and solidity of that which does exist (for the construct is in nature), and the wide generalization and freedom of ideas, for it is through an idea that the construct has been delimited from all the rest of nature.

We are able, then, to think about the natural world, and to set up relations between ideas that are yet also relations between natural entities. The relations may be rather simply empirical: plants wither in the absence of water, lead melts when heated. Or, the relations may be deductive. We may say that if a given construct is present, it follows inevitably that a certain second one will appear: follows, that is, not because we have had experience of the sequence, but because some wider relation between constructs demands the succession. Thus, if a satellite is given a horizontal velocity of 18,000 miles/hour at a height of 100 miles from the earth's surface, we can say from the laws of mechanics, without benefit of previous satellite experience, that it must enter a stable orbit about the earth.

In discussing deductive relations we shall generally drop the explicit use of the term "construct," and instead use such words as "hypotheses," "axioms," "definitions," "consequences," and "statements." These latter are terms that are applied to various elements of a language, and we shall use them because in discussing deductive relations we are talking about logically required relations within a language. In the terms that we have been using, we could say that deductive relations are relations among ideas. It is preferable, however, to say that deductive relations are linguistic relations (with the assumption of a given set of language rules). In any case, since ideas are usually expressed in words, there is a general kind of concomitance between relations among words and relations among ideas.

In any consideration of deductive relations we are not working directly with the entities of nature, but with symbols that refer to these entities. Here again we see the fundamental, suffusive power of the construct; like the soap molecule that brings about the mixing of oil and water because one part of it dissolves in water while the other part is soluble in oil, the construct has a place in the natural world, and *yet also has been so formed that ideas and words can be a direct representation of it.* Words, or the ideas that come with words, are not comparable with the natural world of things; the construct, however, is an arrangement of the world of things to which words and ideas do fit. But further, the construct is not an arbitrary arrangement by man of the experiences that our senses bring to us; rather, it is so formed that it is a part of the natural world, in the only place we can consider it, the realm of ideas and language. I have given a crude pictorial representation of this role of the construct in Figure 2·2.

Without the construct, we would only have words that were of no significance for what nature is and sensations that had no reference or connotation beyond their immediate occurrence; for, ideas and words are not formed in the realm of immediate sensation, but in a realm of concepts. The construct must carry the concept into the world of nature, or, conversely, fit nature into a world of concepts. If the construct is a properly formed one (as it is in good science) it does have its being in the natural world and yet also, because of the way it was formed, it has a connection directly with the conceptual world of ideas and words. The deductive relations among these words must then be relations too among the entities of nature, if, again, the constructs are properly formed. If they are not, our deductive system is

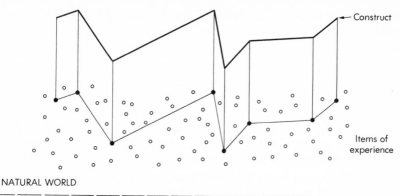

Construct

Items of
experience

NATURAL WORLD

WORLD OF IDEAS AND LANGUAGE

Figure 2-2.   The construct is formed from experience, and is in the natural world. It is in accord with a concept or idea which is in the world of ideas and language. Hence, relations in that realm can give us information about the natural world. The relation between constructs and the data of experience would not always be as direct as here indicated; constructs might be defined only in terms of other constructs (as discussed in Section 3 of this chapter).

not good science, as will generally be made plain by the failure of confirmatory tests (tests in which one looks for the constructs presumed to be associated with consequences deduced in the linguistic realm). The genius of science finds employment in discerning constructs which do lead to the setting up of fruitful deductive relationships.

5   DEDUCTIVE SYSTEMS

It is an ideal of science to derive descriptions of specific natural phenomena from general scientific principles. Such a deductive form has been established in some of the domains of science. The science of mechanics, in which the motions of masses of matter under the influences of forces are calculated, provides an example. This science, when all quantum-theory effects are disregarded (the so-called "classical mechanics"), can be put into the form of a few basic equations and definitions.[6] Then, with the addition of

---

[6] An explicit axiomatization of nonrelativistic classical mechanics of mass particles is proposed by J. C. C. McKinsey, A. C. Sugar, and Patrick Suppes, *Journal of Rational Mechanics and Analysis*, **2**, 253 (1953).

the procedures of mathematics, we have a science which in principle is adequate for determining the motions and locations, as a function of time, of any mass or system of masses in the presence of known force fields, provided that there is adequate information about initial conditions. In general the mathematical difficulties become great indeed, for situations of any high degree of complexity, and also, the neglected quantum effects come to be of essential importance when individual masses on the atomic level, or smaller, are involved. Still, mechanics is a deductive science of immense power and utility in the description and understanding of the physical world, and it stands at the heart of much of physics. The science of electricity and magnetism has similarly been given an essentially deductive form in the electromagnetic equations of Maxwell; from them, and some basic definitions, one may obtain descriptions of all electrical and magnetic phenomena, provided that one does not approach too closely to the atomic level. Thermodynamics, geometric optics, kinetic theory, statistical mechanics, quantum theory: all of these branches of physics are also in an essentially deductive or quasi-deductive form, such that results for specific physical situations follow from a few basic principles or postulates. Other instances in which there is at least partial achievement of a deductive structure could be cited, in the biological as well as the physical sciences.

When a science is in a deductive form the domain of nature to which the science applies is described by a set of general principles, or, as they are commonly called, natural laws. Deductions from these principles, under specific conditions, are descriptive of the situations to which those conditions apply. If the principles can be put in a mathematical form, deductions can be made with the use of all the power and ingenuity of mathematical reasoning. Hence, the deductive science gives both a sense of understanding, because the domain of the science is encompassed by a few basic principles, and a power of prediction and explanation for specific events in the domain. In a significant sense, the ideal of science is a single set of principles, or perhaps a set of mathematical equations, from which all the vast process and structure of nature could be deduced. In a later chapter I shall make some comments on the possibility of science's reaching this goal.

The rules by which consequences are obtained from postulates in a deductive science are, of course, the rules of logic, or, the rules of the appropriate mathematics. We may take both logic and mathematics to be a set of language rules, even aside from considerations of whether or not there may be explicit reduction of all mathematics to logic. It might seem that we are bringing in a realm that is extra-natural in utilizing the laws of logic and mathematics. Detailed discussion of this supposition will also be given later (Chapter 5). I shall only state here that our general argument will be to the effect that natural law and logic-mathematics are not two completely separate and different kinds of discourse; in science we use that mathematics whose assumptions are in agreement with experience, and logic too, in a very broad and general way, reflects the way we find the natural world to be.

We have already referred to the opportunity for genius in science in finding those constructs that will permit the statement of natural laws that span a wide range of natural phenomena. It is to be emphasized that simple generalization does not lead to natural law. Many people before Newton had observed the motions of bodies under the influence of forces, and had, like Aristotle, come to the conclusion (which is precisely what observation of terrestrial bodies confirms) that a body continues in motion only when a force is applied. The development which reached a culmination in Newton's laws of motion required the perceiving, by Newton and "the giants" on whose shoulders he stood, of such entities (constructs) as empty space, velocity, acceleration, force, and mass. These could be put together, as Newton did, into a natural law that was universally applicable in situations involving matter and motion, but this was not done by simple generalization from such situations.

There properly is in a deductive science a certain vagueness, or freedom, in the basic postulates. The terms of the postulates are not completely and explicitly defined in terms of sense-data; for, if they were, the postulates would be no more than direct generalizations of direct experience, and they would not have the latent content that is made apparent when unexpected consequences are deduced from the postulates. If the laws of motion were a simple generalization of observations about the motion of a body when specified physical forces are applied, we would not need to bring in the relatively subtle dynamical concepts of mass, force, and acceleration. But also, such a simple generalization would give us no power to predict the appearance of such phenomena as Coriolis forces, or conservation of momentum for a system of inelastically colliding bodies. We see another striking example in the deductions that were made from Maxwell's electromagnetic equations. The electric and magnetic field quantities which he used were vague, in that there was no complete physical (empirical) definition of their properties. (And the physical attributes of these quantities are hardly any less puzzling today, some 100 years after Maxwell introduced them.) Yet, the equations gave the very important deduced consequence that there are electromagnetic-field waves, including, among others, the waves that constitute visible light.

If a deductive system, then, is to be rich in consequences—as it must be if it is to explain a large and complex range of natural phenomena—it must have postulates whose properties only become apparent as their consequences are obtained. The definition of the postulates is, then, essentially implicit rather than explicit. This aspect of the deductive systems of science has been very well presented by R. B. Braithwaite, in his book, *Scientific Explanation*,[7] where he gives detailed paradigms of deductive systems that can and cannot

[7] *Scientific Explanation* (New York, Cambridge University Press, 1953), Chapter III.

be adapted to novel situations. Braithwaite writes[8]: ". . . theoretical terms can only be defined by means of observable properties on condition that the theory cannot be adapted properly to new situations. . . . It is only in theories which are not intended to have any function except systematizing empirical generalizations already known that the theoretical terms can harmlessly be explicitly defined. A theory which it is hoped may be expanded in the future to explain more generalizations than it was originally designed to explain must allow more freedom to its theoretical terms than would be given them were they to be logical constructions out of observable entities. A scientific theory which, like all good theories, is capable of growth must be more than an alternative way of describing the generalizations upon which it is based, which is all it would be if its theoretical terms were limited by being explicitly defined."

Two general ways of proceeding in a discourse may be distinguished. In one way, which may be styled the Aristotelian,[9] discussion begins with a careful definition of the major terms that are to be used. Then one develops the topic by application of these defined terms. In the other way, which we may call Platonic, terms are at the first given only some identifying definition. The development of the discourse (as in Plato's dialogues) both brings out new properties and gives new clarity for the terms. It might be said that the goal of the Platonic discourse is to obtain definition of the terms; in contrast, in the Aristotelian method one begins wih definitions. Each method is obviously used in science.

In carrying out the consequences of a deductive scientific system we seem largely to be proceeding in the Platonic manner. We do not at all (contrary to what has sometimes been written by philosophers of science) begin with a series of "protocol sentences" which define our basic entities, and then manipulate these entities in a description of the natural world. Rather, in the theoretical work of science we are concerned with various terms and postulates and the implications that come with them. Development of the theory, as in Socrates' questionings in a dialogue, brings out these implications. We hope that when the job is finished we may thereby come to a fairly complete definition of the entities we study. The deductive system, if chosen with insight, can lead us to great new truths, not otherwise apparent, about the natural world.

Some of the information that has been gained about the electron provides an example of the "Platonic method" in science. The pioneer work was concerned chiefly with experiments that showed the existence of the electron as a negatively charged body, and also led to determinations of the value (constant) of its charge, and the value (not constant with velocity change) of its mass. Further properties which must be ascribed to it came, however,

---

[8] *Ibid.*, p. 76.
[9] I am indebted to Professor Richard P. McKeon of the University of Chicago for this suggestion of the two methods.

with the growth of physical theory involving the electron. Its behavior in atomic orbits, and its emission or absorption of radiation in "jumping" from one orbit to the next, became known with the early Bohr theory of the atom. Further development of the quantum theory brought out the remarkable wave properties that the electron (as well as other matter particles) must have. Then the Dirac relativistic quantum theory of the electron confirmed that it must also possess an intrinsic angular momentum (or "spin": this property had earlier been perceived for the electron, on somewhat more empirical grounds, by S. A. Goudsmit and G. E. Uhlenbeck). Further theoretical interpretation of the Dirac theory led to the suggestion of the positive-charge image of the electron, the positron, and to the prediction of creation and annihilation phenomena of electrons and positrons. Confirmatory physical evidence has been interwoven with this development, but it is indeed proper to say that theoretical development has brought forth striking new knowledge about the electron. There are still many puzzles which can give rise to new theoretical (and experimental) developments that will still further define the properties of the electron.

6   DESCRIPTIVE SCIENCE

Science which is not deductive in form is generally referred to as descriptive, or perhaps as "purely descriptive." In descriptive science statements may be made about a particular *kind* of entity or phenomenon: the specific gravity of pentane under specified conditions, the chemical reaction between oxygen and uranium, the life-cycle of the oyster. Or, the description may consist of statements about a single entity or event: the astronomical radio source in Cygnus, a newly found mountain in Antarctica, or a particular case of human illness. The description is usually fairly directly made from sense-data; if it is otherwise, that is, if it is a deduction from more general statements, we think of it as a deduced consequence rather than a directly descriptive statement. The same statement often can be obtained, if it is part of a deductive science, both by description and deduction: we may, for example, find the volume of a gram of helium under standard conditions of temperature and pressure by direct measurement, or we may deduce the volume from the kinetic theory of gases.

There are so many factors that enter into the making of science—observation, deduction, imagination, curiosity, as well as patience and honesty—that one hesitates to single out any one as the basic element of science. Still, description would seem to be as good a choice as any; for, it certainly must be the beginning of our knowledge of the natural world. Description provides the material with which the setting up of general principles of a deductive system can begin, and also, as we have seen, the deductive system points to new properties for which confirmatory description may be achieved. Attaining descriptive information of new domains of nature is quite as much a source of dramatic growth of science as is the development of a successful new theoretical scheme (and is, in fact, generally prior to the scheme). The opening up of a new realm to description has, historically, often been associated with the development of new scientific apparatus: the telescope, the microscope, the cloud chamber, and the particle accelerator are ready examples. Also, we should not forget the part played by intrepid human exploration: one thinks of the "voyages of discovery," and of the first steps that men are taking today into extraterrestrial space.

In making descriptive statements in science one is, of course, using constructs, just as when the latter are woven together into a deductive system. In a science that is close to sense experience the constructs may for the most part be quite directly related to experience. In the physical geography of a given region of the earth, for example, we might think of descriptions that are in terms of very specific visual features: hills, rocks, ponds, forests, etc. But a geography of any wide scope would soon introduce constructs, as mountain ranges or oceans, which go beyond completely direct denotation in experience. And generally, a descriptive science would seem to involve, at a fairly early stage, constructs that are considerably more than the particular bit of nature corresponding to a given set of sense-data. For, we recall that any construct defined in terms of other constructs is not of the "directly related to experience" kind. Thus, the definition in botany of a pistil, "the ovule-bearing organ of a seed plant, usually consisting of ovary, style, and stigma," [10] while referring to a natural entity that is fairly obvious in our every-day experience, is not given directly in terms of sense-data.

The simple accumulation of descriptive statements about an aspect of nature, in an unselected language, can soon lead to an overwhelming mass of facts that "have no meaning." We want facts to be organized in a manner that shows patterns of some kind—if nothing else, an alphabetical ordering that will allow easy reference. The arranging of facts into an orderly pattern is part of scientific description, and here there is opportunity for the creative insight that suggests patterns that are highly useful, and that may even be a reflection of important elements of patterning in nature. The setting up of lines of longitude and latitude is an example of a very useful scheme that permits the organizing of geographical facts into a model of the natural world that is being described. The classificatory schemes of biological taxonomy are likewise of immense and obvious value in biology; and they of course show the groupings of living organisms into kingdom, family, order, species, etc., even though these groups are not as discontinuous from each other, or as inflexible in characteristics, as was maintained by the pre-evolutionary doctrine of immutability of the species. Perhaps the best example of insight into nature that can come with the creation of the proper classificatory scheme is that provided by the periodic table of the chemical elements. Here

[10] *Encyclopedia Britannica*, vol. 17, 1961.

we see a relatively simple arrangement of the elements into "periods" and "columns" which gives an ordering basis for an extremely wide variety of chemical facts (for example, "metallic properties become more pronounced as we go to heavier elements among the nonmetals"). Further, the arrangement of the table helped point to a more basic understanding of chemical properties in terms of the details of the electronic structure of atoms.

Classificatory schemes like the periodic table are not primarily in the form of deductive systems and yet they give great explanatory power to science. They do this because in a sense they are what might be termed "hidden deductive systems." A rubric for classification is a way of stating that all entities that belong under this rubric have certain characteristic properties, and this is a statement of natural law for those entities. Thus, if all elements of the first column of the periodic table are strong reducing agents, we "explain" the energetic reaction between sodium and oxygen by reference to the position of sodium in the periodic table.

But descriptive statements may have explanatory significance even though they are for a single entity or event, if we have a deductive scheme in which to fit the event. Thus, a description of the high winds that blew on a day when I was absent from home may explain the broken tree limb that I find on my return. Or, on a more sophisticated level of meteorology, the observation of change in a high-altitude jet stream may explain a change in pattern of close-to-surface hurricanes. Even without knowledge of natural law that permits the placing of a fact into a causal relationship with the phenomenon to be explained, descriptive facts may have explanatory significance. The occurrence of distinctive bacteria in association with a disease gave an "explanation" for the disease, even without any approximate knowledge of the mechanism by which the bacteria might have their effects. Or, Benjamin Franklin's demonstration of the electrical nature of lightning gave what was accepted as a natural explanation, notwithstanding the absence of information about how charges would be formed in the atmosphere and accumulated at a high electrical potential. Indeed, we might say that careful description, even aside from knowledge of wider natural law, does to some extent constitute an explanation of a phenomenon. To answer the question, "What happened?" is in general not completely different from answering "Why did it happen?"; for, we answer the "why" in science by stating a general principle, a law of nature, and this is a statement of "what happens," but for all occurrences of a natural process rather than a single instance.

7   SCIENCE AND THE NATURAL WORLD

Since science is knowledge of the natural world, it is possible to raise all the traditional epistemological and metaphysical questions of philosophy with respect to the "reality-status" of the world that science tells us about.

Scientists generally have not found it necessary or attractive to devote much thought to these questions; but a few, and including some of the most creative, have given considerable attention to them and have argued for a definite point of view. And in modern physics, particularly with the development of quantum theory, questions have arisen which rather directly require an epistemological position on the part of the physicist who would answer them. We shall consider some of these more specific questions in later chapters, in our discussions of quantum theory and limits or completeness of space–time description; in this section we shall present our general ideas about the relation between science and the existent world.

The world that science describes is the world of experience. The extreme question which some philosophers have raised (although it is hardly a question that even "reflective common sense" would ask) is, "Does the world that experience gives to us actually exist?" This question, I would reply, is not one that is suitable for rational analysis, any more than is, say, the question, "Does the sensation of the color red exist?" In the peace of study, with one's body in health and no unusual sense-data impinging on the consciousness, one may entertain the possibility that the experienced world does not exist, but the merest brush with the world, through our senses, annihilates any doubt that thought may be able to engender. The effect of any kind of external stimulus—the rubbing of a towel on one's skin, the force of another person's voice, the urgency of some practical situation—gives us direct and immediate intuition of the existing natural world of which we are a part.

And yet, even though the work of scientists is directed towards the natural world, a curious trend of argument has led some of them close to a position of skepticism about the existence of that world, a position not unlike that reached by some philosophers through an emphasis on ideas, with relative dismissal of experience. Wishing to be resolutely empirical, the scientist may state that he will make *no* presuppositions about the world beyond that which comes to him as sense-data. He then finds, however, that the inferences he makes from experience do not have the property, ascribed only to the content of sense-data, of being assuredly a part of the empirically experienced world. This is the point of view that is generally described by the term *positivism*. The virtues of this position are not negligible: the very emphasis on empiricism gives its supporters a stout defense against many varieties of metaphysical nonsense. But, to gain knowledge one must have freedom to look for firm paths amidst the quagmire and underbrush; in contrast, positivism gives a stay-at-home safety which is unfavorable to the advance of science.

The leading exponent of positivism among scientists[11] has been the

---

[11] The term has its origin in the philosophy of Auguste Comte. Comte, however, stressed the "positive" aspects of scientific as opposed to religious–philosophical knowledge, rather than an epistemological restriction to sense-data.

Austrian physicist, Ernst Mach. In his hands, positivism was a useful tool in the discussion of metaphysical concepts in science, as, for example, the concepts of absolute space and time. And yet, positivism also led Mach sadly astray in his denial of any reality to atoms, which to him could only be concepts for the organizing of experience. Einstein wittily expressed the good and bad of positivism when it was charged against him that in his general relativity theory he violated the very positivistic canons that influenced his development of the special relativity theory. "A good story," Einstein said, "should not be repeated too often."

The criteria that positivism gives for natural reality are, indeed, highly fallible, and, even though there are times when concepts that have been adopted in science should be destructively criticized, the positivist's criticism is clearly too far-reaching. It can be argued that if positivism is consistently carried out, it leads to the extreme conclusion that the only assured constituents of reality are the sense-data which we have at a given instant: the patch of brown that I call a chair, the ringing that is the noise of the telephone bell, etc. Any extension of these sensations, beyond the "here–now," requires inference and memory, and hence is other than immediate sensation. We see, then, that the positivistic criteria for reality, adopted in good faith as a guaranty for keeping false elements out of science, do in fact lead to a view of what constitutes reality that is altogether inadmissible to a scientist (or, for that matter, to any other kind of person).

The analysis of the epistemological aspects of science in terms of constructs is, I believe, a way of maintaining both the immediate intuition that we have of the natural world and the place of inferred entities within that world. The constructs of ordinary experience—the people, chairs, flowers, rocks, and the rest—are immediately perceived as being part of natural reality, because there is direct association of these constructs with sense-data (which *are* the carriers to us of information about the world). Other constructs become increasingly abstract, that is, increasingly far removed from direct experience. About these, the question can be often raised, as a legitimate scientific question, Are they valid natural entities, or merely imaginative concepts? But no generalizations about all constructs being merely imaginative or conceptual are therefore justified.

Nonetheless, many scientists have expressed the view (and this would in general be the positivists' position) that science is a way of organizing experience, but is without commitment to the existence of the entities which it finds necessary for this organization. Thus, we find as representative of this view the following quotation from a college textbook in physics: "pointer readings, taken in bulk, are the 'irrefutable facts of Nature.' Quantities for which operational definitions cannot be given, i.e., quantities that are not reducible to sets of pointer readings, are called 'unobservables'; they do not belong to the field of science." [12] Positivism, endorsed as the appropriate

[12] David Halliday, *Introductory Nuclear Physics* (New York, Wiley, 1950), p. 4.

philosophy for physics, is characterized thus: "A logical positivist . . . sees no operational way to decide whether a given theory or hypothesis represents 'absolute truth' or not. As a result he discards all concepts like 'truth' or reality in his thinking. His goal is to give as economical a description as possible of the sense perceptions that come (or that can be made to come) within his experience."

Now, as has been indicated, the positivistic approach in the end logically entails an almost complete loss of the natural reality that scientists seek to describe. The grains of truth in support of the positivistic point of view are that the constructs of science are sometimes erroneously inferred from nature, and also, that some organizing concepts are used in science that are scarcely even intended to have the same existence as do the constructs of the natural world which can be directly related to sense impression. *But the determination of whether or not a proposed construct is truly a part of the natural world is a problem for scientific work—frequently of the most challenging and skillful kind—and not a matter to be decided by philosophical generalizations.*

Some illustrative examples may be helpful. In the spirit of positivism, we might say that an electron is merely the name that we give to whatever is responsible for the ions in a cloud chamber on which a certain kind of vapor trail is formed. In justification for such a statement we may say that we thereby avoid the error of picturing the electron in terms of sense-attributes that are associated with large-scale objects which we literally can see and feel. This is commendable caution, and yet it neglects the wide array of experimental evidence that points to the electron as a natural entity, with the same kind of existence in nature that we find for larger bits of matter. Thus, we find that we have firm evidence for properties of mass, electric charge, linear momentum, and intrinsic angular momentum for the electron. We know that it moves, carrying its charge and mass with it, and that its momentum does not change unless forces act upon it. It is true that the electron has some properties that we do not find for large-scale aggregations of matter: notably, its dual wave–particle behavior, and its creation or annihilation along with a positron. But these properties, in view of the evidence for the existence of the electron as an element of the natural world, must be taken as new knowledge about the world: knowledge not obtained from the study of ordinary macroscopic pieces of matter.

In the case of the elementary particle, the neutrino, physicists actually doubted its existence for many years. The particle had been suggested by W. Pauli and E. Fermi because the electron decay processes of radioactive nuclei violated the laws of conservation of energy and conservation of angular momentum unless some unknown particle carried off energy and angular momentum in the decay process. The suggestion of a new particle not discernible by the usual methods of particle detection, just for the sake of satisfying two conservation laws, was not a completely convincing one, even though few physicists would have felt that the conservation laws could be violated. A state of more-or-less suspended judgment prevailed until about 1950, when definite evidence of recoil motion from emitted neutrinos was obtained. Since then, further confirmatory evidence has been found: reactions resulting from the large flux of neutrinos emerging from a nuclear reactor have been observed, in accordance with theoretical predictions of neutrino properties. The question of the literal, natural existence of the neutrino (introduced into physics, as a positivist might say, as an organizing factor) was decided by appeal to experience; the neutrino was suggested as a particle that does exist, and laboratory experiment, by showing whether or not it did have particle properties in addition to those originally postulated for it, did eventually demonstrate its existence.

It is true that some of the constructs used in science are not definite, definable entities of the natural world; but to say whether or not this is so, for a given construct, is also far more a matter for scientific judgment than for general philosophical pronouncement. The defined term *energy*, for example, is widely used in natural science. And yet, there is no assertion that energy is a specific kind of object or substance. Actually, it is a property of physical situations, and as such can be a property of many different kinds of situations. Thus we speak of kinetic energy for the motion of masses, potential energy for work that has been done in bringing about arrangements in electrical or gravitational fields, chemical energy, mass energy for radiation, mass energy for the kinetic energy that can come with disappearance of rest-mass, energy of compression, energy of wave motion, and so on. In all these various situations there is a possibility of quantitative conversion of one kind of energy into another, and hence the basis for the common term. But, there is no reason, experimental or theoretical, for identifying anything as energy, apart from the physical situation in terms of which the energy is defined. Using our construct analysis, we can say that energy is defined only as a property of other constructs, which may themselves, for the particular energy defined, exist independently. Energy is nonetheless a part of the natural world: it would be foolish to say "energy does not exist." But when we are speaking of energy we are speaking of a construct that does not have the properties of existing in itself in the same way as does an electron or a photon; rather, we have kinetic energy only when we have mass in motion, potential energy when we have attracting charges separated from each other, and so on.

The thermodynamic concept of entropy is even more abstract than energy: that is, it is even more a creation of manipulations among constructs rather than of identification between constructs and any conceivable sense-data. When we define the entropy of a thermodynamic system as the integral

$$\int_{T_i}^{T_f} \frac{dQ}{T},$$

where dQ is a heat increment and T is the temperature at which the heat was transferred, along some "reversible path" between T_i and T_f, we are not at all defining an entity having properties that will allow us any direct or indirect way to get a sense impression from it (as we can, say, from an electron by means of cloud chambers or photographic plates). Again, though, entropy is a part of the natural world, but only a derivative part, so to speak, and it does not have the properties that enable it to be identified independently of other entities.

There is a tendency to speak of a defined property like entropy or energy as a "concept," while entities like rocks or flowers, or even molecules or electrons, which have more direct relations to sense-data, are easily referred to as "things." We have in these differences of terminology a reflection of the extent to which the form of the construct is a result of contributions from the scientist. A flower is such an obvious unit, in contrast to its natural environment, and gives such a direct sense impression to us, that we feel there is little that we have done in setting it off from the rest of nature as a distinctive element. Hence, we readily think of it as a "thing" in nature. Entropy, in contrast, is only defined in terms of a fairly sophisticated scientific terminology, and there is no sense of a compelling natural structure that corresponds to it. Indeed, very likely there is an alternative scheme for thermodynamics, as effective as our present one, in which one would not even need to define entropy. Hence, we think of entropy as being rather more chosen by us than presented by nature; that is, we think of it as a "concept." Still, it is a construct, defined in terms of other constructs to which there is eventual relation to experience, and therefore it seems proper to say that entropy, *as defined*, is an element of the natural world. The definition, we have seen, does not give it the same properties that, say, an elementary particle has; but when we say that the gas in a container under given conditions has a specified entropy, we are assigning it a natural property (not a concept), in virtue of which it will behave in a certain predictable manner.

There are instances in physics where the properties of a construct may be very much in doubt. A prime current example is the ψ-function of quantum theory. Here, we do not know the extent to which wave properties, as usually conceived in physics, are properly a part of the construct; or, conversely, the extent to which this construct, the ψ-function, is no more than a mathematical statement of probabilities at various space–time points, with virtually none of the properties normally given to the constructs of the natural world. Here again, though, we can make the point that determination of the reality-status of the construct is a problem for scientific investigation; for, in a valid science the properties of nature are the properties of the constructs of science.

By considering, then, both our direct perception through sense-data of the natural world and our added elements of selection and inference, we are able to present what is, I believe, an adequate account of the relation between science and the natural world. We avoid the positivists' narrowing of existence to what is immediately sensed, and yet we retain the safeguards of the empirical approach of science against inferences that cannot be ultimately confirmed in the data of experience. A last question remains. The constructs of science, we have seen, make up the natural world that science describes. Does this mean that nature is just the world about which science tells us? The answer is, I think, quite obviously "No," but let us first consider the implications of an affirmative answer. We might argue that science at any one time has done the best it can with the experience man has had, and if there is a consistent theory for that experience, then the constructs and properties required by that theory are the natural world. If the world were any different we should have to have had different experiences; or, to put the argument another way, we must accept nature to be as our science has found it, since we by definition have no knowledge of any other nature.

The position that finds the nature given by science to be co-extensive with the natural world has had some support in the philosophy-of-science literature. We can see that if we accepted this position our completeness-of-science problem would readily be solved: if nature is just that which science tells us about, science is by definition complete at any time—for there is no further world to be described. This conclusion, however, cannot seem right to a scientist. And, we further readily discredit the position by considering the changes that occur in science as it develops. If the world that science has discerned and the natural world were one and the same, a change in science would be a change in nature: it would be required, for example, that during the nineteenth century the mass of a material particle was independent of its velocity relative to the measuring apparatus with which it interacted, but after the early years of the twentieth century the mass varied with change in that velocity!

The growth that is characteristic of contemporary science alone gives abundant reason, then, for our feeling assured that the world described by science is but a fragment of the total natural world. Also, the argument supporting a contrary conclusion, that we know of nature only through the science of a given time, seems quite wrong. Science, of necessity, must form abstractions and consider ideal or limiting cases. It is no less valid for this, but still it does not describe the complexities of nature that are presented to us in our direct experience but do not receive formulation in science. It is proverbial in physics that if literal situations are examined in a manner that attempts to take account of all available physical detail, the descriptive equations take on an overwhelming complexity. The control that an athlete has over the behavior of a baseball, for example, may all but defy detailed physical analysis. Similarly, a skilled observer can make valid judgments about people on grounds that are not formulated in books of psychology or medicine. And in general, whereas science is explicitly cognitive, our knowledge of nature must involve a whole spectrum of responses to experience, some of which are rather more intuitive or subconscious than conceptual or logical.[13] In creative new insights into nature, it would seem likely that the scientist generally draws upon his total store of perception of nature, rather than only his explicit scientific knowledge.

We want to say, then, that we have experience and knowledge of the natural world prior to science. This is obviously so: people with little interest in or knowledge of science still have knowledge of their bodies and their surroundings. Our continuing experience of the natural world is a complex stream of sensations of many kinds, some of which are very subtle. It is this continuum of sense impression, beginning at birth (or probably even before) and organized chiefly in accordance with the structures of the natural world, that gives us our basic reservoir of assured information and feeling about ourselves and our world. This knowledge of nature is indeed at the very basis of our living, as well as of our science. But science has also carried our knowledge of the natural world far beyond the ken of ordinary experience, and in these realms we must rely on science for our natural knowledge. The constructs, however, that are only inferences from experience are found to merge imperceptibly with the constructs of the world of our direct sense impressions; there are, for example, no discontinuous changes in the properties which we must assign to matter as we go from rocks and trees down through giant molecules and then to elementary particles. Inferred constructs therefore are properly taken as an extension of the natural world that we come to know and love through our senses.

The continuing possibilities for new knowledge in those domains of nature where we depend largely on science may be endless. But we wonder whether or not there is any sense in which this is not so. To ask this question reminds us of the major theme of our investigation, to which we now return.

---

[13] The importance of that which we know in an other than explicit, conscious manner has been emphasized by Michael Polanyi in his book, *Personal Knowledge* (London, Routledge and Kegan Paul, 1958).

3

Complete Description and Science

1 SIMPLE COMPLETE DESCRIPTION

A SIMPLE, DIRECT DEFINITION of completeness for a science might be that a science has completely described a domain of nature when it has stated every fact about that domain. We could say, then, that our criterion for completeness is the extent to which all the aspects of the domain in question have been duly observed and noted. Of course the problem at once comes to mind, How do we know when "all aspects" have been described? Even aside from this question, however, we can easily come to see the virtual impossibility of ever giving a description of every detail of any other than a very sharply circumscribed natural region.

Suppose, for example, that the chemical material, sodium, is to be described. The appearance of sodium in the chemistry laboratory, its physical properties, the great number of chemical reactions into which it enters, perhaps something about the manufacture and use of sodium: this would constitute the customary textbook material. If the properties of density, electrical and thermal conductivity, thermal expansion, optical reflectivity, bulk modulus, as well as any others that were of interest, had been measured with close precision (as precisely as anyone would ever be likely to want) and if all reasonably likely chemical reactions into which sodium enters had been studied and described, then we might be tempted to say that we had complete knowledge of the sodium in the world. However, the description would not at all have been of particular existing pieces of sodium, but of sodium as a general entity. In effect, the description of chemical and physical properties of sodium is a prediction that any piece of metal that has the identifying properties will behave physically and chemically in a certain prescribed manner. (And, it is to be noted, our world has such properties of uniformity and persistence that such a prediction is justifiable in experience.)

For our "complete description" of sodium we would want not just a statement of how sodium will behave under given conditions, but a statement of where every piece of sodium is. Indeed, for ultimate completeness, we would want to know every point (as far as physics allows us to determine it) at which there is an atom of sodium, not only in the earth but throughout the universe. Furthermore, we would wish to know the conditions surrounding each atom; thus, we would want to know the energy of each atom with respect to surrounding atoms and the kind of electrical, magnetic, and gravitational fields acting on each atom. Also, if the science were complete, we would want to have the information about the location and surroundings for every aggregate of sodium at any desired time. But finally, even this would not be enough. Sodium would have different relations to other entities, in different natural processes, and these varying relations should be taken into account. Some particular sodium might be in sodium chloride molecules, giving a pleasurable sensation of salt taste in a child's mouth. The same sodium could be related to the digestive reaction beginning in the saliva of that mouth. This is only one example, though, of all the relations that the sodium under discussion has to all the other entities of the universe. In complete detail, its relation to every other atom and also to any chosen group of atoms should be available (where "atoms" may be taken to include all the types of entities constituting the world), and at any given time.

A "complete description" of nature with respect to sodium, then, would not be only a set of generalizations about sodium, but would be a statement, for any time (i) of the whereabouts of all sodium; (ii) of the nature of sodium (here there would be reference to basic entities in nature) ; (iii) of all relations of each distinct group of sodium atoms to other parts of nature.

The above is the requirement, for a complete description, on just one component, the atoms of sodium. In our complete description, not only sodium but every other component must also be described, because such groups have properties that are not present in their components. Thus, to take an obvious example, a biological organism has properties that belong to the entire organism and not to each entity constituting it. Inanimate objects too, as a given stone, or the earth, or the sun, must be given the kind of complete description that we outlined for sodium.

If the universe is infinite, it is at once obvious that no finite science could possibly describe the world in every detail. And, we shall make the restriction that our science is to be limited to a finite number of statements. With a finite universe we could conceivably have the kind of scientific description that I have desiderated, but completeness would still only be partially achieved. The reservation is necessary, because we do come into an infinite regress: the very writing of the complete description, or in any other way enunciating it, would itself be a part of the universe, and should be in the descriptions. It might, for example, be the case that sentence 9, paragraph 181, chapter 32, volume 457 of the sodium series describes sodium atoms in Plymouth Rock. But now the fact of the existence of this sentence is also an aspect of the universe; i.e., there should be a descriptive sentence,

"Sentence 9, . . . etc., exists." We have, then, an infinite regress, and to avoid it the description itself must be left out of our complete description of the finite world.

The accumulation of scientific description as itself a part of the world to be described would by no means be trivial. After a certain point it would appear that our description would add more to be described than we in fact do describe. Thus, suppose a box of various items were to be described in high detail. If the descriptive materials (e.g., a sheaf of paper with ink marks) became more complex than the original box and contents, we would have had a "loss," in that there would now be more to describe than at the start of the operation. We might well be no better off if the descriptive device were a magnetic tape or even if it were a man's memory. For, if description became sufficiently detailed there would have to be arrangements in the description whose order exceeded the amount of order in the items to be described. I make this assertion on the assumption that the description of, say, a given atom and its interactions requires at least several atoms in addition to the atom itself. In the limit of descriptive efficiency we would need at least the same number of atoms in the description as in that described; we would then, however, be reproducing the universe in the description, and we could not expect to do that, either physically or logically. (Since the universe includes everything, there could not be two of it.)

We can conclude, then, that there is incompleteness to the descriptive detail which we can give, even if the world should be finite, and therefore a science cannot be complete in the sense of giving description of every last detail of the world.

The limitation on scientific description also suggests that the world cannot be made completely aware of itself: there is no possibility of an awareness or recording of every detail of the universe. Such a self-awareness could readily occur if consciousness were inherent in matter—in each atom, in and of itself. But, on the contrary, consciousness appears to come with a group of atoms so organized (into an organism) that they have purpose, response, and memory. The awareness (or attention) of the organism, whether directed to another group of atoms or to some constituent part of itself, seems to require the elaborate mechanisms of a nervous system; likewise, any machine designed for description, or storage of information, requires elaborate mechanisms. We see, then, that awareness requires organization of atoms which themselves present new domains for which exhaustive awareness would require still further mechanisms, and so on, so that even an organization of all matter into a sentient organism would not lead to complete awareness. The only escape from this limitation would be provided by an organism which could function both as a conscious entity and as an object (in each of its constituent parts) of its consciousness. It seems highly unlikely that this could be so: that the organism, whose parts P_1, P_2, P_3, . . . function in its having awareness, could direct itself to one of those functioning parts,

P_i, and still have its normal awareness functions. In simple illustration, this would mean a camera taking a picture of itself, while in the act of taking a picture of something external to itself, or a man studying his brain operation, while the brain is providing the mechanism for normal awareness of some other aspect of the world.[1] Indeed, there is contradiction in the postulation of a mechanism's giving its attention to an event external to itself, and simultaneously to a part of itself. So, bearing in mind the reasons we have seen against achieving any kind of complete description, we come to a strong naturalistic argument against any kind of total exhaustive awareness of the universe.

2   COMPLETENESS IN A SELECTED DOMAIN

Our conclusion about the impossibility of attaining a complete description of the world does not apply to a limited domain. In an appropriately selected part of nature we might expect to achieve as much detail of description as we wish by use of the facilities and resources of the universe surrounding the chosen region. Thus, a simple piece of metallic crystal might be described in immense detail, both in respect to its own inherent composition and structure and to its relations to the world about it. But in practice we would expect that if we were willing to devote sufficient effort there would always be some further refinement of detail in description or measurement that could be achieved. There are, to be sure, certain limitations *in principle* on the accuracy with which we can make physical measurements (as will be discussed in Chapter 9), but these limitations are on an atomic scale, and are not likely to be reached before the limit of practically desirable description has been attained.

Such completeness of description as we find in a science results, then, from limitation to a selected domain. We obtain completeness, not in any absolute sense of having described every possible detail, but only in the sense of having described as much as we find it worthwhile to describe, within the capabilities of our science, at any given time. There is, we see, a dominant element of what we may call pragmatism in our conception of completeness; that is, the purpose for which we want the description will to a large extent determine at what point we will consider it to be complete.

The selection of aspects of nature to be described may, of course, be made for one of many different reasons. Even if we think of a scientist whose goal is the traditional one of increasing our knowledge of nature, we will perceive that the particular kind of natural knowledge which he is seeking will strongly affect his selection. A zoologist interested in animal morphology,

---

[1] Leon Chwistek discusses the impossibility of a man's talking about what he is saying, at the very moment he is saying it. See his *The Limits of Science*, translated by H. C. Brodie and A. P. Coleman (London, Routledge and Kegan Paul, 1948), p. 42.

a physiologist concerned with reproduction processes, a biochemist concerned with carbohydrate metabolism, and an ecologist studying dependence of biological species on environmental changes, will all study a given kind of animal with different techniques and with different resulting descriptions. Also, some parts of nature may recommend themselves for investigation simply because of their striking aspects: thus, lightning, volcanos, the aurora borealis, an unusual disease, the rainbow. In these instances a selection for description may be guided by little more than the inherent interest in the phenomenon. Frequently a natural entity or process may be exhaustively studied for the sake of the role it plays in a theory, as a critical confirmation or exemplification. The close study that has been given by physicists to the speed of light is an example, as is, also, the elaborate investigations by geneticists of inheritance and chromosome structure in the fruit fly, *Drosophila*. Some research may be for the purpose of a suitably defined kind of completeness, and for no other apparent reason: a botanist may wish to catalogue all the kinds of native plants in his county; a chemist may wish to prepare and study every known compound of a given element; a classical scholar might devote his life to writing an exegesis on every extant work of a chosen Greek author.

When we come to other than "purely scientific" considerations which might strongly determine the choice of a natural domain for study and scientific description, we can find purposes as varied as those which operate in life generally. Food production, military strength, medical therapy, better transportation, faster communication, social amelioration, personal or institutional prestige—these are some of the motives that may give rise to a search for scientific description. And, scientific activity that is carried on for each of these, or other, purposes is, of course, directed to a particular aspect or domain of nature. The agriculturist interested in food production possibilities of a new land and the cartographer interested in preparing a detailed survey map are each going to "see" and describe different aspects of the land, in the light of the goals they have in mind for the particular scientific work they are doing. The richness of nature is demonstrated by the myriad specialities of pure and applied science that have developed. Indeed, we are probably only at the beginning of the proliferation of scientific specialities, in response to the varying needs of man for knowledge and control with respect to his world.

The fact that a selection of a domain is made in the process of creating a scientific description suggests a first workable definition for completeness of a science. We restrict the range of the science to a part of nature or human activity that is appropriate to the methods and scope of the science. Further, since the selection of the domain to be described is made with some purpose in mind, we can make a further limitation by asserting that the science is complete when the purpose for which it is carried on has been approximately achieved. Our definition may then be stated: *a science is descriptively com-*

plete when as much descriptive detail as is desired has been achieved for the domain that is defined for the science. This definition appears to be a satisfactory one, for many of the descriptive sciences, in the criteria that it gives for completeness.

As an example we might consider the physical geography of England. The science constituted by such a description has a limited domain, the country of England, and a somewhat clearly defined purpose, the setting out of the topography of England with detail that is sufficient to the various purposes of the people who are living in or studying that country. To a large extent, considering the variety of maps that are available, it would seem that this science is now complete. For the Earth generally, physical geography obviously is not yet complete, but air flights and land expeditions to the polar and other obscure regions appear to be rapidly bringing about completion. For the Moon, on the other hand (particularly the far side), the science is obviously only in its beginnings.

Another example is provided by the science of inorganic chemistry. The range of this science is defined by the chemical properties of the chemical elements and their compounds, with the exclusion however of the hydrogen-containing compounds of carbon (which form the domain of organic chemistry). In its techniques and fundamental concepts the science merges with physical chemistry and physics at many points, and it is not altogether accurate to speak of it as a dominantly descriptive science. Still, in broad outline, the goals of inorganic chemistry are the identification and orderly description of the chemical elements and their various possible compounds; with the establishment of the periodic table as a valid classificatory scheme, and the description of the readily obtainable compounds, the science achieved a fair degree of completeness. New and interesting aspects of inorganic chemistry do continue to appear: thus, transuranium compounds, complex stereochemical molecules, noble-gas compounds, and new insights into chemical bonding. The science is clearly alive as a research field, and practical uses for various types of new compounds assures continued practical as well as scientific interest. Yet, in terms of the "purpose" of understanding the salient features of our natural world, I believe it could be properly said that inorganic chemistry has made its major achievement, and for this reason we can speak of its relatively high degree of completeness. (It is to be recognized that for some other particular purpose, for example, that of synthesizing a ceramic with certain novel properties of strength and heat resistance, the science might not be at all complete.)

A somewhat different example is provided by the mathematical science of trigonometry. This is a science whose domain is the fairly limited one of the relations between magnitudes of sides and angles in triangles. The science is a complete one, in that the relations that one might expect to obtain have been found, and a great deal of specific information about these relations has been calculated and tabulated (in tables of trigonometric functions). The science is not complete in the sense that every last possible detail has been recorded: this could not be achieved in a finite world, since the values of each trigonometric function could be calculated to an indefinitely large number of decimal places and for an indefinitely large number of specific angles. However, in terms of the definition that we have introduced in this section, completeness has been achieved; for, it would appear that trigonometric functions are usually known with as much accuracy as is desired for the purposes of trigonometric calculations. Further, the methods are available for calculating to greater accuracy if that is desired.

If the amount of information that has been gained in a science is as great as seems feasible, work may virtually cease in the science, even though there might still be a strong desire for further knowledge. In this case one would not properly say that the lack of activity in the science implied that it was complete, excepting perhaps in the case of there being virtually no prospect, even at any future time, for definite advance in the science. An example of a domain about which there was great intrinsic desire for more information, but very little scientific activity for a long period of time, is provided by the planets of our solar system. During the first half of the twentieth century astronomers in general (with, to be sure, some notable exceptions) gave little attention to the physical characteristics of these bodies. All scientifically interested persons would probably have liked to know much more than was available about the planets, but astronomy seemed to have gone about as far as it could in gaining information about planetary surfaces and atmospheres. Still, no one would have been likely to say that our knowledge of the planets was complete. The development of space-exploring rockets in the mid-twentieth century, as well as of new techniques in spectroscopy and radio astronomy, gave us new knowledge of the planets, and the prospect that with sufficient effort further desired knowledge could be obtained. As a result there was a great heightening of interest in the planets throughout the science of astronomy. We would today describe planetary astronomy as a very active but highly incomplete science; fifty years ago it would perhaps have been characterized as highly incomplete and also as relatively inactive.

It is hazardous to essay an example of a science which might be called complete because of the lack of *any* prospects for further knowledge, even though more knowledge is desired. There are, to be sure, limits which seem to come from the very nature of the world, and these will be of concern to us in later chapters; but here I refer only to situations in which less fundamental considerations appear to prevent our having hopes for further knowledge. The future course of science is so unpredictable, and there are so many instances in the past of unexpected breakthroughs to new domains of natural knowledge, that one hesitates to suggest that no more can be gained in any one field of knowledge. The safest examples can perhaps be taken from scholarship that is addressed not to the natural world directly but to human beings and their activities. Thus, we would like to know more than we do about the life of William Shakespeare; the possibility of important new material coming to light cannot be ruled out, but it seems fairly likely that the field of Shakespeare biography is complete in the sense that we shall gain little further significant information. Another example might be provided by an ancient city, whose ruins had been thoroughly studied by archaeologists, and with no remaining prospects for further information.

The extent to which description of a domain is desired may of course change radically, with consequent change in what is considered to be complete description. New interest in practical application of the knowledge of a given aspect of nature would, generally, give rise to new criteria for completeness. Thus, use of steam in engines created a desire for close knowledge of the relations between pressure, temperature, and heat capacity of steam; the possibility of constructing a controlled thermonuclear reaction has led to great interest in the properties of electrically charged gases called "plasmas"; as a result of the development of airplane and rocket travel, we have novel demands for knowledge about the behavior of the human organism in the high atmosphere and beyond—demands that were nonexistent a half-century ago.

Also, the development of science, aside from its applications, leads to changing conceptions of what would be complete knowledge of an aspect of nature. For example, in the early years of this century it would probably have been generally agreed that in our knowledge of sun, planets, asteroids, comets, meteors and dust we had reasonably adequate knowledge of what are the constituents of the solar system. But the discoveries of cosmic rays, and of the charged particles streaming from the sun and surrounding the Earth, set altogether new goals for the knowledge to be gained about what is in the space surrounding us. Investigations of subatomic structure, beginning in 1895 with Becquerel's discovery of radioactivity, brought an even more striking change in demands for knowledge: the atom, which for centuries had been regarded as an ultimate entity about which there was little more that could be learned, came to be known as a complex structure about which an immense amount of detailed information was required before anything like completeness of knowledge could be achieved. Medical research workers of the late nineteenth and early twentieth centuries looked primarily to bacteria for the causes of contagious diseases, but with the discovery of viruses the existence of an entire new group of living entities was established, and medical science, as well as biology generally, was faced with a new domain about which to seek detailed descriptive information. Similar examples of extensions of the demands for complete knowledge in a natural domain are found everywhere in the history of science; for the very process of gaining new scientific knowledge results in change in our expectations for what is yet to be learned.

Our definition of completeness of science in terms of degree of detailed description leads us, then, to the conception that there are varying criteria or standards of completeness for any one domain of nature. Whether in fact there may be absolute limits on the kind of detailed information to be obtained in any one domain is a problem for our later discussions; but the richness of nature is such that an indefinite amount of descriptive detail does seem to be available for observation by the scientific worker, and in any event we cannot expect science to achieve description of every fact of existence and relation. The amount of description that will make a science effectively "complete" for a natural domain must, obviously, vary with the knowledge that we have of what the domain comprises and with changes in the purposes for which we are carrying on the science.

Our first proposed definition for completeness is, I believe, in accord with the attitudes and practices of scientists with respect to the role of science as a description of the natural world. Nonetheless, the definition is not at all adequate in any total discussion of completeness in science. We have already commented, in Section 6 of Chapter 2, on the prime importance of description in science. In that same discussion, however, we emphasized that scientific description does not generally occur except within a framework of some theoretical development in the science. The theoretical components introduce elements that are missing in a definition of completeness which refers only to description.

If science were description only, the completeness definition that we have introduced would give little encouragement to those who wish to find in science some comprehension of the natural universe. That definition suggests that science does no more than carry on a kind of random play upon the surface appearances of nature: that a need for control of a particular group of natural processes carries scientific investigation in some one direction, and then a different need carries it in another direction; or, that a striking new natural phenomenon draws attention to itself, is studied and described, but then some further and perhaps less obvious phenomenon is next considered. In this way, increasingly extensive domains of nature are observed and described—but still the result is no more than a bringing to light here and there of some partial aspects of an infinite domain. It may be that the achievement of science, even with its full theoretical powers, can never be more than such a fragmentary understanding: circles of light that always darken into an unfathomable unknown. We are not ready, however, to come to this conclusion, if at all, without first taking a long look at the prospects that the theoretical structure of science gives for intelligibility in nature. We shall do this by first considering what might be the criteria for completeness with respect to theoretical components, just as we have done for the descriptive aspects of science.

4

Completeness and Explanation

1   DESCRIPTION AND EXPLANATION

SCIENCE ARISES as an answer to two kinds of questions, "What is it?" and "Why is it?" The first kind of question may be thought of as having its roots in a simple need to know what are the properties of the world, for reasons of curiosity or otherwise. How deep is the sea? What kind of life is on Mars? How heavy is plutonium? What is the educational background of people who rob banks? These are samples of the unending series of questions that may be posed for scientific study, and, in some cases at least, answered by scientific description.

The second kind of question is directed not toward matters of fact but of understanding: Why does iron sink in water and wood float? How can circulating blood carry food to animal tissue? and so on. The impulse to raise these questions is more philosophical than for the first kind: there is a desire, in addition to the wonder about what lies beyond the next hill, that asks for pattern and intelligibility. In some cultures this desire has led to myths of spirits and gods who are responsible for what happens in man and the world about him. In our Western science, the desire is satisfied, in part at least, by the structure of natural laws that we have discerned. This structure seems to tell us that there are patterns and regularities among the phenomena of the world; by placing an event or property among phenomena that belong to a known structure, we answer the "why" question; or as is commonly said, we give the scientific explanation.[1]

The distinction between a "why" and a "what" question is, of course, not at all an absolute one. Although an answer to one of the latter kind is

---

[1] There is an extensive literature in the philosophy of science on scientific explanation. A good overall treatment is given by Ernest Nagel, *The Structure of Science* (New York, Harcourt, Brace & World, 1961), esp. Chaps. 2 and 3. See also A. C. Benjamin, *An Introduction to the Philosophy of Science* (New York, Macmillan, 1937), Chap. X. A more detailed study, especially of deduction and explanation, is presented by R. B. Braithwaite, *Scientific Explanation* (New York, Cambridge University Press, 1953).

essentially descriptive science, we have seen (Section 6, Chapter 2) that a description of what happened can in itself have explanatory significance. This is so, I think, because description generally places events within the framework of natural occurrences, thereby removing a sense of mystery that comes with possibility of altogether unknown domains. One characteristic of explanation may be that it expresses a simple relatedness to the familiar. There is immense complexity and mystery about everything in our lives: our own bodies, the growing grass, the earth we stand on. Yet, we most of the time take the world with an easy "this is the way things are" attitude, and with no need for explanation. (Even "unnatural," manmade devices, like telephones and television, are quickly accepted by the majority of people, with no great concern for how they work.) An unusually spectacular and perhaps destructive phenomenon, for example a tornado, is to a considerable extent "explained" when it has been identified (or described) as something that does occasionally happen. President Truman, in announcing the explosion of the first atomic bomb to the American people, gave assuring explanation by speaking of the release of nuclear fission energy as having been going on for a long time in the stars.

The explanation that is associated with description seems to rest, then, on the psychological appeal of that which is familiar, or at least that which has been named and described. However, in the more philosophical sense to which we have referred, explanation is not just a "Because it is that way" answer to a "Why," but rather is a "Because many things are always this way" answer. We may not appear to gain very much by going to the second sort of answer, but actually immense achievements in our knowledge of nature are involved in the step: we go from events, or collections of similar events, to explicitly stated uniformities of occurrence or structure among all events of a given kind. By abstraction and generalization we then comprehend an entire aspect of nature when we state a natural law, or equation or theory, which correctly tells us the structure or behavior for all instances of that aspect. Also, we have then explained any of these particular instances, for we can say, of each instance, this occurs because nature always behaves in this way (and indeed, we may well have been able to give added conviction to our explanation by being able to predict the instance from our knowledge of the general pattern).

If, however, generalizations about nature stood alone, with no connections between them, they would not go very far along the path from explanation by reason of familiarity to explanation by reason of coherence and intelligibility. Happily, one of the primary features of science is that it has developed into an interlocking set of generalizations. The degree of relatedness varies among the sciences, but in physics it is such that we can generally not only explain a fact by referring to a generalization of which it is an instance, but also we may refer the generalization to other laws and theories which require it. In this way we come to see nature as behaving in all its aspects—or at least, in all those that are within the domain of the particular science we are considering—according to a pattern that we can understand. By way of illustrating various kinds of explanation we might consider the everyday situation of a broken pottery dish lying near the edge of a table on which it had been placed. Our first question probably would be something like "What happened?" If, say, a woman working in the room told us that she accidently pushed the dish off the table with her dusting cloth, we would then have a satisfactory explanation-by-description. The dish was pushed and fell to the floor; it is commonly known that objects do fall when unsupported, and also, if they are made of baked clay they frequently break under a sharp blow.

In the preceding explanation we are not only using an appeal to familiar kinds of events, but also our explanation implicitly calls upon generalizations from experience; we have learned about solid bodies falling, unless their size is that of dust particles or smaller, and we know about the fragility of pottery. Suppose, however, that we are in a reflective mood, or are being questioned by a student, and we try to understand more about the dish's falling. Our first explanation in terms of physical science would probably call upon the law of falling bodies, and we could say something to the effect that near the surface of the earth all free bodies fall towards the center of the earth with an acceleration that gives a velocity gain of about 32 ft/sec in each second. This law itself need not be taken, however, without further explanation. We can say that it is a consequence of Newton's law of gravity, which tells us that between any two masses there is an attractive force that is proportional to the product of the masses divided by the square of the distance between them. The proportionality constant is known, and by using it and the known values for the mass and radius of the earth, we might demonstrate the validity of our explanation by calculating that the acceleration of a falling body close to the surface of the earth is about 32 ft/sec². We could say that we have now seen the fall of the dish as an instance of the influence of a universal force which exists everywhere in nature. We might, as scientists have for several centuries, point with justifiable satisfaction to the many natural phenomena, both terrestrial and astronomical, which are described by the law of gravity, and hence explained, because the law is one of universal validity.

But the explanation is still not complete, since we can ask, "Why is there a force as described by Newton's law of gravity?" Until a half-century ago, we could give no answer (although there had been many attempts, none of them at all successful, since the day of Newton). Today, the general theory of relativity does enable us to answer this question, and thereby to give the explanation in terms of a still more inclusive natural law. For Newton's law of gravity, space is an extended nothingness in which matter exists, but with no essential relationship between the space and matter. For Einstein's gravitational equations, matter and space and time are not independent; there is an intimate, essential relatedness such that as a consequence of the presence of matter space–time does not have its usual Euclideanlike geometry but is slightly "curved." The new geometric relationships of the variables of space and time are the source of what we call gravitational forces. For most practical applications these are equivalent to the forces given by Newton's law; however, with very strong gravitational forces there are differences between the values required by the relativistic and Newtonian equations, and observation (specifically of the precession of the perihelion in the orbit of the planet Mercury) is clearly in favor of the validity of the relativistic theory.

With Einstein's general theory of relativity we come to the final stage in our explanation of the broken dish. We proceeded first to an establishment of the breaking as a result of a common kind of occurrence, an accidental push followed by a fall and a breaking. We then asked further about the fall,[2] and came to a law for falling bodies that may itself be derived from Newton's law of gravity. This law in turn is a consequence of a theory about the relation between matter and the basic metric properties of space and time. One could wish to go still further, and Einstein tried for decades to relate not only gravitational fields but also electrical and magnetic fields and the nature of individual elementary particles to the properties of space and time. Such a unified field theory has not, however, been achieved, and for the time, at least, we must gratefully take the gravitational field theory as giving our best understanding of the gravitational force beween bodies.

2   COMPLETE EXPLANATION

A deductive system may be identified with what in mathematics and logic is called an axiomatic system. This is a system which contains (i) primitive terms and definitions which tell us what are the objects or concepts with which the system is concerned, (ii) various symbols of logic and/or ordinary language which serve as "connectives" among the primitive terms, and (iii) a set of axioms that state basic relations among the terms. Various new relations among the primitive terms may be derived from the axioms; it is this process of logical derivation that is the characteristic feature of a deductive system. In such a system we can learn hitherto unknown relations, consequent from the axioms, without first introducing new relations among the primitive terms. Euclidean geometry is the deductive system that is probably best known: the primitive terms are line, point, plane, etc. The connectives are generally ordinary language, without assumption, however, of any specific geometric relations in the language. And, the axioms are such

---

[2] Our attempts at further explanation would probably not have been as successful as they were if we had asked about the accidental push or the breaking; for there we would quickly have come to complexities of physiology–psychology, or of mechanics and solid-state physics, respectively, that are not readily explainable in close detail.

principles as, "If equals are added to equals, the sums are equal to each other."

There is wide freedom in the way we might set up a deductive system for a given body of interrelated propositions (as, for example, plane geometry). What is to be put into primitive terms and definitions, what is to be put into the axioms, and so on, are decisions that to a large extent rest with those who devise the system. But in any event we have for a deductive system the characteristic feature of derived results (theorems, consequences, etc.) that come from the axioms. And, the axioms are assumed principles, perhaps well justified for various reasons, but not in any way derivable within the system itself.

We have pointed out (Section 5, Chapter 2) that the structure formed by the laws of a natural science is that of a deductive system. However, this statement must be taken with reservations. In principle many of the various branches of physics, for example, could be put into a strict deductive system, and in a few instances actually have been. In common practice, however, science is not so expressed in textbooks or review papers. Instead, basic principles are established with regard both for experimental confirmation and consistency with other relevant parts of physics (assumed to be established), and applications to selected special problems are considered. In the application of basic principles deduction is definitely involved: the consequences of the general principle for a particular situation are determined. There is slight disposition on the part of the physicist, however, routinely to present each application, or group of applications, as a rigorous axiomatic system. Instead, he wishes to be informal about when he uses strict deduction (often in the form of mathematical methods) and when he introduces observational or other material.

It can perhaps be said that a relatively highly developed science like physics is *latently deductive*, and can become manifestly deductive in any circumstance as required. The reason that physics and other natural sciences have not been generally put into a strict deductive form I believe, lies in the great variety of ways in which principles are to be used. Nature presents an enormous array—perhaps unending—of different physical circumstances or situations; in applying physical theory to each of these, the relevant special conditions must be brought into the problem. We might, as an example, think of Newton's second law, which gives the relation between applied force and time rate of change of momentum for a material body. The range of application of this law is enormous: falling bodies, vibratory motions, particle collisions, hydrodynamic flow, rotational motions, frictional effects, ballistic trajectories, vehicular motions, rockets, artificial satellites, and planetary orbits are among the many phenomena that are studied with an essential use of the law. But particular circumstances must be introduced with each phenomenon. For falling bodies, there is a gravitational field and perhaps atmospheric frictional effects; vibrations involve masses and restoring forces which must be specified for the particular system involved; when the second law is applied for the determination of the motion of charged nuclear particles moving at very high speeds within an accelerator, relativistic effects which somewhat modify the common statement of the law must be taken into account; and so on. In a textbook on mechanics it is useful for a physicist to derive and elucidate various standard kinds of applications of the second law; but even aside from the problem of including *all* consequences, which will be discussed later, one can readily see that an axiomatic presentation of all consequences would require the introduction of an indefinitely continued series of new primitive terms and definitions. Similar considerations argue against a strictly axiomatic presentation of physics with respect to its other basic theoretical principles.[3]

We can conclude, then, that although many branches of science could be set forth as deductive systems, in practice they retain flexibility and breadth by being expressed as sets of principles to be applied *for their deduced consequences* to special circumstances. This latent deductive quality operates both for science as analysis or prediction and for science as explanation. In the illustration of Newton's second law we thought of the law as a way of analyzing various physical phenomena so as to learn what would be the relations between force and motion. However, by coming to see how the phenomena are described by the second law in these same situations, we come to an explanation of them. And, similarly with other physical principles: in knowing the law or principle which applies for a given phenomenon, we feel that we know its explanation. Here too we see the latent deductive property of science. An appropriate group of phenomena are often said to be *subsumed* under a law (or equation or theory) : this means that those aspects of the phenomena for which the law is applicable are described by the statement of the law. Thus, all instances of forces on charged bodies in electrical fields may be regarded as being subsumed under the equation, $F = Ee$, where F is force, E is the field, and e is the charge. Also, we can both say that we derive[4] the magnitude and direction of the force on a charge in a given field from the equation, and that we explain electrical forces by reference to the equation.

We saw in the preceding section in our illustrative discussion of gravitational force and scientific explanation that explanation need not stop with the general law that is immediately applicable to a phenomenon. The law

---

[3] The problem of deductive structure in physics has been discussed by L. Tisza, with conclusions somewhat similar to mine, in his paper "The Conceptual Structure of Physics," *Reviews of Modern Physics*, **35**, 151, sec. I (1963).

[4] For the purposes of science, any logical or mathematical consequences of a law or equation are necessarily valid (if the law itself is taken to be correct). The question of what difference there is between the necessity of a consequent in a logical system and the necessity of a *natural law itself* is an important one in the philosophy of science. There clearly is a difference: we can readily conceive of worlds with different physical laws (e.g., one in which moving electrical charges do not give rise to magnetic fields) but not of one in which logically contradictory relations exist (e.g., an observer both does and does not, at a given instant, observe a magnetic field associated with moving charges). I shall give a further discussion in Chapter 5 of the relation between logical and empirical statements.

may itself be explained by reference to some still more general physical principle. The latent deductive nature of physical science enables us then, at least in certain cases, to see some aspect of an event as a consequence of a physical principle, that principle in turn as a consequence of some still wider principle, and so on. In this way we proceed to principles that are successively broader in the range of natural phenomena which they encompass and, concomitantly, stronger in their explanatory power.

So, having given some indication of the manner in which sciences can take the form of deductive systems, we are now in a position to consider what complete explanation by science might be. In discussing complete description, our first suggestion was that we attain completeness when we have stated every fact about the domain of concern to a science. Likewise, we now suggest that we have complete explanation when we are able to explain every possible fact: every property and every event in the universe. By explanation of a fact we now mean both that we are able to show it as a consequence of the theoretical situation of the science, and also that the theory itself is satisfactory with respect to our desires for explanation.

This first attempt at a meaning for complete explanation follows from a direct and simple application of the notion of explanation to all factual knowledge. We at once see, however, that the definition does not give us a feasible goal for science. In considering "simple complete description" we found that a complete statement of all facts is both practically and logically impossible; hence we cannot even include a statement of all facts, much less their explanation, in our science. We obviously, then, want some modification of our requirement of an explanation of all facts. The obvious step for elimination of reference to every aspect of every phenomenon is to require explanation only of those facts, in each science, which are considered to form a complete description in the science. In this way we bring our requirement of explanatory detail into consonance with the definition we reached (pp. 35–36) for completeness with respect to scientific description. Hence, we can now expand that definition so as to include explanation: *a science is complete when it gives as much descriptive detail as is desired for the domain of the science and when the theoretical structure of the science satisfactorily explains all of the facts of the science.*

We will want to see how well this definition seems to agree with what is the actual attitude of scientists towards completeness, as indicated by some illustrative examples. But before doing this we should know more about the relation between a theoretical structure and all desired description. Is there, for example, any way of knowing when a set of axioms forms a system that is properly consistent as well as complete with respect to the facts of the science of interest? Also, the proposed definition introduces a large ambiguity in its requirement of "satisfactory" explanation: we must consider whether or not a deductive system can provide such an explanation, or whether it itself always inevitably asks for further explanation. A line of attack on these problems is suggested by the fact that logicians and mathematicians have given attention to the question of what constitutes a complete deductive system with respect to a system of concepts, and we shall next see what we can gain from their results for our consideration of a complete science.

3   CONSISTENCY

From the point of view[5] of logic or pure mathematics, an axiomatic system is a statement of relations in some freely chosen conceptual realm, as natural numbers, Euclidean geometry, or Riemannian geometry. There is no objection at all to inconsistencies between the axioms or consequences of two different systems; rather, from the point of view of axiomatic logic, it is only the consistency within a given system that is of significance. In considering the deductive systems of natural science, we see at once that there cannot be contradiction between systems. The scientist's conception of the world requires it to be unique, and hence there cannot be contradictory accounts of any one aspect of the world, without one of the accounts being wrong. (This is not to deny, of course, that at different times in the historical development of science contradictory statements, both of which have seemed justified and even empirically confirmed, have been maintained for some single aspect of nature. But, because nature is one, we must always believe that in science there is a correct choice between two statements which give contradictory properties to *precisely* the same natural entity or event.) As natural scientists, then, we cannot, for example, hold both Euclidean and non-Euclidean geometry to be valid for physical space, *with similarly defined physical terms*, in the way that a mathematician might consider these geometries to be equally proper. The geometries are not mere formalisms for the mathematician, empty of content; they are sets of relations between definite concepts of line, plane, angle, etc. But for him, *qua* mathematician, there is no basis external to the system for preferring one to the other.

If a deductive system is to be acceptable, the scientist requires it to be consistent just as does the logician or mathematician. If a system is consistent, there are no contradictory statements in it. Or, alternatively, if a system is consistent, not every sentence of the system is provable; for, if there is one false (or inconsistent) statement in a deductive system, then any statement expressible in the system may be proved within the system.[6] This property of deductive systems may readily be demonstrated. Suppose an inconsistency

---

[5] The logical material of this and the following section is largely taken from: R. L. Wilder, *The Foundations of Mathematics* (New York, Wiley, 1952), Chapters I and II; A. A. Fraenkel and Y. Bar-Hillel, *Foundations of Set Theory* (Amsterdam, North-Holland, 1956), Chapter V; I. M. Copi, *Symbolic Logic* (New York, Macmillan, 1954), Chapter 6.
[6] The great Cambridge mathematician, G. H. Hardy, so a story goes, once commented in a college dinner conversation that if $2 + 2 = 5$ then any other statement can be proved; to the challenge of a table companion, "Prove that I am the Pope," Hardy replied, "By subtraction of 3 we get $1 = 2$, and hence you and the Pope, two, are identically you, one."

in a system to be expressed by the assertion that both A and not-A are valid. Further, let B be any other desired statement. It is the case that if A is true, then it follows that either A is true and B is false or both A and B are true. However, it has been asserted that not-A is true; hence, since we must have either A or B, and we do not have A, we must have B.

But even though any single instance of inconsistency does tell us at once that a system is inconsistent, the demonstration of consistency for a formal system, regarded purely as a system of symbols and axioms of relationship, is in general not feasible in any direct manner. There are an indefinite number of consequences which may be derived from the axioms of other than very simple systems, and further, it may be difficult to determine whether or not a given pair of theorems (consequences) is mutually consistent. If one can show that there is one sentence of the system which is not provable, then one has shown consistency of the system, since, as previously stated, any statement could be proven in an inconsistent system.[7] But if attempts to disprove a statement have not succeeded, the system is not necessarily inconsistent; perhaps it is only that the attempts have not been sufficiently ingenious.

A system may, however, be judged for consistency by an indirect test. The logician considers a system to be consistent if it has a "sound interpretation" or a *model*. A formal system may be set up to express and elicit true statements about a domain. It does this by putting into axioms and definitions a set of concepts that are basic statements about the domain and by enabling consequent theorems to be derived. The truth or validity of the system may be found from the truth or validity of the theorems: do they, or do they not, make valid statements about the domain? After we have given meanings to the terms of a system its axioms and theorems form an *interpretation* of the system. We see, then, that an interpretation transforms a system from a formal arrangement of symbols, related in accordance with prescriptions and implications contained in the axioms, into a set of meaningful statements about some entities. If now, we further can say that the sentences of the system are true under the given interpretation, then we say we have a model. If the original set of uninterpreted axioms is called a "formalism," an interpretation that gives true premises and true consequences is a model of the formalism. Thus, "line," "point," and "plane" may be given various meanings: they lead to a model of the structure–formalism of geometry when interpreted, for example, as the lines, points, and planes of common experience.

Our practical test for consistency of a deductive system comes, then, to a test of adequacy of the system for the concepts encompassed by the system. *If a deductive system leads to true statements about the domain it covers, the system is consistent.* In science, deductive systems are generally models, in the sense we have defined, which have been set up as formalizations of an intuitively conceived theory. The confirming of the deductions of a theory is, then,

---

[7] This is the "Post criterion for consistency," first enunciated by the American mathematician and logician, E. L. Post.

both a proof of the validity of the theory, in a physical sense, and a demonstration of the consistency of the theory in a logical sense. Just as the proof of the pudding is in the eating, so, in science, the test of consistency is in the correctness of the results.

Although deductive scientific theories are almost invariably what we have termed models, there has been some attention given to the possibility of the role of pure, uninterpreted formalism in natural science. P.A.M. Dirac, who has argued that purely formal structure is becoming increasingly important in physics,[8] has nonetheless also stated that "although the main object of physical science is not the provision of pictures. . . . One may, however, extend the meaning of the word 'picture' to include *any way of looking at the fundamental laws which makes their self-consistency obvious.*[9] The model, in other words, has at the least a role in aiding in the discerning of consistency. It has also been cogently argued, however, that all the deductive systems of science are models; that there is, in fact, no role in natural science for an uninterpreted formal structure. We shall not further discuss this allegation, except to comment that certainly at some points any useful scientific theory must have an interpretation which relates its terms to the experienced constructs.[10]

The electromagnetic theory of J. C. Maxwell provides an excellent example of a deductive system in science. The (interpreted) axioms are four basic equations, and they, with associated definitions of terms of the equations, form the theory. The theory grew out of a long tradition of mathematical formulation of electrical and magnetic phenomena, but its unique form, and success, rested on intuitive concepts of electrical and magnetic fields first formulated by Michael Faraday. The four equations of the theory were expected to describe all electromagnetic phenomena; or, to put the matter another way, all electromagnetic phenomena were to be subsumed under the theory and hence explained by it. The theory achieved this comprehensive description and explanation, and further, it brought the phenomena of light and other electromagnetic waves, not previously recognized as electromagnetic in nature, into its domain.

The Maxwell theory was eventually found lacking, after we came to learn something of the sources of electromagnetic phenomena: Maxwell knew

---

[8] "Quite likely . . . it will be beyond the power of human intelligence to get the necessary new ideas by direct attempts to formulate the experimental data in mathematical terms. The theoretical worker will therefore have to proceed in a more indirect way. The most powerful method of advance that can be suggested at present is to employ all the resources of pure mathematics in attempts to perfect and generalize the mathematical formalism that forms the existing basis of theoretical physics, and after each success in this direction, to try to interpret the new mathematical features in terms of physical entities . . ." *Proceedings of the Royal Society,* A133, 60 (1931).

[9] P. A. M. Dirac, *The Principles of Quantum Mechanics,* 3rd ed. (New York, Oxford University Press, 1947), p. 10.

[10] For further discussion, see Mary B. Hesse, "Models in Physics," *British Journal for the Philosophy of Science,* IV, 198 (1953); also E. Nagel, *The Structure of Science* (New York, Harcourt, Brace & World, 1961), Chap. 6.

nothing, for example, of discrete charges. Also, even on the level of macroscopic phenomena the theory, as customarily interpreted, was found to make an incorrect prediction in the matter of the Michelson–Morley experiment. It is interesting to notice how modification of a deductive system proceeded in this situation. One element in the original Maxwell theory was that electromagnetic waves are oscillations of an all-pervading aether, and hence that light has a constant velocity with respect to this aether. This interpretation of light velocity was, then, part of the model that comprised the theory. After the Michelson–Morley experiment failed to detect a constancy of light velocity with respect to the aether, the model was reformulated, notably by Albert Einstein, without an aether and with a constancy of light speed with respect to the observer. The new formulation brought certain changes in the terms of Maxwell's equations for observers moving with respect to electromagnetic fields, but the essential form of the equations remained the same. The new model did give theorems which were true (were in agreement with observation) whereas the old one did not. In its new form, then, the theory may be judged to be consistent (neglecting its possible deficiencies on the microscopic level). In this instance, the change in the model involved a change in the postulated properties of the domain covered by the axioms: it was not consistent to find in nature an aether which maintained electromagnetic waves, but a deductive system which required these waves always to move at the same speed with respect to an interacting observer was found to be consistent. We see that in science consistency involves both an "internal" correctness of logical structure, and a proper adjustment of axioms and interpretation to the group of entities or concepts that are the subject matter of the system. The interpretation by which the system appears as a consistent one is not to be chosen arbitrarily but is forced, so to speak, by the characteristics of the natural world.

4   COMPLETE DEDUCTIVE SYSTEMS

Given that a deductive system is consistent, what is required for it also to be formally complete? Several meanings of completeness for a deductive system may be considered. The most general, perhaps, is that of "expressive completeness": a system is complete if every statement about the subject matter of the system can be formulated in the system. This kind of completeness is desirable but not very demanding, since any sufficiently wide collection of terms, regardless of whether or not conditions for deductive relations are stated, will permit it. If we provide enough words to name everything we give expressive completeness to a system.

We gain a more significant definition of completeness by putting a requirement on the provability as well as expressibility of the sentences of a system. We may say, then, that a system is *adequately complete* if it is consistent and if all of the statements of the system *which are true for a given interpretation* are also provable within the system. In this definition we assume that the criterion for truth is outside of the system: that by reference to the domain of the interpretation there is a way of determining whether or not a statement of the system is true. For the deductive systems of science the test of experience provides, of course, either directly or indirectly, the external criterion of validity for the sentences of a system. If the theorems of the system satisfy this empirical test, and if also they do encompass all of the descriptive facts of the domain (all of the statements which are true) then the system is complete.

There is yet a third definition of logical completeness which we wish to consider. A consistent system is said to be "deductively complete" if for every statement of the system either the statement or its negation is provable. That is, by logical deduction within the system we may show either that *any* sentence of the system is a valid consequence of the axioms and definitions or that its negation is a valid consequence. There are, then, no statements about which the system leaves any doubt with respect to validity. This kind of completeness is stronger than that defined in the preceding paragraph; that definition does allow for certain sentences to be unprovable (not disprovable) within the system. A deductive system, then, may be adequately complete, as defined, but not deductively complete. The lack of deductive completeness for certain logical systems was first shown by K. Gödel, in what has come to be known as "Gödel's incompleteness theorem." The relevance of this kind of incompleteness for science is not immediate, and we shall not further discuss deductive completeness and Gödel's theorem at this point. But, because the theorem is of great intrinsic interest, and is important for some questions about completeness in science to be considered later, we shall give a detailed discussion in the following chapter.

A fourth kind of completeness should be mentioned, even though it would not be wanted for a scientific system. An inconsistent deductive system is complete for the domain of its terms and axioms—in a sense, even deductively complete—because *every* statement expressible in the system can be proven in the system. If a scientific theory seems to be giving too much, with various investigators finding conflicting results, an inconsistent deductive system may be the source of the trouble. The relativity theory discussions of recent years about changes with relative motion in time rates of clocklike systems, including biological organisms, are perhaps an illustrative instance. One can scarcely doubt the validity of the special relativity theory, or its application to time-rate changes in physically interacting high-speed systems, but the controversial results for physically isolated clock systems suggest an inconsistency in the particular deductive system formed when relativistic equations are applied to these systems.

With a deductive system which is "adequately complete" we have one which fulfills a first requirement for complete explanation. Since every descriptive statement of the domain of the science in question is a theorem of the adequately complete system, we are able to explain every fact of the domain by reference to the basic principles (the axioms) of the system.

We would generally expect the adequately complete system to give more than the immediately descriptive statements of the science, for we have learned that only a small part of the structure and processes of nature can be directly described by us. Most scientific theories involve entities that have been imaginatively constructed (see our discussion in Chapter 2), and statements about these entities are part of the science, just as are the more directly descriptive statements upon which justification of the constructs of the science must ultimately rest. The statements which go beyond empirical test cannot, of course, be given their truth warrant directly in terms of experience. If, however, we have confidence in the system of axioms and defined quantities (constructs) that we have set up, we are generally ready to accept statements that are valid only as deductive theorems. There is always a desire to corroborate these by appeal to experience, if possible, but such corroboration is usually of more interest as a test of the entire theory than of a particular theorem. We have no hesitation in accepting the use of a firmly established theory like Newtonian mechanics even for phenomena that are beyond observation, if the theory should be valid for those phenomena: for example, for the motions relative to each other of a pair of stars that form a spectroscopic binary system (which is known only by inference as a double-star system). On the other hand, an application of general relativity theory, a theory which has not yet received abundant empirical confirmation, to, say, the motion of artificial earth satellites, is of interest primarily as a test of the consistency of the theory.

Elements of a deductive system that go beyond direct experience are generally necessary if we are at all to have a deductive system that will encompass, and hence explain, a descriptive domain. Science has today achieved many theories that are latently deductive systems and that do explain the phenomena of some given domain of nature. The definition of completeness of a science that we gave in Section 2, p. 46, does then seem to be capable of fulfillment, if one is willing to accept the explanation of a natural domain by a set of basic principles as constituting satisfactory explanation. Clearly, this is an important *if*, for one does want to ask, "How do we explain the basic principles?" We shall return to this question in the following section, but for the time let us assume that a gathering together of a field of science into a comprehensive theory does constitute a satisfactory explanation, and with this assumption consider some examples of possible completeness in science.

Our definition of completeness for a science requires that the science give as much descriptive detail as is desired and also a deductive structure that is satisfactory for explanation. The science of mechanics has often been regarded by physicists as a prime model for a completed science. This science gives the principles governing the relations between motions of various kinds of material bodies and the forces and restraints applied to the bodies. Classical mechanics, as the science is called, may be extended and modified to include the situations of very fast relative motion, with speeds comparable to that of light, which are covered by the theory of relativity; and indeed, "relativistic mechanics" would properly be the more inclusive science, since it contains the Newtonian mechanics of ordinary motions as a special case. The behavior of very small particles, for which wave properties of matter become significant, is definitely excluded from classical mechanics, and belongs rather in the province of quantum theory. But, for the domain of matter and motion to which it is presumed to apply, mechanics is a highly successful science, and it does in principle fulfill the requirements we have given for a complete system. There are many phenomena of the motion of matter that have not yet been fully analyzed in terms of the basic principles of mechanics (for example, the motion of fluids through various kinds of orifices) but there is no reason to think that there are inadequacies in the principles.

It is to be noted that when we speak of mechanics or examine a treatise on the subject, we do not find a vast collection of descriptive sentences, properly explained by the principles of the science. As we have already pointed out in discussing the latent property of deductive systems in science, the principles of a highly general science are usually presented somewhat independently of the many facts which they explain. The investigator, having learned the principles, may then apply them to a wide variety of different physical phenomena. The descriptive detail which is desired will then generally be given in association with the various fields of special interest. Because of the frequent separation in presentation of descriptive and deductive (theoretical) aspects of science, we can in practice speak of a theoretical science like mechanics as being complete, even though the science does not include descriptive detail for a specific domain of nature. The range of application of a theoretical structure in science is generally to be regarded as universal—as being applicable to all instances of the kind of phenomena covered by the structure. The concentration on theoretical aspects, which leads us to speak of a science as being complete when it gives us a theory alleged to be adequate for all special situations, has a parallel in the complete descriptive science. We said, for example, that the physical geography of a country was a complete (descriptive) science when all desired facts had been noted. Here we use the word complete even though the theoretical component is relatively small; likewise, we speak of a theoretical science as complete even though only slight descriptive detail is given with it.

The science of thermodynamics, like that of mechanics, is a system of universal generality, covering energy transfer and change of state for all physical systems. Insofar as it is applied to physical changes between equilibrium states it is a complete science; it too, though, is generally presented as a deductive system (sometimes in a quite rigorous form), apart from descriptions of the phenomena everywhere in nature for which it gives understanding and prediction.

Electrodynamics, as applied to electromagnetic phenomena of ordinary experience, is also a system that is generally regarded as being "adequately deductive," and indeed this completeness to a considerable degree carries over even to phenomena on an atomic level.[11]

Other fields of science that are complete to a reasonable degree may readily be cited: kinetic theory of gases for a specific state of matter; the theory of evolution for development of new species among all living organisms; the theory of diseases from pathogenic bacteria; atomic structure theory for types of chemical reaction and bonding. Every scientific reader could give further examples on varying levels of comprehensiveness. Today there probably are few, if any, of the latently deductive systems of science that are absolutely and rigorously complete, even with the modest requirement on explanation that we have provisionally adopted. (The very problem of demarcation of the domain of a science would be troublesome: at what point, for example, in considering material particles of decreasing size would we say that effects peculiar to quantum theory are neglible and those of classical mechanics entirely adequate.) But we gain appreciation of the completeness that has been achieved by considering some examples (with which the history of science is obviously replete) of deductive systems which failed for want of completeness.

An example on the level of widest inclusiveness is provided by the hypotheses of the particlelike atom as the ultimate physical reality. This concept, which had its origin among the Greek atomists and was given a classic statement in Lucretius' *De Rerum Natura,* was a dominant notion in the physics of the nineteenth century. According to it, the world is basically atoms in the void of space, and in their properties the atoms, although very small, are like the larger pieces of matter which we directly experience. The science of this century has shown the concept to be irreparably deficient as a basis for a deductive system that will explain what we find in nature. Atoms are not tiny pieces of "matter," but are complex systems of other particles, and these particles have properties quite different from those that we assign to matter on the basis of direct experience; the elementary particles do not even persist indefinitely, but may be annihilated and created; space is not a featureless void, but an active physical entity which participates in the propagation of electromagnetic waves, in the formation of gravitational forces, and in the creation of inertial mass and electric charge from energy.

Although we now have a highly successful theory of the atom, the theory of the specific kinds of elementary, subatomic particles is at present

---

[11] Thus, in a report on "Electron Theory" to the Solvay Conference, Brussels, Sept.–Oct. 1948, J. R. Oppenheimer wrote: "In the theory of the electron and the electromagnetic field, we have to do with an almost closed, almost complete system, . . ." Reprinted in *Quantum Electrodynamics,* edited by J. Schwinger (New York, Dover, 1958), p. 148.

an example of an incomplete system. During the first decades of this century, until the early 1930's, the electron and proton were assumed to be the basic building blocks of nature. Atomic and nuclear structure and experiments with radioactivity and atomic-particle collisions were interpreted and explained on the assumption that these two were the only elementary particles. Various new experiments, as well as theoretical considerations, led to the discerning of new particles: the neutron, the positron, the neutrino, and many others. Even the nuclei of atoms, it was learned, are composed not of protons and electrons, as had been believed, but of protons and neutrons. Today, although the elementary constituents of matter in its ordinary states are believed to be known, new facts about elementary particles are still being learned, and a satisfactory theory of the particles, and why they are as they are, has yet be to achieved: from either the point of view of description or explanation, the science is incomplete.

Still, it may be that continued experimental and theoretical work, within the framework of present-day physics, will lead to a satisfactorily complete science of the elementary particles. The incompleteness, in this instance, is perhaps a consequence of the science not yet having been developed to a sufficient degree. In other cases, incompleteness seems to have resulted because of a clearly wrong principle at the foundation of the science. The aether concept in physics, which did not give a basis for a correct theory of effects of relative motion on electromagnetic fields or on matter, might be an example. Or, in biology we might cite the concept of *elan vital*; in view of the apparent differences between animate and inanimate nature, its existence would not seem to have been an unreasonable hypothesis, and yet in the end it was a fruitless concept in understanding biological organisms.

There are cases where a science has been developed to a considerable degree, and then been dropped because of the obvious inadequacy of its postulates. One might think of phrenology, held by many in the nineteenth century to be a valid science of human personality and capability. But today, in view of what we know about constitutional psychology and the other biological and cultural factors of determination of human behavior, the simple hypothesis of a strong relation between head structure and personality is easily dismissed as hopelessly inadequate.

The extent to which science has achieved completeness is justifiably a source of pride: in many of nature's domains a fair share of the descriptive knowledge has been obtained and theoretical development has led to a discerning of unifying structures and processes. Yet, every scientist knows of questions still unanswered in his field of work, of synthesis and deeper understandings that still lie far away. We have proposed criteria for completeness of particular sciences, each concerned with some given aspect of our world. Can we, however, find any meaning for completeness of all science? In the next section we shall see something of what is involved in such a universally complete explanation.

5   LIMITATIONS OF SCIENCE

We will now drop our provisional assumptions that we have a satisfactory explanation when the phenomena of a natural domain have been covered by a complete science, and ask what further explanation might be desired. Any deductive system has a set of axioms as its basis, and the statements deduced in the system cannot (as long as we stay within the system) go back to any more fundamental statements. A scientific theory, then, which is generally a latently deductive system, rests on postulates which are in no way explained by the theory itself. In practice, of course, we usually have justification for the postulates in two ways: (i) the consequences deduced from the theory, assuming them to be in accord with experience, give support to the validity of the postulates; (ii) the theory is usually constructed with postulates that have some plausibility, either in terms of experience or intuitive insight. However, if we are persistently curious we want more than justification for the theory; we want also to know why are its postulates as they are.

Newton's law of gravitation, we have seen, is a law that describes and explains universal phenomena of attraction between material bodies, and yet is itself explained by the general theory of relativity, of which it is a consequence. We have here a paradigm for what we might work toward with every successful deductive scientific system; each set of axioms, explanatory of a domain of phenomena, would in turn be themselves explained as a result of being consequences of some still more inclusive theory (deductive system). Our ideal for science would then be some one master theory or deductive system from which all other laws and equations of science would ultimately follow.

The ideal of an ultimate unification of science has been widely discussed in the philosophy-of-science literature, often as "reductionism" or "the unity of science." [12] The concept is an appealing one, and much of what has already been achieved in science supports its feasibility. The division between living and nonliving things, once seen as a clear break in the natural world, has come to be regarded as a continuum: crystalline viruses, for example, display properties of both realms. Throughout biology generally there is a strong trend toward molecular biology, in which biological processes are investigated in terms of physical and chemical properties of molecules. This same tendency away from ascribing any irreducible factors to living things has been apparent in medicine, psychology, and even sociology–anthropology. A naturalistic point of view generally prevails, with little support for a soul or psyche that is nonphysical in origin. If human and animal behavior and thinking may be understood in terms of biology, and biology in terms of physics and chemistry, and these in turn in terms of a

[12] See, e.g., E. Nagel, *The Structure of Science* (New York, Harcourt, Brace & World, 1961), Chap. 11.

master theory, then each complete deductive system of a special science could eventually be explained by reference to that master theory. The various special sciences would presumably not only explain the natural world as we know it, but also account for the development of all structures and organisms, from the universe of galaxies through the realm of biological organisms.

There are considerations that may be advanced against the likelihood of science's ever coming to the kind of complete synthesis just outlined, but at present it is hardly possible to argue with any conclusiveness either for or against that possibility. Assuming, though, that the successful master theory as well as all necessary subtheories should have been formulated, we see that we would still not have gained any final answer or explanation. The master theory itself would rest on postulates, or would itself be a set of axioms. Suppose, for the sake of concreteness, that the theory were along the lines of the unified field equations of relativity theory, and implicitly gave a statement of the properties and laws for matter, energy, charges, and force fields of all kinds, and spatial and temporal extensions, in terms of a basic space–time plenum. We would still be led to ask, Whence came that plenum as the basic entity of the universe, and why is it formed so as to give the natural laws and properties that we find? There is nothing in the procedures of science to indicate any stopping point in the regress that carries us from one level of explanation to the next. We observe nature, generalize our observations, and find a set of constructs that explain those observations. Scientific genius may carry us to yet another set of constructs and relations that give further explanation, and from there perhaps yet further, and so on. This empirico-deductive method gives us insight, understanding, and the power of broad generalization, but, as scientists have long observed, each new achievement in science seems to open new domains for new investigations.

We shall return in the concluding chapter to the question of the elusive final explanation, but for now we can stop with the limitation on explanation that is inherent in the deductive structure of scientific theory. Deductive systems rest on axioms, and somewhere, in a finite science, there must be a primary set of postulates, not deduced from a prior, more general set.

A first limitation on the completeness of science comes with the selection of subject matter in any science. We said that a complete science is one in which all desired description has been achieved, and that this diminution from all descriptive detail was necessary because of the indefinitely large amount of the latter. There is, however, no reason to think that selection will necessarily be of the most essential aspects of nature. Even when the science of zoology, say, is complete in our defined sense, we may have overlooked significant aspects of animal life. Thus, to give a hypothetical example, we know that many animals perform striking feats of navigation, as, for instance, the flights over thousands of miles by migrating birds. These trips can apparently be achieved as a result of sensitivities which, among others, may be to scents, magnetic fields, stellar configurations, or slight temperature differences. These would be sensitivities that are innate with some animals but are only obtained by human beings through elaborate instrumentation. We cannot know, then, but that in studying animals in terms only of factors that are obvious to our sensibilities we are failing to learn essential things about animals.

Or, we might think of the bias about what is important in the universe that comes with our particular size. Have we actually selected for study those forces and structures which are of greatest significance for the nature of the universe? It is a common observation in physics that gravitational force, which is of highest importance to a human being's locomotion, would be a trivial matter to a small insect who would find air resistance, air currents, and surface tension (when it is in contact with liquids) to be of much greater concern.

Selection of certain aspects of nature is determined not only by what is most egregiously presented to us for understanding or control, but is also to a considerable extent determined by scientific theory itself.[13] Scientists tend to look for that which they can understand in the terms of their accepted scientific theory, and to solve the problems that are tractable with that theory. The behavior of gases, although important indeed, is not obviously of more importance in ordinary experience than that of liquids and solids; yet what student of physics or chemistry is given college instruction about the latter, for which the theory is fragmentary and difficult, comparable in extent to his study of the relatively easy and well-understood kinetic theory of gases? Questions of how inherited traits go from generation to generation have certainly been of interest for centuries; yet, apparently slight scientific attention was given to them before the first dvelopment in the nineteenth century of a proper genetic theory.

One might argue that the importance of theory for selection is only another way of stating that while science is still incomplete, not all desired facts will have been obtained and not all domains brought within the compass of a theory. Still, if it is agreed that there is always some selection, it follows that there is always some arbitrariness in the theory, and hence some limitation on completeness.

Putting the matter of limitations in the least favorable way, we can say that the understanding which we gain from science is always highly incomplete, because we are at best only carried from one set of questions to another. And, we might grimly add that the basic ideas, the stopping points, of one scientific epoch are frequently replaced by quite different concepts

[13] The influence of accepted theory on the aspects of nature selected for study is emphasized by Thomas S. Kuhn in his book, *The Structure of Scientific Revolutions* (Chicago, The University of Chicago Press, 1962).

at a later epoch, so that we cannot even have much confidence in the ultimate postulates of science at any time. Further, since any science gives only a partial picture (only, say, the physical aspects, or the chemical, or the biological, or the economic) for the object it studies, we never see anything whole in science. We have, then, carried a notion of completeness in science as far as the highest expectations for future success would allow, and still we have found these limitations inherent in the method of science: we can have neither total description nor ultimate and final understanding.

There is, I think, no escaping these limitations, and scientists are generally aware of them. Nonetheless, there is no cause for us to falter in our carrying on of science as a successful way of learning about the universe. Although we do not see a path to a final closed theory, we have immediately with us the richness of insight into nature that has come with science and continues unabatedly to grow. Also, even though first principles of science do change, we need not therefore feel altogether skeptical about the concepts of our day. Sometimes, it is true, a widely held theory is found to have been altogether wrong: thus, there simply was no fluid substance constituting heat, as required in the caloric theory. But commonly, discarded first principles are valid for the experience on which they were based, and remain so under special assumptions of the broader theory. Newtonian mechanics is still true and adequate for most physical situations in our natural world, even though it is now a special case of (as Philipp Frank phrased it) "relativity; a richer truth." Even the comparatively naive atomic theory of the ancients is, if one does not push it too far, a first approximation to a basic statement of the nature of matter.

In thinking of the position in which science leaves us with respect to unexplained postulates, we should recall too that there are possibilities for surprises as great as those in the past. When the group of philosophers at the University of Paris in the fourteenth century were doing the work in mechanics that laid the groundwork for the first flowering of modern science, they can little have suspected how the world they discerned would be sundered by science. The coherent medieval cosmos, once so fresh and appealing, with its final causes and ultimate purposes readily traced to a God who was described in virtually every aspect of life, was gradually replaced by the natural world constructed by science. This world has the firmness and conviction that come with empirical verification, but it is open, fragmentary, and not obviously meaningful. A return to the theological assurance of a medieval world cannot be expected, but by its very openness there are possibilities that science may yet show us more ultimate intelligibility in nature than has as yet been disclosed.

Finally, even though the element of selection is inevitable in science, it is to be noted that selection is not by chance. To some extent, the elements which are most prominently available for study in nature do tend to be the most important; the sun and planets, for example, properly are the basic components of the solar system, and it is fitting with a natural order of importance that they should have been observed and studied before the streams of charged particles in interplanetary space. When matters are not at first correctly judged with respect to what is important, the search for causal relations does tend to lead science to the most basic and pervasive elements. Chemists did after a time come to a realization of the significance of a constituent of air for combustion, even though superficial observation seemed to show fire coming of itself out of burning materials. Scientists certainly do select that which is amenable to their methods, for detailed study and explanation, and by this procedure it is the "easier" problem which tends to be solved. Yet, there is a working away at the difficult, complex problems as a science seeks to achieve completeness in its domain. Even the solid and liquid states of matter, which are complex in contrast with the gaseous, are now yielding to the application of basic physical and chemical theory. As noted before, and perhaps of greater significance and interest, there is the considerable achievement that biology, biochemistry, and biophysics have already made in using that theory to understand living structure and processes.

The feature about selection that is to be emphasized is perhaps not its inevitability, but that scientists can select the aspect of nature for study where we most want knowledge. Understanding, then, need not come only where the development of science happens to be able to give it, but in some degree it can be sought for in what seems most significant for our knowledge of nature.

With these comments on the limitations of science we conclude a first approach to the completeness problem. Our discussion has been in terms of rather general features of science and logic, and it has led us to a plausible characterization for completeness of a science, as well as to some conclusions about limitations for science. But we want also to consider in detail some of the specific results of natural and mathematical science; some of the things that science discovers about the world are as necessary for consideration of the possible completeness of our understanding as are the methods and structure of science. We shall first, however, discuss the rather recondite result of logical studies, Gödel's theorem, for which a presentation was promised.

5

The Gödel Incompleteness Theorem

1   INTRODUCTORY COMMENT

THERE has been wide comment on "Gödel's theorem" in philosophical and quasi-philosophical writings, usually to the effect that the theorem disclosed a necessary limitation in our knowledge. There is a sense in which such statements are clearly correct; it is a major consequence of the theorem that, granted their assumptions, most systems of logic and mathematics that are of interest to us can never again be regarded as having the possibilities for demonstrable certainty which had been attributed to them. It is not obvious whether or not there are any direct consequences of the theorem that are of importance for natural science. But, we shall find in our discussion that propositions similar to the kind established by the theorem can be of definite relevance to the problem of completeness in science, and possibly even to the specific content of physics.

The theorem is a statement about formal, deductive systems that was enunciated and proven in 1931 by the Austrian–American mathematician Kurt Gödel.[1] It shows that in any logical system of sufficient complexity which is internally consistent, one may always describe propositions which cannot be proven or disproven within the system. The phrase "within the system" is of key importance. In a larger system, the so-called metasystem, in which the original system is included and in which it may be discussed, the propositions

[1] The original paper is K. Gödel, "Über formal unentscheidbare Sätze der Principia Mathematica und verwandter Systeme I," *Monats. für Math. u. Phys.*, 38, 173 (1931). A translation into English has been made by B. Meltzer, with an introduction by R. B. Braithwaite, *On Formally Undecidable Propositions of Principia Mathematica and Related Systems* (Edinburgh, Oliver & Boyd, 1962). A popular account has been written by Ernest Nagel and James R. Newman: *Gödel's Proof* (New York, New York University Press, 1958). Other discussions which I have also found helpful are the book by Andrzej Mostowski, *Sentences Undecidable in Formalized Arithmetic* (Amsterdam, North-Holland, 1952); the account in R. L. Wilder's *Introduction to the Foundation of Mathematics* (New York, Wiley, 1952); the paper by J. Findlay, "Gödelian Sentences: A Non-Numerical Approach," *Mind*, 51, 259 (1942); and the detailed exposition in Herman Weyl's *Philosophy of Mathematics and Natural Science* (Princeton, N. J., Princeton University Press, 1949).

may generally be proven or disproven; but Gödel's theorem requires that in this larger system it will again be possible to make statements which cannot be proven or disproven in that system, and so on for any further system which one develops. Gödel's theorem tells us, then, that a consistent deductive system is always incomplete, inherently and of necessity, since it is always possible to formulate statements of the system which are *undecidable* within the system. In contrast, before Gödel's work it had generally been assumed that a statement made with the prescribed terms of a given system could be shown by deductive methods within the system either to be or not to be a logical consequence of the axioms of the system. The property of an inconsistent system, that every proposition stated in the system may be proven, does of course indicate why Gödel's theorem is applicable only for consistent systems.

It is not the case that every deductive system is incomplete in the manner required by Gödel's theorem, and in fact Gödel has proven that certain systems among the so-called "first-order functional calculi" are complete. However, in general, the higher-order functional calculi, systems in which there is quantification of functional variables through the appearance of terms like "all" or "some," or in which there are statements of relations of relations or relations of properties, are not systems for which ordinary completeness may be demonstrated. Specifically *any* system constructed in a conventional manner which is broad enough to contain the formalized number theory that gives us arithmetic is one to which Gödel's proof of incompleteness does apply. Most of the axiomatic systems in which some part of mathematics is formalized do meet this criterion, and certainly the language of natural science is generally rich enough to contain arithmetic; hence, the exceptional systems for which Gödel's incompleteness cannot be demonstrated are of little concern to us.

Gödel constructed the proof of the existence of undecidable statements for an arithmetical system, that is, for a system containing whole numbers and the operations of addition and multiplication. His result, therefore, explicitly tells us that it is possible to formulate propositions in a given system of arithmetic which are not decidable in that system.

On first meeting with a statement of what Gödel's theorem establishes, a person is inclined speculatively to search for illustrative undecidable statements. What assertion in arithmetic, for example, could be shown to be such that it can never be proven or disproven? One might think of some theorem concerning prime numbers far in the reaches of the number system, where explicit calculation could not give a result. The undecidable Gödelian sentences, however, as they have been formulated, are not of this nature. They are not primarily expressive of results pertaining to the content of a system, or to what we learn by using the system. If the sentences were content-sentences of this kind, we would hardly expect them to have the property that even though the undecidability may be removed in a metasystem, a new undecidable sentence may always be formulated in *that* system, to be in turn removed in a still more inclusive system, and so on. Rather than making assertions about term properties, or about relations between terms of a system, the undecidable sentences of Gödel's proof are of a kind that make assertions about the provability or unprovability of a certain sentence. And further, the sentence about which the assertion is made is commonly the very sentence itself that is making the assertion. There is, then, a primitive logical property of deductive symbolic systems that is manifest in Gödel's undecidable sentences. This elemental property gives his incompleteness theorem wide validity for systems which are of a certain minimum level of complexity.

It should also be emphasized, however, that the Gödelian sentences are propositions of arithmetic. It is because they are, that their existence entails the incompleteness of proof in arithmetical systems. The construction and interpretation that show the undecidability of the sentences give them their significance. It is quite conceivable, however, that undecidable sentences might be found to have mathematical significance, in their ordinary interpretation as statements about number. As yet, however, no significant mathematical results (apart from the question of decidability itself) have been found for any Gödelian sentences.

Gödel remarks in his paper that there is an analogy between his result and the logical antinomy known as Richard's antinomy; and also, a close relationship to the "antinomy of the liar." The latter is particularly simple, and we may discuss it alone as indicating the kind of reflexiveness that is characteristic of Gödel's proof. The liar antinomy is illustrated by a situation in which a man makes the declaration, "The statement I am now making is false." The paradox is evident. If the statement is true, then it must be false in consequence of what the statement says about itself. On the other hand, if the statement is false, then it must state an untruth in saying that it itself is false, and instead it must be true. The declaration gives us contradiction, and therefore tells us that it is possible within the rules of the English language to be led to statements which contain contradiction, even though one does not make outright contradictory assertions.

Our language, of course, in all its richness and subtlety, can include many regions of inconsistency and ambiguity. A language such as a logical or mathematical system, however, which is to be used as a tool for precise communication and for exploration of deductive relationships, must be consistent. Gödel found that certain mathematical statements could be interpreted as referring to their own provability, as does the statement of the liar to its own truth, and could not be decided in a mathematical system if the system were still to be consistent.

2   GÖDEL NUMBERS

A notable technical achievement of Gödel in his proof of undecidability was that he devised a way in which a system could "talk about itself," within its own system of symbols. A mathematical system contains defined symbols, operations, and axioms or basic rules of inference. From these, formulas of various kinds and proofs of formulas are constructed. We consider the explicit arrangements of symbols that make up a formula, or the groupings of formulas into a proof, to be essential parts of the system. However, discussions of how a given formula is reached, that is, discussion of operations in the system such as substitutions in a formula, sequential arrangement of formulas, status of a formula as axiomatic or derived, are carried on in a "metamathematical" system (in English-speaking countries, normally some part of the English language). By an arithmetization procedure Gödel assigned numbers to formulas and terms, so that these metamathematical statements could be made in the terms (numbers) of the system itself. In this way he could within the system present considerations bearing on the provability of a certain sentence.

We shall not attempt to proceed so far into the technical details of the incompleteness proof as to show the particular sequence of formulas, each of which has a number-equivalent, which Gödel uses. It is desirable, however, that we see what his arithmetization procedure is. His basic logical signs or symbols are the following, with the number assigned to each symbol written below it:[2]

0	f	$\sim$	$\vee$	Π	$($	$)$
1	3	5	7	9	11	13

Individual variables, like $x, y, z, \ldots$, which range over the natural numbers and may be infinite in number, are assigned prime numbers $17, 19, 23, \ldots$. Functions of the first order, $F_1, G_1, H_1, \ldots$, for classes of individuals, are assigned numbers $17^2, 19^2, \ldots$. Variables of the third type, for classes of classes of individuals, are given numbers $17^3, 19^3$, etc. And in general, variables of type n are given numbers p^n, where p is a prime > 13. Certain sequences of numbers correspond, then, to formulas of the system; e.g., the sequence $17 \; 17^2 \; 11 \; 19 \; 13$ corresponds to $xF_1(y)$.

The *Gödel number* of a formula is not, however, merely a sequence of symbol numbers, although the latter is used in formulating the Gödel number. Suppose there are m symbols in the number sequence; then, the first m prime numbers are associated with the number sequence of the formula, the first prime with the first number of the sequence, the second with the second, etc. (1 is not taken as a prime.) The Gödel number of the formula is the *product* of the m primes, with each prime raised to the power of the symbol-number associated with it. Thus, the Gödel number for the formula $xF_1(y)$ is $2^{17} \cdot 3^{17^2} \cdot 5^{11} \cdot 7^{19} \cdot 11^{13}$. There is a unique formula associated with every Gödel number, because for every natural number not itself a prime there is a unique resolution into prime factors.

The Gödel numbers of formulas may be used to construct still one further kind of Gödel number, the *sequence number* of any given sequence of formulas. This number is the product,

$$2^{n(1)} \cdot 3^{n(2)} \cdots p_k^{n(k)},$$

where again we have a product of primes, with each prime raised now to the power of the Gödel number of the formula that corresponds to that prime. Thus, $n(1)$ is the Gödel number of the first formula in the sequence of formulas, $n(k)$ is the Gödel number of the kth formula. This sequence number is also unique, for any given sequence of formulas, and, because of the uniqueness of factorization into primes, one number corresponds at most to a single sequence. Hence, for any number 0, 1, 2, 3, . . . we may determine "whether the number is the Gödel number of a basic sign, or of a series of basic signs, or of a series of series of basic signs, or is not a Gödel number at all . . . ; and if the number is a Gödel number, the rule [i.e., the arithmetization procedure] specifies uniquely which string [sequence] it is of which it is the Gödel number." [3]

By means of the Gödel numbers, it is possible to discuss the structure of the system in terms of the numerical elements of the system. In his paper, Gödel speaks of the metamathematical concepts as being expressed in an "isomorphic image of the system," [4] the image being formed by use of the Gödel numbers in the domain of arithmetic. More specifically, Gödel writes, [5]

"Accordingly, then, a formula is a finite series of natural numbers, and a particular proof-schema is a finite series of finite series of natural numbers. Metamathematical concepts and propositions thereby become concepts and propositions concerning natural numbers, or series of them, and therefore at least partially expressible in the symbols of PM itself. In particular, it can be shown that the concepts, 'formula,' 'proof-schema,' 'provable formula,' are definable in the system PM, i.e., one can give the formula $F(v)$ of PM—for example—with one free variable v (of the type of a series of numbers), such that $F(v)$—interpreted as to content—states: v is a provable formula."

We may give still one further statement on the role of Gödelian numbers, this one a quotation from J. Findlay's paper[6]: "The sentence considered by Gödel does not, however, directly say of itself that it is not demonstable, but only that a certain *number*, which is uniquely correlated with the sentence in question, is characterized by a numerical property which corresponds to indemonstrability. It therefore raises the issue of undecidability in the arithmetical as well as the linguistic realm."

[3] R. B. Braithwaite, introduction to K. Gödel, *On Formally Undecidable Propositions of Principia Mathematica and Related Systems*, translated by B. Meltzer (Edinburgh, Oliver & Boyd, 1962), p. 8.
[4] K. Gödel, *ibid.*, p. 39, note 9.
[5] K. Gödel, *ibid.*, p. 39. The symbols "PM" refer to A. N. Whitehead and B. Russell's *Principia Mathematica*; Gödel used as his system those parts of *Principia Mathematica* in which the arithmetic of natural numbers is established.
[6] J. Findlay, "Gödelian Sentences: A Non-Numerical Approach," *Mind*, 51, 260 (1942). The interested reader will find a concise, *purely verbal* expression of an undecidable Gödelian sentence in this paper.

3   EXPOSITION OF THE THEOREM

We shall now present an informal sketch of the proof procedure that Gödel uses; our treatment is suggested by that of Mostowski.[7]

We suppose that our system S (which contains the arithmetic of integers) has in it a defined infinite sequence of sentence-forms,

$$W_1(p), W_2(p), \ldots, W_n(p), \ldots, \tag{1}$$

where each sentence has one free variable p that runs over the integers. The sentences W_n are definitions of properties of integers, and it is possible to state these definitions by means of the Gödel numbers. Thus, to state the property of provability for a number p, we would show that p is the Gödel number of the final formula of a derivation, whose sequence number defines a W_j corresponding to provability.

We wish, however, to state for an integer n that n cannot be shown to possess the property expressed by W_n. We may write this statement as,

$$\text{The sentence } W_n(n) \text{ is unprovable in } S. \tag{2}$$

With the writing of (2) we have specified a particular property, the unprovability in S of $W_n(n)$, that is to be expressed by one of our $W(p)$'s. We will write that $\phi(n, p)$ for any n, p is the Gödel number of the sentence $W_n(p)$. Also, we let T be the class of Gödel numbers of the theorems of S. The property (2) may be restated,

$$\phi(n, n) \text{ is not a member of the class } T. \tag{3}$$

The sentence (3) expresses a property of a number, and, since it is such a property, it may be expressed by some one sentence, W_q, of the sequence of sentences (1). Further, as already noted, by means of the arithmetization procedure these sentences may be expressed in S by Gödel numbers. Specifically, we may in principle find the Gödel number for $W_q(p)$, a number which would have the interpretation that there is not a Gödel number such that the formula with the number p is deducible (provable) in S. We say that this Gödel number for $W_q(p)$ is q.

We now substitute the qth numeral for the free variable p of $W_q(p)$, so that the property W_q is now applied to its own number. We now have $W_q(q)$, where in place of a variable p in the formula we have the definite number q. (The number q itself referred to a formula with a variable p.) But since $W_q(q)$ is a formalization in S of (3), it says the same thing as does "$\phi(q,q)$ is not a member of class T." That is, $\phi(q,q)$ is the Gödel number of $W_q(q)$, but also $W_q(q)$ is an expression of (3), with $n = q$. Since (3) and (2) are

[7] A. Mostowski, *Sentences Undecidable in Formalized Arithmetic* (Amsterdam, North-Holland, 1952), pp. 5–9.

equivalent, $W_q(q)$ states that the sentence $W_q(q)$ is unprovable in S. Or, in the realm of Gödel numbers, $W_q(q)$ in effect says that its own Gödel number does not belong to the class of Gödel numbers of provable statements (theorems) of S. We have stated that $W_q(q)$, which is the unprovability of ascribing property W_q to number q, is unprovable in S, and, we have given the prescription, in principle, for finding the number in S, $\phi(q,q)$, which is equivalent to this statement.

The proof of undecidability of the sentence $W_q(q)$ now readily follows. If the sentence $W_q(q)$ were proven we would have a contradiction, because its content states that $W_q(q)$ is unprovable. On the other hand, if it were proven that $W_q(q)$ is false (i.e., if the negation of $W_q(q)$ were provable), we would have proven that $W_q(q)$ is provable. But this again would be contradictory, because $W_q(q)$ states that $W_q(q)$ is unprovable. It almost seems, as Weyl suggests,[8] that an explosion should occur if we write the Gödel number, $\phi(q,q)$, that is the arithmetic equivalent in S of $W_q(q)$. The numbers ϕ and q are definitely prescribed, and yet nothing of the kind occurs. Instead, we must conclude that $W_q(q)$ is neither provable nor unprovable, since, if it were either, our system S would not be consistent. We say, then, that if S is consistent the sentence $W_q(q)$ is undecidable in S.

We may restate the situation, in its verbal construction, as follows. $W_q(q)$ is, q has the property W_q. What is this property? It is the property that it is not provable that W_q belongs to some specified integer. Thus, $W_q(q)$ assigns to integer q the property that it is not provable that W_q belongs to integer q. Now, in order to give a quasi-pictorial representation of the need for undecidability, if consistency is to be maintained, we will use a wavy line over a group of words to mean that the proposition constituted by those words can be proven, and a straight line over a group to mean that the proposition expressed by them cannot be proven. Then, by virtue of the definition of property W_q, $W_q(q)$ has the meaning: $\overline{W_q \text{ belongs to } q}$. So, if $\widetilde{W_q(q)}$, we have both $\overline{W_q \text{ belongs to } q}$, which is the relation of W_q to q expressed by $W_q(q)$, and $\overline{W_q \text{ belongs to } q}$, which is the property that q has by virtue of the nature of the property W_q. Hence, we have a contradiction. On the other hand, if $\sim\widetilde{W_q(q)}$, where "$\sim$" means negation, we at once have $\overline{W_q \text{ does not belong to } q}$. However, the *property* W_q is $\overline{W_q \text{ belongs to } q}$, and the expression immediately preceding states that it can be proven that q does not have this property. But if it can be proven that q does not have the property $\overline{W_q \text{ belongs to } q}$, it must be possible to prove that W_q does belong to q, i.e., $\widetilde{W_q \text{ belongs to } q}$. Again, then, we have a contradiction. So, as before, we conclude that if the system is consistent $W_q(q)$ can neither be proven nor

[8] Hermann Weyl, *Philosophy of Mathematics and Natural Science* (Princeton, New Jersey, Princeton University Press, 1949), p. 229.

disproven. The key point in the proof presented by Gödel is the "self-reflection" of W_q: W_q is a property of a number, to the effect that this very property is not provable.[9]

Although Gödel found a sentence that was undecidable in the system to which it belonged, he further showed that this same sentence was provable (was a true sentence) in the metasystem in which the sentence and system were discussed. We can indicate his argument with our sentence W_q of system S. We have shown, in the metalanguage, that $W_q(q)$ is undecidable because of the contradictions that arise within the system if $W_q(q)$ is proven or disproven (within the system). This means that we cannot prove that the property W_q belongs to q. But our sentence $W_q(q)$ that is undecidable in system S is precisely just that "The sentence $W_q(q)$ is unprovable in S." The sentence, then, is a true sentence, provable in consequence of our metalinguistic considerations about the undecidability of the sentence in S. Or, as Gödel puts the matter in the introductory section of his paper[10]: "So the proposition which is undecidable in the system PM yet turns out to be decided by metamathematical considerations."

Our result is a remarkable one. We find a sentence that is undecidable in a system, and yet our very consideration that the sentence must be undecidable[11] in its system requires that it be a true sentence in the metasystem of our discussion.

One might well ask, if we find that the undecidable sentence of system S is a true sentence, provable in a larger system, may we not add to the axioms of system S a statement to the effect that the sentence is provable? We could then presumably say that the system S', formed of system S plus the new axiom, is complete. However, the system S' including the new axiom is subject to the same "arithmetization" process (the formation of Gödel numbers for formulas and proofs) as was the system S. It may be shown, then, that some new sentence $W_{q'}(q')$ may be formed, which states "the sentence $W_{q'}(q')$ is unprovable in S'." We shall not give any indication of detailed proof of this result, except to point out that the proof of the undecidable sentence in S involved no reference to any specific axioms, and hence one might expect also to come to an undecidable sentence in S' by following a similar procedure. There would be a failure to do so if the sentence $W_{q'}(q')$ that was constructed were found to be identical with the sentence $W_q(q)$, which now,

---

[9] It may be pointed out for the mathematical reader that Weyl [*Philosophy of Mathematics and Natural Science* (Princeton, New Jersey, Princeton University Press, 1949), Appendix A] finds an interesting similarity in structure between the Gödel proof of incompleteness and the Cantor diagonal proof of nondenumerability of real numbers. In that proof (to be discussed in Chapter 6), a new nonterminating decimal can always be written from the diagonal terms, $N(i,i)$, each changed in value, and hence it follows that all numbers cannot be counted with the integers. In the Gödel proof, we can write all sentences $W_q(q)$, or Gödel numbers $\phi(q,p)$, for the nonprovability property as long as $p \neq q$. But when $p = q$, we come to a "diagonal" sentence that cannot be included among the sets numbered by the integers.

[10] K. Gödel, *On Formally Undecidable Propositions in Principia Mathematica and Related Systems*, translated by B. Meltzer (Edinburgh, Oliver & Boyd, 1962), p. 41.

[11] Unprovable, not *dis*provable.

in S', is not undecidable. The construction procedure would not come to this, however, because the statement (3) requires the sentence $W_{n'}(n')$ to be unprovable in S', and this property is not one which would obtain in S' for $W_q(q)$. The new undecidable sentence can be decided in a still more comprehensive system S''; however, yet another undecidable sentence may be constructed in that system; and so on. Mostowski points out that "the problem of how long the construction of different systems can be continued is at present still far from solution," although it is clear that the number which can be constructed is greater than any finite number.[12]

4 SIGNIFICANCE OF THE THEOREM

There is a quality about Gödel's proof of incompleteness that might make it disappointing to the natural scientist. One rather expects the undecidable sentence to indicate some subtle properties of the world that are forever beyond our knowledge. Instead, one learns of propositions that speak of nothing more than their own unprovability; one's response is likely to be that the undecidable sentence is a contrived singularity rather than any indication of substantial incompleteness.

We must not forget, however, that the Gödel theorem is a theorem about undecidability in an arithmetical system, and may also be considered as an arithmetical proposition; hence, however trivial the theorem may appear in a verbal account, it does introduce a limitation on the completely deductive property of arithmetical systems. One cannot at all foresee what total implications such a limitation may have. As an immediate result, Gödel's theorem changed the minds of mathematicians and logicians about what are the possibilities for demonstration of rigorous and complete proof in mathematical systems. There is not just the fact of necessary incompleteness in mathematical systems containing arithmetic. We recall that the undecidable sentences of a system may be shown to be true in a more inclusive system, the metalanguage of the system. This means, then, that the truth content of a mathematical system cannot be completely expressed by the deductive methods of the system itself. The demonstration of this fact was a severe blow to hopes that by mathematical–logical methods one could rigorously demonstrate the deductive completeness of mathematics.

Gödel's work has in general stimulated an immense amount of work on questions of consistency and decidability in mathematics.[13] Some mathematical

[12] A. Mostowski, *Sentences Undecidable in Formalized Arithmetic* (Amsterdam, North-Holland, 1952), pp. 111–112.

[13] See e.g., A. A. Fraenkel and Y. Bar-Hillel, *Foundations of Set Theory* (Amsterdam, North-Holland, 1958). It should be noted that Leon Henkin (discussion and references in Fraenkel and Bar-Hillel's book, p. 289) has in fact demonstrated that the completeness property *does* hold for calculi of higher order than the first, if we admit a wide class of models in which the range of the predicate variables is not uniquely determined by the range of the individual variables. These models seem not to be of much mathematical interest.

systems of not very high complexity (examples are elementary Boolean algebra and the elementary theory of Abelian groups) have been shown to be decidable. But a long list can be given of mathematical systems in addition to arithmetic which have been shown to be undecidable: for example, in algebra, the elementary theories of groups, rings, fields, and lattices, among others; also, both elementary group theory and set theory. To have radically changed the expectation for work in the foundations of mathematics, to have introduced specific decidability limitations in wide fields of mathematics, and to have profoundly altered philosophical conceptions of the kind of deductive completeness that may be obtained with the methods of logic and mathematics: these effects show the error in an attitude that would find the work of Gödel, and of those who further developed his discovery, to be trivial. And, it is perhaps reasonable to expect that there may be surprising developments yet to come in technical mathematics and logic from the lines of investigation that were initiated by Gödel's proof; for the proof of undecidability is on a level of basic significance in those fields, and it is from basic theoretical changes that we generally expect far-reaching advances throughout a field. The status of the undecidability theorem is well expressed by R. B. Braithwaite in his introduction to the English translation of Gödel's paper: "Gödel's discovery of this incompleteness [of arithmetic], presented in this paper, is one of the greatest and most surprising of the intellectual achievements of this century." [14]

Given the great mathematical, logical, and philosophical import of the incompleteness theorem, we expect that it should have relevance to our consideration of completeness in the natural sciences. A science that has achieved a fair degree of theoretical organization usually contains the body of arithmetic within itself, and hence should be subject to the formulation of undecidable statements. In the words of J. G. Kemeny,[15] "We know that each body of theories in Science is an interpreted mathematical system of a fairly advanced type. Hence it has some unanswerable questions in it. What we don't know is whether any of the unanswerable questions concern predictions. But we have no reason to suppose that none of them do . . . . This suggests the interesting possibility that, not only must we expect an endless advance on the part of theoretical scientists, but that this progress must go hand in hand with the endless progress of the mathematicians, if it is to be of use to mankind."

And yet it is, on first inspection at least, difficult to see how Gödelian incompleteness would be of significance in any of the natural sciences. The propositions of science that are of interest to us as scientists are those which assert properties or relations for the constructs of the natural world. Or, in

[14] R. B. Braithwaite, introduction to K. Gödel, *On Formally Undecidable Propositions in Principia Mathematica and Related Systems*, translated by B. Meltzer (Edinburgh, Oliver & Boyd, 1962), p. 32.

[15] John G. Kemeny, *A Philosopher Looks at Science* (Princeton, New Jersey, Van Nostrand, 1959), pp. 192–193.

brief, the statements of science are directed to the world of natural entities. In contrast, with the interpretation that is superimposed on their arithmetical structure, the undecidable sentences of Gödel's proof point to a property of sentences, with no reference at all to the natural world. (In the Gödelian sentences which we saw in the previous section, the reference of the sentence was in fact to a property of its own self, but it has been shown by E. L. Post that the Gödelian sentence need not necessarily be directly self-referential in that manner.[16]) It is true that discussion of the natural world might be on a purely linguistic rather than a "thing" level: we might for example choose to say, "all statements that assert the principle of conservation of energy are true statements," rather than simply to say that "energy, taking into account its possible forms, is never destroyed or created in a manifest physical process." But the reference, through one intermediate step, is still to natural processes, and regard for inductive knowledge would therefore enter into assessment of the validity of the sentence. In contrast, the reference of Gödelian sentences, to repeat, is altogether noninductive: one is asking (in numerical terms) only about provability of a certain type of sentence with regard to the provability techniques defined within the system. Systems of logic and mathematics are set up on axioms which are not determined in any direct sense by reference to experience, and it is entirely in these systems that Gödelian undecidability arises.

It might be argued, along the lines of the quotation from Kemeny, that the existence of undecidable sentences in mathematics ensures that undecidability will arise in any science which is developed in a close association with mathematics. Here again, though, a counterargument may be presented. The difficulty of finding the solution for a scientific problem frequently does lie chiefly in the realm of mathematics because a calculated solution is desired, or because consistency must be demonstrated. In principle, however, the natural sciences are asking questions about the experienced natural world, and the constructs which we devise do rest on experience, even though the path from construct to observation may be highly indirect. It seems reasonable to suggest, then, that any question about the validity of a construct or its relations to other constructs may be decided by inference from observation. Practical difficulties of observation may seem insuperable, as, for example, if we ask questions about the interior of a star; and also, we must not ask questions that are physically meaningless, as, say, what is the color of an electron; but such undecidability as may occur in a question about the natural world seems clearly not to be of the Gödelian kind which arises out of the inconsistency that proof or disproof would engender in the system.

We have seen that there are Gödelian undecidable sentences which are decidable in the metasystem in which the undecidability is discussed. We might analogically say that the body of observational statements which are

---

[16] For discussion and references see John Myhill, "Philosophical Implications of Mathematical Logic," *Review of Metaphysics*, **VI**, 184 (1952).

relevant to a science constitute an essential element in an ultimate meta-language for the science. Then, by reference to these statements we remove the undecidability which may arise with respect to questions in the science. In a given Gödelian logical system the total set of decidable and undecidable sentences is greater than the set of decidable sentences, and, likewise, in a natural science with a given achieved body of data the set of all possible sentences is greater than the set of decidable sentences. (We have already seen that in practice we do not attempt to answer all possible questions, or to make all possible observations.) So, for the logical system or the natural science, we can remove undecidability by reference to the metasystem. The use of description of the natural world as an ultimate metalanguage is again, however, very different from the way in which decision about a Gödelian sentence is reached in the metalanguage of the system in which the sentence is undecidable.

In order to make more concrete the argument against any significance for Gödelian sentences as statements of natural science, we might consider what consequences for science could follow from such sentences. The science of mechanics is one for which a formulation as an explicit axiomatic system has been developed,[17] and it is reasonable to assume that arithmetic (which in practice certainly forms part of mechanics) could readily be incorporated into the axiomatic system. We know, then, that we could make Gödelian sentences in the system. Insofar as the sentences were only concerned with assertions of their own unprovability they would not, as has already been pointed out, have any content for natural science. Let us suppose, however, that we found that we were able to involve the properties of mechanical systems in the undecidable sentences; we might, for example, have a mapping between Gödel numbers and an observable (directly or indirectly) property, such that the undecidable Gödel sentence had the interpretation of leaving the disposition of the property in an actual mechanical system undetermined. It is not unreasonable, at least in principle, that we might be able to make such a mapping. We have pointed out that the undecidable Gödel sentences are sentences of arithmetic, and may be given an ordinary arithmetical inter-pretation, as well as the interpretation with respect to decidability which the Gödel-number method gives to them. Since mechanics utilizes arithmetic, it is conceivable that undecidability of an arithmetical proposition could be reflected in the undecidability of a proposition of mechanics (even though, as we have noted, no Gödelian undecidability has as yet been found to have important pure-arithmetic significance). At the very least, just as Gödel's proof implies the impossibility of a complete axiomatization of arithmetic (because there are always true arithmetical propositions that are not provable in a system, though their truth can be demonstrated in a metasystem), like-

[17] See J. C. C. McKinsey, A. C. Sugar, and Patrick Suppes, *Journal of Rational Mechanics and Analysis*, **2**, 253 (1953).

wise the proof would also prevent the complete axiomatization of mechanics, since mechanics does contain arithmetic.

If we were faced with Gödelian undecidability for a proposition of mechanics, we could take the following possible further steps:

(*i*) Since we are assuming the undecidability to be strictly of the kind possessed by a Gödelian sentence, it could be removed by considerations of the metalanguage discourse about the sentence. Hence, there is no question of any genuine undecidability with respect to physical properties of the system. It is of course true that Gödelian sentences could be formed in the metasystem, and *these* sentences might have physical content, and so on.

(*ii*) Taking the undecidability as presented in the original system, one might seek to remove it by recourse to observation-statements (where these function as a type of metasystem, as previously suggested). Such a removal would mean that the undecidable sentence was either true or false, on empirical grounds. The system is therefore inadequate, in that it fails to yield a scientific statement with respect to a certain observation. Again, however, no permanent undecidability with respect to physical knowledge would have been introduced into science as a consequence of the Gödelian sentence; we would only have learned that a given system was not adequate with respect to the empirical information available about the natural domain presumably described by the system.

We are not at all wishing here to say that there is no incompleteness of physical knowledge.[18] Rather, the point to be made is that Gödelian incompleteness is in a realm different from that of natural knowledge. In the words of H. Weyl,[19] "We are not surprised that a concrete chunk of nature, taken in its isolated phenomenal existence, challenges our analysis by its inexhaustibility and incompleteness; . . . But it is surprising that a construct created by mind itself, the sequence of integers, the simplest and most diaphanous thing for the constructive mind, assumes a similar aspect of obscurity and deficiency when viewed from the axiomatic angle."

A first examination of the reference of scientific statements seems to lead us to the conclusion, then, that Gödel's undecidability is not a problem for the natural scientist. Science is not confined within a linguistic realm, as are systems of logic and mathematics. It is true that science is a system of statements, and that it adjusts itself to suitable logical–mathematical systems; but also, its ultimate ground for acceptance or denial of a statement

---

[18] We will see in a later chapter that there is inherent physical undecidability about mechanical variables; although it enters in a way far different from the logically formal way in which we gain Gödelian undecidability, we shall explore the possibility of there being any significant analogy.

[19] Hermann Weyl, *Philosophy of Mathematics and Natural Science* (Princeton, New Jersey, Princeton University Press, 1949), p. 220.

is always outside its linguistic system, and is in the way experience finds nature to be. Hence, we should not expect undecidability which arises out of consistency problems within a language system, and yet is always solvable in some more extensive language, to arise in a substantial, irresolvable way in natural science. There may well be questions about nature which are undecidable because an answer seems not to be obtainable from nature, but any question of undecidability about the natural world that arises purely from linguistic undecidability properties should be resolvable by appeal to the natural world. We can say that an "adequately deductive" system, which allows the Gödelian possibility of true statements not deductively demonstrable in a system, does not imply essential undecidability in a science.

The conclusion that we suggest in the preceding paragraph is a plausible one, and, with a strict interpretation of Gödelian incompleteness as being precisely just the undecidability that Gödel's theorem demonstrates for logical–mathematical systems, I think it is not likely that instances will arise that contradict the conclusion. But with a somewhat relaxed definition of an undecidable sentence I think we can find that incompleteness of a kind analogous to that which Gödel found may appear in natural science. We came to our conclusion about undecidable sentences in science by tacit use of a strict separation between logic (including mathematics) on the one hand, and the natural world, as reflected in descriptive and observational statements about it, on the other. And yet, we might wonder, Does not logic too reflect the way the world is? And if that is so, and there is incompleteness in logic, should we not find some similar incompleteness in science? We shall submit answers to these questions in the remaining two sections of this chapter.

5   LOGIC AND SCIENCE

There is a long tradition in philosophy for the making of a clear distinction between the propositions of logic and those of natural science. Logic is considered as being true in a manner that is independent of the natural world. Thus, for example, the Principle of Noncontradiction, which states that a statement S and its contradiction not-S cannot both be valid, is held to be a statement that would be true in any world. The same may be said for other customarily accepted principles of deductive logic. To the extent that the axioms of a mathematical system are simply those of logic, its propositions also, according to this traditional view, share the characteristic of being true without regard for the nature of the experienced world. The term "analytic" is applied to these propositions, whose warranty for truth lies either in their being basic "necessary" logical truths, or consequences (according to rules of inference implied by the same basic logic) of these truths. Further, it is appropriate to say that for any axiom system the logical or mathematical consequences are analytic with respect to the base axioms. The undecidable sentences of a Gödelian system would also, then, be analytic, since they are deduced consequences in the system.

In contrast, the statements of natural science, or of any knowledge resting on experience, are known as "synthetic" propositions. These are statements that give information about the properties and relations of the world of natural entities, and cannot be regarded as necessarily true in any possible world whatsoever. A rough-and-ready reasonably precise way of distinguishing between the two kinds of statements is by asking just the question, "Can I conceive the contrary to be true?" For an analytic statement, the answer would be "No"—a contradiction within the domain of discourse that is being used appears at once. Thus, we consider the proposition, "It follows from the statement 'all trees require water' that the trees of Michigan require water." If we attempt to conceive the contrary, to wit, that it does not follow from the statement about all trees that the trees of Michigan require water, we come to a contradictory statement that we must reject as false. In contrast, we take the following as an example of a synthetic statement: "The electrical force between two point charges varies as the square of the distance between them." Here we can consider the contradictory statement without offense to our sense of reason; the force might observationally be found not to vary as the inverse square power, but as, say, the -2.01 power of the distance. The inverse square law has been sufficiently well established and related to other physical concepts that a physicist would see many changes in his science to be involved if there were a deviation from the law. But, he could accept nature as being that way, and seek to adjust his science accordingly, without feeling that there had been a break with his sense of rationality.

The precise nature of the distinction between analytic and synthetic propositions is a matter of continuing interest and discussion among philosophers. Some see analytic propositions as being essentially linguistic in nature: one sets up certain rules for how language is to be used, and the rules of logic are basic linguistic conventions. Others see analytic statements as a reflection of an order in reason (and/or the universe) which is of a more fundamental kind than the order discerned by the natural scientist. Still others have suggested that the analytic–synthetic distinction is not a clear-cut one, and is a matter of difference of emphasis rather than of complete difference in reference of proposition. I shall have more to say about this view. In any event, we can see that there is a high relevance for our attitude toward Gödel's theorem: the relation of statements of logic to those of science could determine whether or not the Gödelian incompleteness of logical systems must also appear in natural science.

In the preceding section we came to a conclusion about Gödel's theorem and science that was based on the assumption, in effect, of a strict separation between analytic and synthetic propositions. An expression of a different conclusion, based on a different view of the relation of logic and science, is the following[20]: "If, as agreed, the formal systems can be used to systematize fields of knowledge, and if the Gödel theorem applies to such applications, it would mean that no field of knowledge so systematized can ever be complete. At any stage there will always be questions formulable in the system that need a wider system for their solution. Since it is the contention of the author of this book that logic and mathematics do tell us something about reality, the Gödel theorem tells us that there can never be a complete and final theory of reality, i.e. metaphysics."

The view which Katsoff expresses, "logic and mathematics do tell us something about reality," is one that finds support in the arguments against a complete separation of analytic and synthetic statements. We can argue that logic is valid by definition, but that the choice of what is so defined does itself reflect something about the nature of the world. The Principle of Non-contradiction would seem, by the very definition of what we mean by validity or truth, to be a necessary principle, one to which the mind must give assent. Yet, we might think of a region of our natural world (say the interior of a star) where the temperatures are such that there is no stability of atom or molecule whatsoever. We would then have a world of continual flux: of transitions between matter and radiation, with no entity remaining itself, or fixed in position, for a long enough time by any ordinary human standards to be given definite properties. Hence, the noncontradiction principle applied to matter, in the sense that any entity either has or does not have a given property, would perhaps not be formulated; for, no stable entities to which properties could be ascribed would be discerned. Instead, a logic that emphasized aspects of change, without use of statements about existence or nonexistence of entities or properties, might be suitable, since in a domain of constant change physical existence as we think of it would perhaps be a highly subtle and sophisticated concept.

The illustration just given is a far-fetched one. Nonetheless, it is difficult to accept that the determination of our forms of thought can be altogether independent of the natural experiences of mankind (and looking to the line of his evolutionary development, of other animals as well). And, it seems in fact to be the case that philosophers have not been able to give a characterization of analytic statements which does altogether separate them from experience. The views of the eminent contemporary logician, Willard Van Orman Quine, may be given in support of this statement. Quine writes[21]: "It is obvious that truth in general depends on both language and extralinguistic fact. . . . it seems reasonable that in some statements the factual component should be null; and these are the analytic statements. But, for all its *a priori*

---

[20] Louis O. Katsoff, *A Philosophy of Mathematics* (Ames, Iowa, Iowa State College Press, 1948), pp. 194–195.
[21] W. V. O. Quine, "Two Dogmas of Empiricism" (reprinted from the *Philosophical Review*, Jan., 1951) in *From a Logical Point of View* (Cambridge, Mass., Harvard University Press, 1953), p. 36.

reasonableness, a boundary between analytic and synthetic statements simply has not been drawn. That there is such a distinction to be drawn at all is an unempirical dogma of empiricists, a metaphysical article of faith."

Quine presents and rejects various ways of defining "analytical statement." He then considers that the analytic–synthetic distinction may be saved by appeal to a definition of synthetic statement as one which may be confirmed or disproved by appeal to sensory experience, whereas the analytic statement is true no matter what experience may find. Here too, however, he finds that the total isolation of synthetic or analytic from the other is untenable; for an isolated statement has by itself insufficient meaning to provide a test against experience. Thus Quine writes: "My countersuggestion . . . is that our statements about the external world face the tribunal of sense experience not individually but only as a corporate body." [22]

It is to be accepted that the laws of logic and mathematics are true by definition, or, if one prefers, by axiomatization of basic principles. The laws are, however, applicable to the world of experience, and I believe that in an essential way there is therefore a synthetic element (an element derived from experience) in them. The development of alternative systems of mathematics for a given set of terms illustrates the role that experience can play in the determination of the validity of a system of presumably analytic propositions. Before the development of non-Euclidean geometry, Euclidean geometry was generally accepted as necessarily true, i.e., as a body of statements that were valid independently of any sense experience. (Immanuel Kant's philosophy had its origin to a considerable extent in the question of how a science like geometry, which he regarded as synthetic in that it gave information about spatial properties, could yet also be *a priori* with respect to experience.) With the development of non-Euclidean geometries, equally as consistent internally as Euclidean geometry, it became clear that nature did not *necessarily* fit into the theorems of the latter; and, with the advent of general relativity theory, it became an open question, to be decided by appeal to observation, which geometry was adequately descriptive of physical space.

There are many different kinds of logical or mathematical systems which may be devised, some of which would yield theorems that are far removed from a correct description of the physical world. And yet, it seems clear that the development of the main body of mathematics has been one that is closely associated with perceptions of the natural world. Arithmetic surely has its basis in a world of integral things to be counted, and geometry in a world of physical lines, areas, and volumes. Likewise, calculus grew up with problems of areas under curves and the difficulties of defining velocities and accelerations of material particles. Even in the sophisticated and abstract

---

[22] W. V. O. Quine, "Two Dogmas of Empiricism" in *From a Logical Point of View* (Cambridge, Mass., Harvard University Press, 1953), p. 40. In our discussion of constructs in Chapter 2 we have emphasized that there is a conceptual (or linguistic) element even in the terms of science that seem most immediately derived from sense impressions.

mathematics of today it may be conjectured that physical reasoning is a factor in significant advances. That this (and more) is indeed the case was maintained by the eminent mathematician, John von Neumann, who wrote[23]: "I think it is a relatively good approximation to truth—which is much too complicated to allow anything but approximations—that mathematical ideas originate in empirics, although the genealogy is sometimes long and obscure . . . at a great distance from its empirical source, or after much 'abstract' inbreeding, a mathematical subject is in danger of degeneration . . . the only remedy seems to me to be the rejuvenating return to the source: the reinjection of more or less directly empirical ideas. I am convinced that this was a necessary condition to conserve the freshness and the vitality of the subject and that this will remain equally true in the future."

Even more than with mathematics, the scientist feels that logic must be an expression of the way things are: that logic directly tells of irrevocable conditions on our thinking about the world, without even the mediation of number and quantity that comes with mathematics. Yet, systems of logic which are not in accord with our customary ways of thinking can and have been devised: the multivalued logics, for example, in which there are "truth-values" other than simple "true" or "false." The scientist can see logical necessity, then, as not quite absolute; as having a specified formal structure, and a deep and firm consonance with our way of thinking and doing science; but also, as having some possibility for conceivable modification in an altogether different natural world.

The existence of a synthetic element in logic and mathematics, and of an analytic element in science, finds explicit support in the fact that propositions of science, of direct origin in experience and hence dominantly synthetic, may in the development of science become a consequence of mathematical reasoning and therefore apparently analytic in their nature. A good case in point is the geometric ratio π. It was at first an observable, determined only by measurements of diameter and circumference of circles. Archimedes, however, in the third century B.C., with the use of Euclidean geometry, learned how to calculate π from the properties which a circle has by its very definition. The quantity then became one which was essentially analytic. (One might add that π varies with the curvature that is assigned to space, and so with general relativity theory and the assertion of a dependence of space curvature on the matter that is in the space something of the original synthetic element is returned to the concept of π.)

The late Sir Arthur Eddington hoped to find that the basic constants of physics, including such specific numbers as the total amount of matter in the universe, could be calculated from logical–mathematical considerations; that is, he hoped to find that natural science, at least with regard to its basic quantitative properties, was essentially analytic.[24] Whether or not science can

---

[23] John von Neumann, *Collected Works*, Vol. I (London, Pergamon Press, 1961), p. 9.
[24] See E. T. Whittaker, *From Euclid to Eddington* (New York, Cambridge University Press, 1949). The illustrative case of π is given by Whittaker on p. 185.

be expected to become analytic in the sense that Eddington anticipated is a complex and interesting question, but we shall not attempt to discuss it here. The following, however, is an alternative to Eddington's view which is, I think, more congenial than his to the general outlook of scientists and yet at the same time allows an increasingly analytic character for science. This point of view was put forth some one hundred years ago, by the Cambridge predecessor of Eddington in the philosophy of science, William Whewell. He suggested that as elements of science become more and more firmly established, and a large body of science is developed around these elements, they come to have the character of analytic propositions; so much would topple if they were false, that they come to be regarded as necessarily true. In the words of a present-day student of Whewell[25]: "Whewell's position on necessity may then be summarized thus: The mind, prompted in part by experience, invents modes of connection which it imposes upon experience for the purpose of organizing the latter. It describes the nature of such hypothetical connections in propositions in which there occur the names given to these modes of connection. It then verifies these propositions by appeal to further experience; and, if in this continual process of experiential verification, it is successful with some proposition, it makes the proposition true by fiat, re-interpreting it where necessary to maintain its truth. Finally, the proposition may become inextricable from a corpus of knowledge except by dismemberment of the latter, and may have been so long accepted as true that it is invoked unconsciously, involuntarily, and habitually. At this point, we stop verifying the proposition deliberately, and concern ourselves only with its deductive consequences. . . . Such a proposition is a necessary truth."

If logic and science (or analytic and synthetic propositions) are indeed not two separate and distinct realms, we might expect to find in empirical science manifestations of incompleteness similar to those found by Gödel in logic. We shall now exhibit some synthetic sentences that do show an incompleteness in science. Their content may fairly be termed trivial, and I do not at all mean to say that I have shown Gödelian undecidability in a natural science: to show this would mean to demonstrate with complete rigor for sentences with explicit empirical content the same kind of logical undecidability within a system that Gödel found. I only assert that an incompleteness may be found in empirical science which seems analogous to that found by Gödel in logic and mathematics.

6   LIMITATIONS ON SENTENCES OF SCIENCE

In Section 4 of this chapter I suggested that Gödelian-like undecidable sentences would not normally be expected to appear in science. The grounds for this suggestion were that the referents of scientific sentences are outside of the *language* of science, and hence the sentences may ultimately be decided

[25] Harold T. Walsh, in "Whewell on Necessity," *Philosophy of Science,* **29,** 144 (1962).

by observation of the natural world of which the referents are a part. Science, however, may take any part of the world as a domain for its study, and hence its own language, or its own self, may provide the referents of its sentences. When this occurs we do come to undecidable sentences in science, as well as to certain limitations on what science can describe.

In discussing descriptive science (Chapter 3) I pointed out that if science continued to grow the very artifacts associated with accumulated knowledge would become part of the world to be described; books and libraries, for example, are themselves part of the world to be described by a complete descriptive science. Further, the description of books of science would itself constitute science, which should in turn be described, and so on. We have then an infinite regress in the attempt to achieve completeness of description.

The "infinite regress" limitation is not a form of undecidability, but rather is a limitation simply arising out of the fact that description constitutes an event or series of events that invite further description. But by making use of statements in science that are about statements of science we can readily introduce an undecidability akin to that of Gödelian sentences in deductive systems. Thus, suppose that in Volume Z of a work of scientific description, the 11th sentence of Chapter 5 reads as follows: "The 11th sentence of Chapter 5 of Volume Z is not a valid[26] sentence of scientific description." If this statement is a valid part of our science, it follows from the content of the assertion that there is a contradiction in the science. But likewise, if the 11th sentence is not valid, then it follows from the invalidity of the assertion that it is valid. So, again we come to contradiction. Hence, *if our science is consistent,* the sentence in question cannot be a decidable sentence, and no judgment can be made about whether it is valid or invalid.

The undecidable sentence of descriptive science which I have shown is easily recognized as being similar to the antinomy of the liar. It will be readily conceded that no role of importance is apparent in natural science for this type of sentence; in the words of a biochemist with whom I discussed the sentence, "Why would one ever want to introduce such a statement into a scientific work?" And, yet, it would be rash to say that science would never have occasion to use a sentence of this kind. In any event, we see here a singular point at which descriptive science does yield undecidable sentences, as a consequence of setting up a particular kind of statement about its own self. The undecidability in this case, as in the Gödelian sentence of a deductive system which was presented in Section 3 of this chapter, is concerned with the validity of a sentence which refers to itself. Further, it is a sentence which, because of its undecidability (presuming the science to be consistent), may be judged by the person considering the sentences of the descriptive science

---

[26] I use "valid" rather than "provable," in recognition of the fact that I am now considering an empirical science, with possibilities in the science for establishing statements on the basis of observation.

to be a true sentence, since, if undecidable, it is not valid, and this is what it asserts about itself. Here, the domain of "outside referents" by which the validity of the sentence is judged is just the system of the sentences of the science. In looking at this system, we see that sentence 11, Chapter 5, Volume Z, is not a valid sentence (since it is undecidable), and therefore correct in its statement about itself. Again, though, in the description that we are now making of Volume Z of the descriptive science, there could again be undecidable sentences, of the kind hypothesized in Volume Z, and so on.

We have, then, an analogy between the Gödelian undecidable sentence and a sentence of descriptive science. I would argue that the existence of sentences (as is already indicated by the presence in our language of antinomies like that of the liar) in descriptive language that are similar to those in rigorously deductive systems is an indication of a common element in logic and descriptive science. This element is *the property that in a language one cannot consistently speak of the validity of statements when the statements themselves have properties which contradict that validity.* This characteristic of language is an instance, I suggest, of the general fact that *an activity or process cannot display a property which is explicitly forbidden by the activity or process.*

We may more concretely show this basic limitation by considering not a sentence of descriptive science which refers to its own properties, but instead a scientific device which reports on itself (thus making the device rather than sentences of a scientific language the object of reference of the descriptive science). Suppose a machine M is able to describe various aspects of its environment, including its own behavior. It writes or prints what it describes, and in doing this it thereby creates descriptive science. Further, we suppose that there are mechanisms built into it such that it can, to some determined extent, describe its own behavior at future and past times. Thus, the machine may produce a sentence of the form, "At the future time t machine M will be writing." However, suppose the machine writes: "At the present time, t_0, machine M is not writing." In writing this statement, the machine contradicts the precise content of the statement it writes, to wit, that the machine is not writing.

There is, then, a clear and absolute limitation on the descriptive power of the hypothetical machine. By use of various sensing and computing devices it can be developed, in principle, so as correctly to describe almost any desired aspect of the world. But there is one singular aspect which it cannot report: its own inactivity. I see no way to circumvent this limitation on descriptive science; always, whatever is doing the describing cannot describe its own not-describing. A period of inactivity of the machine M could, of course, be simultaneously described by another machine, but then we would have the limitation that this pair of machines, regarded as a single science-producing device, could not describe its own inactivity (for as long as one machine was operating, the device would not be inactive). Or, alternatively, we could say that even if there are many machines, each of which can describe the activities of all the others, we have the limitation that the situation in which all of the machines are inactive cannot be simultaneously described by the machines. If one wished one could generalize this limitation to the obvious fact that a completely inactive universe could not describe itself.

The inability of a describing machine (or, equally well, one could say "of a scientist") to describe its inactivity, while it occurs, is a kind of singularity in descriptive science. I shall in later chapters discuss limitations in physical science which arise out of particular features of the physical world. The limitation that I am now discussing is one, however, that has its basis quite directly in the noncontradiction principle of logic. One may think of the processes of making descriptive science as giving description of virtually any part, at any time, of our incredibly vast and complex universe. One slight fact, however, remains always descriptively unobtainable; any description, by a process, of inactivity of that process that is simultaneous with the description, would be in contradiction with the inactivity.

The writing of a statement such as "Machine M is not writing at the present time t_0" would not be an undecidable sentence, but would be a clearly false sentence. Thus, if we consider the sentence to be true, we have contradiction, since M in fact is writing at time t_0. If we consider the sentence to be false, we say it must then be the case that the machine is writing, and this is in fact the case. Hence, the attempt of the machine to describe its own inactivity leads to a false sentence, because making the description violates that which was to be described.

It is interesting to notice the difference between the (false) sentence the machine might write about its inactivity and the undecidable sentence, "The 11th sentence of Chapter 5 of Volume Z is not a valid sentence of scientific description," which we have considered. In the case of the undecidable sentence we also have a contradiction between the content of the sentence and the assertion of validity for the sentence. Also, if we postulate that the sentence is invalid, we are in effect asserting the opposite of what the sentence says, since we are then saying that the sentence is valid. It is because we are operating entirely in a linguistic realm that we are able by postulate so to alter what has been said. But since this assertion of validity violates the postulate, that the sentence is not valid, we again have contradiction. In the case of the machine's sentence, the assumption that the statement is false does *not* alter the fact that the machine is still engaged in the activity of writing. Hence, the statement written by the machine literally is false, and there is no contradiction consequent upon the assertion of falseness of the statement. With the machine, an unalterable activity, the machine's writing, is the standard by which validity or invalidity of the machine-written sentence may be determined. For the "11th sentence," the validity or invalidity of the sentence is the standard by which the sentence is to be judged, because the content of the sentence is an assertion about its own validity, not about a physical activity like writing. We thereby alter the standard simply by postulation of validity or invalidity of the sentence, and hence come to contradiction in either case, since the sentence is invalid if assumed valid, and valid if assumed invalid. Thus, the manner in which reference to an extra-linguistic situation will give truth or falsity, rather than undecidability, is nicely illustrated. We might say that we gain, so to speak, in having the external activity as object of our statement, since we then avoid undecidability. The concomitant effect, however, is that we lose the flexibility of the sentence that refers entirely to a linguistic realm and which can arbitrarily assert validity or invalidity about itself.

7 SUMMARY

Our discussions of Gödel's theorem and its relations to science have shown us that proper Gödelian sentences do not have any apparent reference to the natural world, and the incompleteness that they entail seems therefore to be confined to systems of logic and mathematics. I argued, however, that there is no clear break between the languages of logic and of descriptive science, and that therefore we might expect an incompleteness in science that is akin to the Gödelian incompleteness of logic. A necessary incompleteness (although not undecidability) arises with the infinite regress of description of scientific description. Genuinely undecidable sentences may be formed in a science if one of its own sentences is taken as the object of description, and the sentence makes assertion about its own validity. A limitation (again, not an undecidability) may also arise in science when a descriptive sentence of the science is concerned with the activity of making the sentence.

None of the limitations discussed in this chapter have the appearance of seriously curtailing the scope of natural science. In a later chapter, however, when I discuss the one place where definite physical limits have been found in science, that is, in quantum theory, I shall return to the considerations of this chapter. We shall then see that some of the limitations which we have found, trivial as they may appear, may be regarded as analogous to a broad and significant incompleteness principle of physical science.

6

Concepts of Infinity

1 INTRODUCTION

WE HAVE CONSIDERED the incompleteness of science which arises from the impossibility of describing every detail of nature, and that which comes from the fact that an explanatory deductive system rests on assumptions which are themselves not derived. Gödelian incompleteness, we have seen, is of yet another special kind, and arises within a system, without direct reference to the natural world. We now want to ask about some of the ways in which specific properties of nature may put necessary limitations on our scientific knowledge. Our first concern will be with the possibly infinite extent of the universe, and with those concepts with which we try to comprehend such a world.

The lack of any apparent limit in extent is perhaps more explicitly suggestive of a necessary incompleteness in our natural knowledge than is any other aspect of nature. The astronomical universe, with no discernible boundary to its immensity, calls forth a response of awe, and the feeling that comprehension is impossible in the face of such overwhelming magnitude. This limitlessness of nature seems not to be in spatial extent alone. Any thought of the continued occurrence of events leads to contemplation of a series of units of time reaching indefinitely into the past or future. It is often possible to reconstruct the recent past of physical or biological systems for which we know the present state, and also to project what early future states might be. But as we move farther from the present, ignorance increases; what hope is there of gaining knowledge of systems, trivial or primary, for times that are indefinitely removed from the present? And the very question of what is the temporal extent of the natural world comes to our minds.

Besides spatial and temporal vastness, there is another facet of nature which raises a question of apparent infinity: How far on the scale of smallness does the complexity of nature continue? We have found aggregates of matter to consist of molecules, molecules to consist of atoms, and atoms to consist of protons, neutrons, and electrons. Are these elementary particles to be still further subdivided into relatively tiny subparticles with all the complexity of relationship among them that we find within the atom? And, those subparticles might yet again be subdivided, and so on. Our observations of nature do not at all so strongly indicate an unending sequence of ever-smaller structure, as they do indicate indefinitely large extensions in space and time; however, the infinite hierarchy of worlds, each within the other, is a conceivable one, and would also seem to narrow our possible knowledge to a finite part of a domain that is infinitely extended to the small as well as to the large.

I shall consider the possible infinities in nature from the point of view of the scientific knowledge that we have today. In this way, we shall hope to come to some estimate of how overwhelming the limitations of infinite magnitudes in nature actually are. A preliminary step, however, is to discuss the concepts of infinity as they have been developed in Western thought.[1] In this way we shall gain some mathematical tools, and some precision of meaning, for use in the exploration of unboundedness in nature.

2   THE INFINITY OF NATURAL NUMBERS

A quantitative formulation of the concept of infinity arises quite directly from our system of natural numbers. These are the numbers (we also call them positive integers) 1, 2, 3, 4, 5, . . . , where the dots are to indicate that the series of numbers extends indefinitely. It is because the numbers do continue without bound (we are always able to add another) that the number of natural numbers is not finite but is infinite. We are able, further, to define the infinity of numbers by means of definite properties, in addition to that of not being finite.

Suppose that we take particular integers, for example, those that are even, and set up a one–one correspondence between these integers and the entire group of natural numbers. We here mean by a one–one correspondence that with each even number we associate one number of the entire group of natural numbers, and, conversely, with each of these numbers there is associated one even number. Thus, our one–one correspondence is as follows:

$$2 \ 4 \ 6 \ 8 \ 10 \ 12 \ 14 \ . \ . \ .$$
$$1 \ 2 \ 3 \ 4 \ \ 5 \ \ 6 \ \ 7 \ . \ . \ .$$

[1] There is a good exposition of the mathematical theory of infinite quantities in the book, A. A. Fraenkel, *Abstract Set Theory*, 2nd ed. (Amsterdam, North-Holland, 1961). No specialized mathematical background is required for the study of this topic, whose rudiments are indeed beginning to be taught in the elementary schools of the U.S.A. The reader who wishes a less professional discussion will find it in an excellent book by Richard Courant and Herbert Robbins, *What is Mathematics? An Elementary Approach to Ideas and Methods* (New York, Oxford University Press, 1941).

It is evident that we will always be able to find a natural number to associate with each even number; for, given any even number, $2n$, there is a number n to be associated with it. Likewise, given any number n, there is an even number $2n$ to be associated with it. Now, the totality of natural numbers is in some sense greater than the totality of even numbers, because there are natural numbers that are not even numbers. And yet, we have seen that for every even number there is an associated natural number. Putting the matter in another way, we can say that a part of the natural numbers is equivalent, with respect to how many there are, to the entire range of natural numbers. This property, that of a part being quantitatively equivalent to the whole, is a key property of an infinite number of items (in this case the natural numbers), and it is, clearly, a property that is not possessed by a finite number of entities. Four apples are a part of five apples, but we could never set up an equivalence, or one–one relation, between the four and all five.

We can discuss the mathematical concept of infinity more satisfactorily by introducing the term *set*. By a set of things or entities of any kind we merely mean a collection, such that there is some defining property by which we are able to tell whether a given entity does or does not belong to the set. I might refer to the set of movable objects on my desk, or to the set of maple trees in East Lansing, or to the set of tensors of rank 2. And, I may refer to the set of natural numbers. The number of items in a given set is referred to as the cardinal number of the set, and we are able to arrange a one–one correspondence between any two sets that have the same cardinal number (finite or infinite). Thus, the apples of a set of four apples may be put into one–one correspondence with a set of four children but not with a set of three or five. Two sets that may be put into one–one correspondence with each other and which therefore have the same cardinal number, are said to be *equivalent*. Also, we may define a part of some given set as a *subset* of the set; three of the apples in a set of four are a subset of the set, or likewise, father is a subset of a set made up of a family of parents and children. Even all the members of a set may be said to comprise a subset, since they are part of the set, but the mathematician speaks of a proper subset as one that does not contain every member of a set.

We can now refer to the natural numbers, 1, 2, 3, 4, . . . , as the *set* of natural numbers. And, what we saw illustrated in the one–one correspondence between the even numbers and all the numbers is the fact that for the set of all natural numbers there may be a one–one correspondence between the set and a proper subset. We may take this equivalence, of "a part being equal to the whole," as the defining property of an infinite set. This property gives us a sharp difference between an infinite and a finite set. When we say that a set is *unbounded* in its number of entities, we have a notion of a cardinal number for the set that is arbitrarily large ("unbounded" would mean that against any natural number chosen as a cardinal number of the set, one could always select a larger one). But, the set so defined would be conceived as being "infinite" just because the number to be applied could always be regarded as being larger and larger. Still, one is always thinking of finite numbers, large as they may be. But now we say that if a set is infinite, it has a cardinal number that is radically different from any natural number; for the infinite set is such that merely some members of the set are equivalent in number to all members of the set. As we have already noted, a finite set does not have this property.

We regard the set of natural numbers as the basic infinite set: the one to which we can point as the prime example, and which can be identified by anyone with knowledge of number and counting. Just because it is infinite, there is no finite cardinal number that can be assigned to this set. Georg Cantor, who is the major figure in the mathematics of transfinite numbers, assigned the symbol $\aleph_0$ (aleph-zero) to the cardinal number of the set of all natural numbers. Any set, then, whose members may be put into one–one correspondence with the natural numbers also has cardinal number $\aleph_0$. In addition to the even numbers there are many other subsets of the set of natural numbers that may be put into such correspondence, and that therefore also have cardinality $\aleph_0$. There are still other sets too. For example, the set of rational fractions, m/n, where m and n are integers, has been shown to have $\aleph_0$ members. In the physical world, if it is infinite, with matter everywhere dispersed about as we see it in our observable universe, there would have to be $\aleph_0$ atoms, or also, $\aleph_0$ galaxies.

The number $\aleph_0$ has arithmetical properties that are different from the properties of finite numbers (these novel properties are related to the equivalence between an infinite set and certain of its subsets). Thus, for a finite number n, $n + 1 \neq n$, but we do have $\aleph_0 + 1 = \aleph_0$. Also, $\aleph_0 + n = \aleph_0$, $\aleph_0 + \aleph_0 = \aleph_0$, $n \cdot \aleph_0 = \aleph_0$, and even $\aleph_0 \cdot \aleph_0 = \aleph_0$.

The preceding relations show us how very differently we must conceive of an infinite set from one that is finite, but, at the same time, they help us in making the jump in understanding that is necessary for comprehension of an infinite set. Suppose we think of an infinite set of space intervals, each of some finite unit of length, laid out one immediately after the other in a straight line. The set has cardinal number $\aleph_0$, which means that its members may be put into one–one correspondence with the natural numbers. The conception of infinity as unbounded extent gives us the image of the line extending forever, with the necessary addition of more units of length whenever the mind pauses at a suggested end point of the line. This image of infinity is by itself, however, unsatisfying psychologically; even though one increases the line indefinitely, there is never a point at which you can say, "Now I have achieved a concept of an infinite set of lengths."

But with the arithmetical properties of $\aleph_0$ we are able to give additional meaning to the concept of the infinite set. Let us think of the set of unit lengths as forming not a line that can always be made longer, but rather one that is an achieved infinity, one that does contain $\aleph_0$ unit lengths. This line cannot be given greater extent; for, since $\aleph_0 + n = \aleph_0$, the addition of more unit lengths has no effect on the number of lengths in the line. In its property of "going on forever," the infinite line has already achieved as much length as it can have, and no finite addition can increase it. Indeed, we may double the number of unit lengths, triple it, or even multiply the number by $\aleph_0$ itself, and still we do not achieve a longer line. In this property, that ordinary addition or multiplication gives no increase in total cardinal number, we see a characteristic property of an infinite set. It is different from a finite set, in that already it contains all the elements that we can number or count. We get no more by adding to what already comprises as many as can be counted if we use all the natural numbers; we merely again have as many as can be counted. Or, we may go back to our defining property. If the line is actually already infinitely long, we may select, say, every third unit length (or, in general, every nth), and pair up these lengths with the total set, such that every selected length is paired up with one of the total set of lengths. We can, we see, take away an infinite set of elements from an infinite set, with an infinite set still remaining, and find the extracted set to be no greater or less in cardinal number than the original infinite set. These arithmetical properties seem strange indeed, in contrast with the rules of finite arithmetic, but they are mathematically consistent, and can actually be descriptive of possible infinite magnitudes in the natural world.

3   FROM FINITE TO INFINITE

It is to be noted that the "infinity" symbol "∞" which is commonly used in finite mathematics does not have the same meaning as does $\aleph_0$. In fact, ∞ does not indicate a specific number at all, but rather, that a quantity is to be taken to be as large a finite number as is desired. Thus, when we write

$$\lim_{x \to \infty} \left(\frac{1}{x} \right) = 0$$

we mean that x becomes so large a number that $1/x$ becomes as close to zero as we wish to bring it. It is sometimes said that in this process we are allowing x to approach the transfinite number $\aleph_0$, but, to repeat, we do not actually give x a value that goes beyond the realm of finite numbers. We might say, then, that ∞ is an indication of an operation rather than a number.

One might next wish to ask, "How does one leave the realm of finite numbers, and finite arithmetic, and achieve the transfinite numbers and their arithmetic?" We say that the cardinal number of all natural numbers is $\aleph_0$. Does this mean that we may eventually pass through these numbers and come to $\aleph_0$? The answer is No, if by "passing through" we mean any kind of counting procedure. The natural numbers do extend indefinitely, as finite numbers, and addition of another finite number must again yield a finite number.

The following question then arises. If we write the sequence of natural numbers, 1, 2, 3, 4, 5, . . . , the number of numbers that we have set down, from the first one to any given number, is just that number. For example, at 27 we have put down 27 numbers. It would seem then, that if the set of all natural numbers has cardinal number $\aleph_0$, we should have $\aleph_0$ as a member of the set. In fact, however, every member of the set is by definition a finite number. In raising this problem, we see how careful we must be in going from the realm of finite to that of transfinite numbers. There is, we say, an infinite set of finite numbers; but, no number reached by the ordinary processes of finite mathematics gives us the cardinal number of the infinite set. Instead, we must essentially hypothesize that there is such a number, descriptive of the set. No finite number describes the set, because there is no last finite number, and we therefore require one that is different from any finite number. We have seen how very different that number is, in our discussion of the arithmetic properties of $\aleph_0$. We cannot expect that any operation of finite mathematics, as going from number n to a different number $n + 1$ by the addition of 1, will ever bring us to $\aleph_0$, because the very rules of operation for an arithmetic that contains $\aleph_0$ are different. So, we must on other grounds take the concept that there is an infinite set of finite numbers. If, conceivably, the finite numbers were all written down, they would be $\aleph_0$ in number, even though each is finite. But, their infinitude in number comes because there *is* no end to the number that would have been written. Here is the disjunction that we must accept: the natural numbers, on the one hand, each finite in value; on the other hand, an endless quantity of these numbers, the magnitude of this quantity being a number (infinite) that exists within its own set of arithmetical rules.

We have seen that these rules give to $\aleph_0$ properties different from those of the natural numbers. And yet, we have come back again to boundlessness, the lack of an ending, as the characteristic feature of an infinite set of numbers, or of an infinite set of anything else. We might retreat from our concept of infinity at this point, as being but a wisp of the imagination: symbols and rules for the infinite, easily enough made up, but never exemplified in any set that can be actually written, or seen, or counted, in its infinite totality. However, the champion of what is, I believe, a more adequate realism can reply that of course, by its very nature, the infinite set cannot be readily displayed. "But," he might go on to say, "we recall, in the words of Hermann Weyl,[2] 'that it is the function of mathematics to be at the service of the natural sciences.'" Our world gives many evidences, in space, in time, and in multitude of atoms, of just that endlessness which we express in our mathematics of infinity. We therefore have genuine need as natural scientists, just as does the mathematician in many of his constructions, for the concepts that

[2] H. Weyl, *Philosophy of Mathematics and the Natural Sciences,* Princeton University Press, 1949, p. 61.

will express and describe infinity. The question of concern is not whether an infinite set is an imagined construct; for in a sense, as we have seen, so are all of the entities of natural science. Our hope is rather that we may some day discover by the methods of science what quantities of nature, if any, are infinite in extent.

4   THE SHANDY PARADOX; INFINITE TIME

Bertrand Russell has nicely illustrated[3] the characteristics of infinite time in a discussion of the autobiography that Tristram Shandy, in Laurence Sterne's novel, proposed to write. Tristram found, after two years of writing, that he had covered only the first two days of his life; understandably, he despaired of ever finishing. Russell asserts, however, "If he had lived forever, and not wearied of his task, then, even if his life had continued as eventfully as it began, no part of his biography would have remained unwritten."

Russell's argument goes as follows. The series of days to come has no last term, and likewise there is no last term in the series of years ahead. Tristram Shandy writes of the nth day of his life in his nth year, where n is a finite number. Since for every nth day there must also be an nth year (assuming that he does live forever), there will be an appropriate year in which he can write of any one day. Or, which is to say the same thing, there is a one–one correspondence between the day of an event and a year in which he writes of that event. Because there is no limit to n, the events of any chosen day will be included in the autobiography.

Common sense, accustomed only to finite numbers, may want to protest: after all, each year is some 365 times longer in duration than a day, and so surely Tristram Shandy will fall farther and farther behind in his writing. So he would, if he had only a finite time to write, but because of the property of an infinite set, that a proper subset may be equivalent to the entire set, he can find a year for the writing of the events of each day. He must, of course, have years corresponding to all of the finite numbers available to him, that is, a set with cardinal number $\aleph_0$, in order to find the year for any day. If we think of his beginning to write in, say, 1729, then at any future year that we can denote with a finite number, the days yet unwritten about will indeed have accumulated ahead of the years. But, if Tristram's life were infinite, there must be, if the infinity is actually achieved, a year for each day.

We can be playful about Shandy's writing paradox; we know it involves a purely imaginary situation, because in fact a man never lives an endless number of years. But the discussion does bring in the concept of the infinite

[3] Bertrand Russell, *The Principles of Mathematics*, 2nd ed. (London, G. Allen, 1937), p. 358 *et seq.*

extent of time; and this is an important one for our consideration of limits on the completeness of natural science.

It is convenient to associate finite units of time, as, say, years, with the positive and negative integers. We may then express future time by the ordered sequence of positive integers,

$$1, 2, 3, 4, 5, \ldots$$

denoted by mathematicians as an ω sequence. Similarly, an ordered series of negative numbers, each number indicating that many years ago, may be used to represent past time,

$$\ldots, -5, -4, -3, -2, -1.$$

The ordered series of negative numbers is referred to as an $*\omega$ sequence. The ω sequence, we see, is ordered such that each member, $n + 1$, is greater than the preceding member n. There is, obviously, a first member, but no last member for the sequence. The $*\omega$ sequence is likewise regarded as ordered, such that the $(n + 1)$ member is greater than the nth member. There is, then, a last member, -1, in this ordered series, but there is no first.

The ω and $*\omega$ sequences give a representation of the serial property of our time measure; each unit-time interval may be placed as earlier or later with respect to any other interval. Also, the sequences represent an infinite extent for time. Just as the integers proceed without limit, with increasing or decreasing magnitudes, the time measure associated with the integers extends forever into the future or the past. It is important to note, however, that any member of these sequences is a finite number. It follows, therefore, that *any* chosen future unit-time interval, denoted by a number in the ω sequence, is only a finite number of years in the future. A similar remark may be made about any chosen past unit interval of time that is associated with a number of the $*\omega$ sequence; the time elapsed since that interval must also be finite. And yet, the cardinal number of the total set of unit intervals (or, of the total set of members in the $*\omega$ or ω series) is $\aleph_0$. The past or future, then, is infinite, because it contains an unending number of unit-time intervals. But, any one interval is only a finite number of intervals removed from the present. We meet, here again, the obdurate property of the infinity of natural numbers: that each number is itself finite, but the accumulation of all the numbers is infinite. The cardinal number $\aleph_0$, although descriptive of the number of members in the ω or $*\omega$ series (or, also, in both taken together), is not itself a member of either sequence.

It is the ascription of an infinite extent to time—an ascription that is inherent in a representation by $*\omega$ and ω sequences—that enables us to argue for Tristram Shandy's ability to complete his autobiography (if he never died). There are arguments that have been advanced, however, against the logical possibility of any being or any thing ever actually enduring through an infinite extent of time. Some people have asserted, for example, that one cannot consistently maintain that the universe has existed for an infinitely long time. Those who argue this way intend, I believe, a duration of $\aleph_0$ years, or other appropriate time units, when they refer to such an infinity. We might want to say that an infinite past goes back to as large a negative number as we wish, in the $*\omega$ sequence, but does not include *all* the numbers of the sequence. This "infinity", although not without elements that are in accord with our intuitive conceptions of infinity, would still give the universe a finite past. Any chosen negative number would still be a finite number, and the universe would be growing older with the addition of each current year to its age. If, however, the transfinite number $\aleph_0$ is the number of years of its past existence, the universe does not have an origin at the unit interval associated with any finite number, and also, since $\aleph_0 + n = \aleph_0$, it is not any older as the result of the passage of any finite period of time.

We take it, then, that an argument against an infinite past is one against an existence through $\aleph_0$ time units. Immanuel Kant wrote as follows: "Now the infinity of a series consists in the fact that it can never be completed through successive synthesis. It thus follows that it is impossible for an infinite world-series to have passed away, and that a beginning of the world is therefore a necessary condition of the world's existence." [4] A contemporary endorsement of Kant's argument has been given by G. J. Whitrow, who writes: "An elapsed infinity of acts is a self-contradictory concept." [5] The essential point of the objection to an infinite past seems to be that there could not conceivably be an infinite series of past events, each requiring a finite time, between some given past event and the present. Or, and this would be entirely equivalent, there could not be an infinite number of unit-time intervals between any past event and the present. An infinite set of intervals, the argument would run, is an endless set, and therefore one could not have come through such a set to the present time P from any past time O; for the set from O to P is necessarily bounded by those times. Only if it were not bounded would it be endless, and then one could not have come through it.

The argument is not to be lightly set aside. I believe, however, that it is fallible, and that no logical inconsistency is involved in the concept of an infinite past. It is to be granted that a series of finite time intervals between two end points, as O and P, could not be an infinite series. A series of intervals with one end point may very well, however, be infinite, as illustrated just by the ω or $*\omega$ sequence. We require, then, in our conception of an infinite past, that we not begin from a given event or time in the past, or, at the least, not from any time associated with a number in the $*\omega$ sequence. If the past is infinite, it must include all of the time intervals of that sequence, and there-

[4] Immanuel Kant, *Critique of Pure Reason*, translated by Norman Kemp Smith (London, Macmillan & Co., Ltd., 1933), p. 397. It should be stated that Kant also gives a parallel argument that the world has *no* beginning in time: these arguments are part of his presentation of the "first antinomy of pure reason."
[5] G. J. Whitrow, *The Natural Philosophy of Time* (London, Nelson, 1961), p. 32.

fore the beginning point cannot be anywhere in the sequence, since the number of intervals between any point in the $*\omega$ sequence and the present is finite.

But, given that we can dismiss the objection of the past's being a bounded series, we still have the problem of how the world comes through the infinite series to the present. In Kant's words, how can the infinite set of intervals be "completed through successive synthesis?" Certainly, we cannot in any finite time go through an $*\omega$ (or ω) sequence of finite intervals, although it sometimes seems that those who argue against an infinite time extent are asking that it be fitted into some indefinitely large but yet finite extent of time that is extrapolated from experience. The stronger statement of the argument, however, is from the endlessness of infinity; if there is no end to the series, by what device can it ever be completed? The refutation of the argument lies in the realization that an infinite sequence is not primarily conceived in terms of a counting of its terms (which indeed we cannot complete) but in terms of concepts which define the numbers of the sequence and the order of arrangement among them.

There are finite sets that are best constituted by simple denotation. Thus, the captain picking his baseball team from among a group of boys simply points and says, "I want him and him and him. . . ." But also, we commonly use only defining properties for the members of a set, with no specific selection of each member: all American citizens over the age of twenty-one, or all books published in 1964. In the case of an infinite set, our only way of selecting the set members is by statement of a defining set-concept. We used such a concept in defining the set of natural numbers. Also, if we have an ordered set, we generally specify the ordering in terms of a relation among the members. The relation may be of many different kinds: in the $*\omega$ and ω sequences it is simply that of "greater than by one" between any member and its successor. The infinite set of unit-time intervals, then, with each interval associated with a number, in no sense requires a counting of all intervals for its establishment. It requires the notion of a time unit, the concept of number (which can be very carefully defined by logicians), and the ordering relation among the numbers. To say that the world cannot have existed through such a set of intervals seems arbitrarily restrictive. There is no need for our being able to count all of the intervals of the infinite set, and there is no necessity for an origin point for the set; hence, it seems that the case for the logical impossibility of an infinite past is not valid.

The importance of the defining class-concept in permitting the conception of an infinite set has been emphasized by Russell. Thus, he writes: ". . . a whole whose parts are the terms of a class is completely defined when the class-concept is specified. . . . And to say, of such a class that it is infinite, is to say that, though it has terms, the number of these terms is not any finite number—a proposition which, again, may be established without the impossible process of enumerating all finite numbers." [6] With respect to Kant's argu-

[6] Bertrand Russell, *The Principles of Mathematics*, 2nd ed. (London, G. Allen, 1937), pp. 349–350.

ment, which he rejects, Russell presents the defined class relation as the essential element: " 'Completion by successive synthesis' seems roughly equivalent to enumeration, and it is true that enumeration of an infinite series is practically impossible. But the series may be none the less perfectly definable, as the class of terms having a specified relation to a specified term." [7] In our consideration of infinite time, we shall accept Russell's arguments, and similar ones of this section, and regard infinite time as a possible property of the natural world.

5   NONDENUMERABLE INFINITY

The infinite set with cardinal number $\aleph_0$ carries our concept of number beyond that which we apply to any finite, bounded set. It might seem that this enlargement is as far as our concept of magnitude can be extended; that since we now have a number that characterizes an endless set, there could be no larger number. Georg Cantor showed, however, that in fact we can conceive of sets that are greater than those with cardinal number $\aleph_0$. Some of these sets have an important role in mathematics, and yet they cannot be put into one–one correspondence with the set of all natural numbers. We say that these sets have a cardinal number that is a nondenumerable infinity, because we cannot count the members of the set with the natural numbers. Any set with number $\aleph_0$ is, in contrast, a denumerable infinity, because its members may be put into one–one correspondence with the natural numbers, which, of course, form a set with cardinality $\aleph_0$. Or, in brief, the members of a denumerably infinite set may be counted (even though there is no end to the counting).

Cantor's discovery of numbers greater than $\aleph_0$ will be discussed. However, first, let us examine a method for showing quite directly, that the set of all rational numbers forms a denumerable set. These numbers, also known as the common fractions, are defined as all the numbers m/n, where m and n are integers (for simplicity, we shall only consider the positive fractions). We might expect the rational numbers to be more numerous than the integers alone. Thus, suppose m_1/n_1 and m_2/n_2 to be two different fractions, with $m_2/n_2 - m_1/n_1 = p$, a positive, nonzero quantity. The difference p may itself be divided into an infinite number of quantities, by division into $k = 1, 2, 3, \ldots$ parts. Hence, by adding these fractions p/k to m_1/n_1 we may obtain an infinite number of rational numbers between m_1/n_1 and m_2/n_2. So, we can say that in a sequence of rational numbers, ordered according to magnitude, there are an infinite number between any two chosen rational numbers. Nonetheless, we find that the total set may be put into one–one correspondence with the natural numbers.

Let us write the numbers n along the top of a square array and the

[7] B. Russell, *The Principles of Mathematics*, 2nd ed. (London, G. Allen, 1937), p. 459.

values of m along a side (Figure 6-1). Then we form a fraction m/n at each intersection of an m row and an n column. We have then an infinite array of fractions, with every possible m/n value present if we consider the array to be formed by all possible m and n numbers. Next, we systematically traverse the array as indicated in Figure 6-1, starting with $m/n = 1/1$, and assigning a natural number to each fraction as we come to it. We see from the figure that after $1/1$ the second fraction is $1/2$, the third is $2/1$, the fourth is $3/1$, etc. We take a route that carries us along diagonals, such that we move through all of the m and all of the n values on each diagonal. In this way we can be certain that we will not be diverted into counting an endless number of fractions with increasing m or n value only. *Our method of traversal will eventually bring us to any chosen m/n, after having counted only a finite number of fractions.* Hence, we are able to say that we may associate a natural number, as used in counting, with any m/n whatsoever. It follows that the set of m/n's is denumerable, with cardinal number $\aleph_0$.

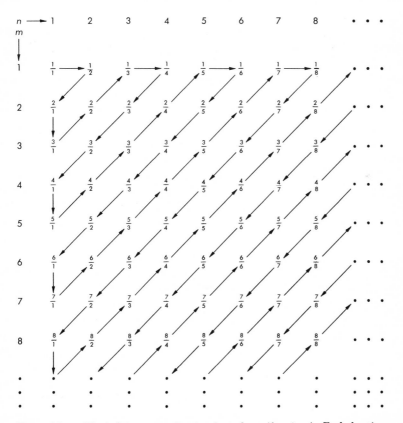

Figure 6-1. The infinite array of rational numbers (fractions). Each fraction may be reached after a traversal through only a finite number of fractions.

The counting of the fractions could have been carried out in accordance with other geometric patterns, and, also, a purely algebraic proof of the denumerability of the set can be given.[8] The procedure we used does not include the negative fractions (m a negative integer), but we can readily make them part of the denumerably infinite set that we counted by specifying that the fraction $-m/n$ be counted after each m/n is counted. The set of natural numbers, we notice, is included in the fractions, since the m/n values in the $n = 1$ column are just those numbers (and also there are other m/n values that will reduce to natural numbers on division of n into m). It is the case, then, that the natural numbers are a proper subset of the rational numbers. By now, we should not be surprised that even so we can set up a one–one correspondence between the two sets of numbers, for an infinite set has the property of being equivalent to a proper subset. Still, without explicit demonstration it would hardly have been obvious that the rational numbers do not have a cardinal number larger than the set of natural numbers.

As promised, we shall now find a set that does have a cardinal number larger than does the set of natural numbers, so that we are not able to count the members of this larger set, even though we use all of the infinitely many natural numbers. Suppose we ask, How many different subsets can we form from a set of n integers? We write the natural numbers as a_1, a_2, a_3, . . . , a_i, . . . , a_n. A given subset contains some particular combination of these integers. Thus, if $n = 5$ one subset consists only of $a_1 = 1$ and $a_3 = 3$; another might contain only $a_5 = 5$, and another none at all. We will indicate whether or not the number corresponding to a given a_i is present in a subset by writing "1" for that number if it is present and "0" if it is not. Thus, 10100 indicates that subset of the first five integers which contains 1 and 3. Considering, now, a set of the first five integers we see that we have two possibilities for whether or not 1 is present, these possibilities being indicated by 0 or 1. But for *each* of these possibilities we have two possible subsets depending on whether 2 is present or not, giving us four possibilities, to wit, 00, 01, 10, or 11. But again, for *each* of these four we have two possible subsets, depending on whether or not 3 is present, giving us $2^3 = 8$ possible different subsets in all. This procedure may be continued indefinitely, giving us, in general, 2^n different subsets from a set of n integers. If, for example, the integers are 1, 2, and 3, the eight different subsets are (1), (2), (3), $(1, 2)$, $(1, 3)$, $(2, 3)$, $(1, 2, 3)$, and $(\quad)$, the last subset being the null set, which has no members.

Since there are 2^n different subsets for a set of n integers (or other items), there are more subsets for a set than there are members of the set. (This statement is obvious for n any finite cardinal number, since $2^n > n$.) However, as long as n is finite, the number of subsets, 2^n, is a finite number; for, we can always double a finite number and still obtain a finite number. Suppose, however, that we now take as our initial set *all* of the integers. Then, the number of different subsets is not any finite number, 2^n, but is the infinite

[8] See, e.g., A. A. Fraenkel, *Abstract Set Theory* (Amsterdam, North-Holland, 1961), pp. 36–39.

number $2^{\aleph_0}$, since $\aleph_0$ is the number of members of the original set. Obviously, there are subsets among those formed from the $\aleph_0$ integers, in addition to the integers taken individually; but can we count all the subsets by using the integers? We saw that the "more numerous" rational numbers, m/n, could be counted by the integers, and we might similarly expect that the integers are a proper but equivalent subset of the set of all subsets of the integers, such that we can set up a one–one correspondence between $\aleph_0$ integers and $2^{\aleph_0}$ subsets.

Cantor found, however, that the number $2^{\aleph_0}$ is not equivalent to $\aleph_0$, and that it must be regarded as a larger cardinal number than $\aleph_0$. I shall now give a proof that in general an equivalence (i.e., a one–one correspondence) cannot be found between any set and its subsets (as is obviously true for finite sets). We indicate a set as S, and its members as x. We will denote any subset of S as s. Our problem is, Can we set up a correspondence such that each s is associated with a single x, and vice versa? We will distinguish two kinds of subsets s (Figure 6-2) : (i) those labeled s_1, each of which contains the element x with which it is associated in one–one correspondence, and (ii) those labeled s_2, which do not contain the elements x with which they are associated in one–one correspondence. Finally, let us form the subset T which consists of all the set elements x that have their correspondence with a subset s_2. Now we assert that T is a subset s such that there is no element x of S with which it can be in a one–one correspondence.

A proof of this assertion follows. T cannot be in a one–one correspondence with any x that is contained in T; such an x would violate the condition of formation of T that its set elements x have their one–one correspondence with subsets of type s_2. But also, T cannot be in a one–one correspondence with any x that is *not* contained in T; such an x, by the definition of T that it be composed of all x's that have their one–one correspondence with s_2-type sets, would be a member of T and we therefore would violate the correspondence between T and an x not contained in T. We have found, then, that it is contradictory to assume a one–one correspondence between the subsets and members of S, and that at least one subset, among the subsets of a set, cannot be associated with a member of the set. It follows that the cardinal number of the set of all subsets is larger than the cardinal number of the original set.

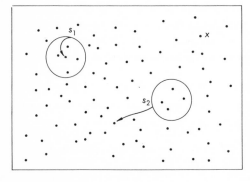

Figure 6-2. The elements x of the set S are symbolized by the dots. One subset s_1 and one subset s_2 are indicated by circles enclosing the elements x that belong to each. An arrow from the circle shows the element x with which the subset is in correspondence; for subset s_1, x is in the subset, while for s_2, x is not in the subset. The x's that are in correspondence with s_2 make up the subset T.

We must take it, then, that $2^{\aleph_0}$ is a larger cardinal number than $\aleph_0$. Cantor gave the symbol $\aleph_1$ to this number, and we write $2^{\aleph_0} = \aleph_1$. We may interpret $\aleph_1$ either as the cardinal number for the set of all subsets of a set of cardinality $\aleph_0$, or alternatively, we may, in accordance with the significance of the exponent in finite arithmetic, regard $2^{\aleph_0}$ as indicating 2 multiplied by itself a completed infinity ($\aleph_0$) times over.[9]

The reader who is not well acquainted with transfinite numbers may wish to see another way of demonstrating the inequality $\aleph_1 > \aleph_0$, without reliance on the proof about nonequivalence between a set and its set of subsets. Such an alternative proof is nicely given in Cantor's "diagonal procedure"; although this procedure is basically similar to the one based on the proof about subsets, it has the advantage of being in a kind of diagrammatic form. Referring back (p. 96) to the ordered sequence of natural numbers, 1, 2, 3, . . . , symbolized as a_1, a_2, a_3, . . . , a_i, . . . , a_n, we notice that any infinite sequence of 0's and 1's which we may form can represent a given subset of the natural numbers, with 0 again having the significance that the number a_i corresponding to the position of the 0 is not present and 1 indicating that the integer is present. Thus, in Figure 6-3 we have written ten different sequences, with each indicated as continuing forever beyond the ten terms actually written. Also, one of the natural numbers n has been associated with each subset (i.e., with each sequence). We can continue writing different sequences, and thereby form different subsets, as long as we like, because we can always add new terms, 0 or 1, to the sequences. Any new sequence can therefore be made different from those already written by writing it with a last term different from that for the others. It appears that we are able to count the sequences, because we are associating a number n with each sequence. The number n and the associated column of sequences go on forever, so a cardinal number $\aleph_0$ seems to be indicated for the subsets (sequences), just as for the number n.

Cantor's diagonal procedure shows, however, that we cannot exhaustively count the subsets with natural numbers. Consider a sequence that is formed by taking the terms along a diagonal through the array of sequences (Figure 6-3) and changing each of these terms. That is, we change each 0 term on the diagonal sequence into a 1 and each 1 into a 0. *The diagonal sequence that is thereby formed must differ in at least one term from every sequence of the original array.* We assert that it is impossible to count all of the subsets with the natural numbers: it is *always* possible to form new sequences, corresponding to new subsets, in addition to the sequences that have been counted. The attempt to set up one–one correspondence between subsets and natural numbers fails.

It is worthwhile to dwell on the difference between the nonequivalence exhibited in the Cantor diagonal procedure and an equivalence that we did find with the natural numbers. When, for example, we made a one–one cor-

---

[9] A. A. Fraenkel, *Abstract Set Theory* (Amsterdam, North-Holland, 1961), p. 110. It is to be noted that $\lim_{n \to \infty} 2^n$ would not be $\aleph_1$, but would in fact be a finite number, "as large as desired."

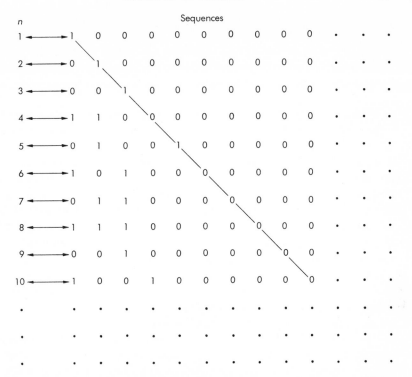

Figure 6-3.   Cantor's diagonal procedure: each horizontal sequence is different from every other, and the sequence formed from the diagonal (with change of each term) is different from all the others.

respondence between every integer n and the rational fractions m/n, we were always able to find an n to associate with the m/n's, and vice versa. It is true that because the set of integers is infinite, we have not exhaustively performed all the one–one correspondences, when we have set them up for integers up to a given m or n. But, again, for the set considered, the correspondence is complete, and we can foresee continued completeness of correspondence for all values of n. The diagonal procedure shows, however, that for any correspondence between a selected group of subsets and the appropriate n, there inevitably is at least one additional subset that can be formed from the members of the selected group. It is true that there is always an $n + 1$ with which this additional sequence may be associated, but then, again, there will be the possibility of forming still another diagonal sequence not in the one–one correspondence. Counting is a serial procedure, with the items to be counted set "one after the other." Cantor's proof shows that in *any* serial arrangement of the nonterminating sequences that correspond to subsets, we are never able to count all the subsets that can be formed by the numbers that make up the sequences; at least one more subset, which has not been counted, may be formed as prescribed by the new diagonal sequence. What one can now foresee is that even though n does grow forever, there will never be one–one correspondence between the chosen n and the possible subsets that can be formed from the members of an associated set of sequences. Since sets of equal cardinality are by definition those that can be put into such a correspondence, it follows that the cardinal number of the set of all the subsets of the natural numbers must be greater than $\aleph_0$.

Our set of subsets may be of little help in giving intuitive meaning to the cardinal number $\aleph_1$ We can, however, readily go from the set of all the subsets of the numbers to an equivalent set, that of the number of points on an interval of line. That this set should have cardinality $\aleph_1$ does perhaps give some intuitive significance to the number $\aleph_1$.

The mathematical points are associated with the real numbers. We have already seen in our discussion of the rational numbers that between any two of these there is an infinite $(\aleph_0)$ number of other rational numbers. And yet, the rational numbers do not exhaust the possible numbers. There are numbers that cannot be expressed as a ratio of integers, m/n; for example, $\sqrt{2}$, one of the so-called irrational numbers. It can be shown[10] that any rational number is a periodic decimal, one in which after some finite group of digits has appeared, the same digit or group of digits will repeat itself indefinitely often. The real numbers, however, may be associated with the general class of infinite decimals; the rational numbers, represented by the periodic decimals, are a proper subset (and, we know, denumerable) of the real numbers. An infinite decimal is of the form $n.b_1b_2 \ldots b_i \ldots$, where each b_i is a digit and n is an integer.

We can now readily show that the set of all real numbers in an interval is nondenumerable, i.e., has cardinal number $\aleph_1$. To do this we will consider the interval between the numbers 0 and 1. An infinite decimal, then, will represent a number or point in this interval if it consists only of digits b_i after the decimal mark, with $n = 0$. Further, there is no necessity for our number system to be based on the number 10. We can just as well express our "decimals" in a binary system, in which 0 and 1 are the only digits.[11] In such a system, 0.1 is $\frac{1}{2}$, 0.01 is $\frac{1}{4}$, etc. The upper bound of our interval would be

$$0.111111111 \ldots = \sum_{n=1}^{\infty} \frac{1}{2^n} = 1.$$

We see, then, that the sequences which we used, as in Figure 6-3, to represent subsets of the natural numbers may also be interpreted as infinite decimals. Each sequence must merely be regarded as being preceded by a decimal point in order to convert it into a proper infinite decimal. The diagonal procedure which led to a proof of the nondenumerability of the set of subsets of the

[10] See, e.g., R. Courant and H. Robbins, *What is Mathematics? An Elementary Approach to Ideas and Methods* (New York, Oxford University Press, 1941), pp. 66–67.
[11] In this system the natural numbers 1, 2, 3, 4, 5, 6, 7, are 1, 10, 11, 100, 101, 110, and 111, respectively. In general, 2^n in the decimal system becomes 10^n in the binary system; thus, 16 is 10000. The number 23 would be $2^4 + 2^2 + 2 + 1 = 10111$.

numbers will now serve equally well as a proof for the nondenumerability of the set of infinite decimals over the unit interval. Or, and this is mathematically equivalent, we have a proof that the number of points on a line, in a unit interval, is nondenumerable, with cardinal number $\aleph_1$.

If we associate rational numbers with points on a line, in a way, say, such that 0 and 1 are the end points, it is readily seen that the points are densely packed on the line; for, between any two fractions (points) m/n, we can insert a denumerable infinity of other fractions (points). Our result for the cardinality of real numbers tells us, however, that we can envision still many more points on the line; that, considering the irrational numbers, the points associated with the rational numbers form only a countably infinite subset of the uncountably many mathematical points that may be associated with an interval of the line.

Suppose the line is not a unit interval in length, but is infinitely long. It may be shown that the number of mathematical points on the line is still $\aleph_1$. This result may be taken as following from the transfinite arithmetic equality, $\aleph_0 \cdot \aleph_1 = \aleph_1$, which implies that if we have not a unit-interval line but one made up of countably infinite unit intervals we still have no more than $\aleph_1$ points. Or, the equivalence between points in a unit interval and in an infinite line may be readily shown by a geometric mapping. Thus, suppose a unit interval of line, AB, to be formed into three equal segments in relation to a point S as shown in Figure 6-4, with $A'B'$ a segment of an infinite line. We see that rays drawn from S will either intersect both AB and the infinite line or will intersect neither. Any ray which intersects both provides a mapping, or one–one correspondence, between two points, one on the interval AB and one on the infinite line. Such a ray may be drawn from any point of AB to one corresponding point on the infinite line, or vice versa.

The cardinal number $\aleph_1$ that characterizes the set of points on a line is often referred to as the "power of the continuum," in reference to the continuous distribution of mathematical points on a line *or in space*. The italicized phrase may be included because the set of points in space is found also to have the same cardinality as the set of points in a finite interval. A key step in the proof of this equivalence is to show—contrary to what one's intuition would suggest—that the number of mathematical points in an area is the same as in a line. We consider a unit square, with one side along the x-axis and one

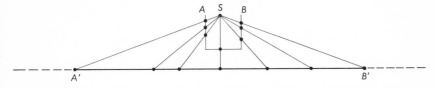

Figure 6-4.   The points of the line of unit length, AB, may be put into one–one correspondence with the points of an infinite line, of which $A'B'$ is a segment.

along the y-axis of a Cartesian coordinate system. The x coordinate of a point may be written as an infinite decimal, $0.a_1a_2a_3a_4a_5 \ldots$, and similarly the y coordinate as $0.b_1b_2b_3b_4b_5 \ldots$. Now, we write an arbitrary point of the square, (x, y), as $z = a_1b_1a_2b_2a_3b_3a_4b_4 \ldots$. We then put this point into one–one correspondence with that point on the x-axis which has the same sequence of digits, $0.a_1b_1a_2b_2a_3b_3a_4b_4 \ldots$. In this way, each point of the square may be associated with a point on the unit interval along the x-axis. Hence, the set of points of the square is equivalent to the set of points on the line interval.

The equivalence of sets for the points on a unit side and in the unit square may be extended to sides and squares of any magnitude, since, as we have already seen, finite and infinite lines contain the same number of points. Further, the extension from one dimension (line) to two dimensions (square) may be written as an infinite decimal, $0.a_1a_2a_3a_4a_5 \ldots$, and similarly the y of mathematical points in any three-dimensional space, finite or infinite, is given by the power of the continuum. But we may go still further, and extend to a space of $4, 5, \ldots, n$, or even $\aleph_0$ dimensions. The set of points in a space of $\aleph_0$ dimensions, with an extension of $\aleph_0$ units along every dimension, is still one with cardinal number $\aleph_1$.

The concept of the continuum of mathematical points is an important one, and it is impressive that mathematicians have won through to a convincing analysis of the numerical magnitude of this set of points; particularly, in view of the fact that elaboration and distinction had to be made in the already difficult domain of infinite number. It has been found to be mathematically meaningful, and useful, to elucidate infinite sets even larger than that of the continuum; a whole sequence of the alephs, $\aleph_0, \aleph_1, \aleph_2, \ldots$, may be defined. For our purposes, however, it is sufficient to be acquainted with infinite sets of cardinality $\aleph_0$ or $\aleph_1$. It is indeed doubtful, as we shall see, that any set of finite *physical* objects with cardinal number $\aleph_1$ can exist. But the concept of such nondenumerable sets can be helpful just as a limit *not* to be found in the natural world.

7

Cosmology

IF THE UNIVERSE is infinite in extent in space or in time, there clearly is a limitation on the completeness of science; for, we then cannot expect to have detailed knowledge of the entire natural world. We might still hope, however, that in the scientific knowledge which we gain of an available sample of the universe we learn basic principles and structures characteristic of all parts and times of the universe. And, if sufficient interdependence is established between the large-scale structure of the universe and the local physical properties that we study, we can perhaps even establish something about the total structure of the universe. The fact of infinity or conceivably of finitude of the universe might be discerned in some such indirect way.

There is today a branch of astronomy and physics, known as cosmology, which is concerned with the question of the overall structure of the universe. Properly, perhaps, we should refer to it as astronomical or physical cosmology, in contrast to cosmological speculations that are primarily guided by the metaphysical studies of philosophy or by the religious convictions of theologians, but for simplicity we shall omit any qualifying term. There have, of course, been cosmologies in every age, and the scientific work in cosmology today is the attempt of our age to fashion its best answer to the question of what is the natural universe in its entirety, even considering the regions beyond those parts about which we have any direct information. As sciences go, cosmology is highly speculative, and no one claims that we have any certain answers to the essential questions. And yet, some things have been established, and from what has been learned about the universe we can perhaps make a rash guess about the prospects for a completed cosmology.

Any attempt to survey the entire field of cosmology would be beyond the goals set for this book.[1] We shall, however, consider some of the salient fea-

---

[1] Some recommended technical presentations are: H. Bondi, *Cosmology*, 2nd ed. (New York, Cambridge University Press, 1960); G. C. McVittie, *General Relativity and Cosmology*, 2nd ed. (London, Chapman & Hall, 1964); O. H. L. Heckmann and E. Schücking, in *Handbuch der Physik*, edited by S. Flügge (Berlin, Springer, 1959), vol. 53; R. C. Tolman's *Relativity, Thermodynamics, and Cosmology* (New York, Oxford University Press, 1934), may be recommended for discussion of principles, even though it is out of date in many respects. *Fact and Theory in Cosmology* by G. C. McVittie (London, Eyre and Spottiswoode, 1961), gives an excellent quasi-popular presentation. G. J. Whitrow's *The Structure and Evolution of the Universe* (New York, Harper & Row, 1959), and William Bonnor's *The Mystery of the Expanding Universe* (New York, Macmillan, 1964), are altogether nontechnical expositions.

tures of current cosmological thinking, particularly with reference to the problem of the infinity of the universe.

1   SOME FIRST IDEAS

Astronomical observation has not given any direct evidence of a limit to the universe, as, for example, in the form of a thinning out of galactic density at great distances from the earth. It is a plausible assumption, then, that the universe of stars and galaxies extends forever. And, it probably is the general assumption, among those who at all consider the world from a scientific turn of mind, that the cosmos is infinite. We explore as best we can in the universe around us, but always in the background is the endless unknown, an unfathomable mystery, but scarcely menacing because it is so remote from the familiar world which is the subject of most scientific study.

And yet, there actually is some quite clear and definite indication that there is a strong element of finitude about the universe. Further, the empirical evidence is as straightforward as could be desired—it can be seen every night, in the obvious fact of the darkness of the night sky. The question of the finitude is not, of course, a simple one, like determining whether the extent of a box on each side is a centimeter, a kilometer, or is infinite. We would hardly expect so simple a measure, applicable to objects *in* the universe, to apply to that which is no less than the totality that contains and comprehends all things that *are* the universe. Finitude and infinitude might be expected to be interwoven, in subtle and complex ways. What we have learned so far does indeed indicate some such complexity.

The significance of the night sky for cosmology is brought out in the argument commonly known as "Olbers' Paradox." [2] Olbers pointed out that if the universe extends infinitely far in every direction, the radiation that we see in the sky should be everywhere as bright as that close to the surface of a star. This result follows from the fact that although light decreases in intensity according to the inverse square of its distance from its source, the number of stellar sources would increase with the cube of the distance from a point of observation. Hence, assuming the inverse square law to be exact, even over very large distances, the increase in number of radiating sources, as we consider volumes of astronomical space around a given point, will win out over the inverse-square decrease in intensity and give more and more radiation at the point as larger volumes are considered.

The argument may be easily expressed mathematically. The key assumption is that stars and galaxies exist everywhere in infinite, Euclidean space, with approximately the same number density of galaxies as we find in the observable universe around us. We designate this density as ρ. Also, we assume

[2] H. W. M. Olbers, *Astronomisches Jahrbuch für 1826*, edited by J. E. Bode, pp. 110–121. The same argument was apparently presented almost a century earlier by L. de Cheseaux [see discussion by Otto Struve in *Physics Today*, **14**, 54 (April, 1961)].

that in differential volume element dV the number of sources is $\rho \, dV$, and that at unit distance from the volume element these sources give radiation of intensity $I_0\rho \, dV$. The intensity of the radiation reaching a given observation point, for example, the earth, is $dI = I_0 \, \rho \, dV/r^2$, where r is the distance of the volume element dV from the earth. The total radiation I to be received at the point of observation is given, then, by the summation over the dI's from all of the matter in the universe:

$$ I = \int_{V_\infty} \frac{I_0\rho}{r^2} \, dV, $$

where V_∞ indicates that integration is to be made over the entire volume of the universe.

The volume element dV may be taken as being $4\pi r^2 \, dr$, the volume of a spherical shell around the given point; all parts of the shell are at distance r from the observation point, since the shell thickness dr approaches the limit zero. With this expression for dV we may integrate over all space by letting r increase indefinitely from zero. That is,

$$ I = \int_0^\infty I_0\rho \left(\frac{4\pi r^2}{r^2}\right) dr = \int_0^\infty 4\pi\rho I_0 \, dr = 4\pi\rho I_0 r_\infty. $$

We see, then, that the intensity of radiation I received at the point of observation becomes infinitely large as r increases without limit.

We expect from Olbers' considerations, however, not to see "infinitely" intense light, but a sky that is everywhere as bright as the surface of the sun or other stars. Matter absorbs radiation as well as emits it, and stars are considered, in Olbers' Paradox, to be in equilibrium with the radiation surrounding them. If the radiation field around a star, from sources other than the star, became more intense than the radiation emitted by the star itself, we would expect the star to have a net absorption of radiation. The equilibrium between all stellar matter, and the radiation in space, would therefore keep the heavens from blazing with light even brighter than that at stellar surfaces.

In any event, what we observe is far indeed from the brightness that Olbers' argument predicts. The night sky is essentially dark. There are the moon and some very bright stars; further, telescopes show indefinitely more radiating sources, as we increase their light-gathering power. But the essential background is one of darkness, and not at all the overwhelming rush of radiation, accumulated through infinite reaches filled with glowing stars, that would be expected if the universe as we see it did extend indefinitely far in space and time.

One might advance as a flaw in Olbers' argument the possibility that space is filled with opaque materials which screen off the light from distant galaxies. Each place in the universe could then be regarded as protected from the radiation of very distant sources by the accumulation of absorbing materials between it and those sources. This criticism is not, however, a tenable one. There is dust and gas in space, in addition to stellar material as such, and one could envision any given photon of radiation as being absorbed if it traveled sufficiently far. But, if there were an infinite background of stars the absorbing materials would have come into the same high-temperature, radiating state as is characteristic of the stars. The absorbers, then, would simply serve as new sources of radiation, and, just as if they were not there, the sky would be filled with radiation at the equilibrium intensity of radiation immediately surrounding a star.[3]

Olbers' argument tells us, then, that the simple conception of an infinite universe of stars is incorrect. We have instead the fundamental fact that there is a limit of some kind on the astronomical universe, and we are thereby given some hope that we may be able to discern structure and extent for the universe. There would have been, in contrast, a kind of blunt meaninglessness in a world that appeared simply to go on forever, with endless repetition of stellar sources, all sending light to us as from the stars that we do observe.

What are the possibilities for the finitude that is assured by the night sky? One is that the element of limit on the universe is not at all a spatial one, but is purely temporal. Light and other electromagnetic radiations move through space with the finite speed c, and therefore a time $t = r/c$ is required for radiation from a source at distance r from a point to reach that point. An entire infinite universe may have come into being at a time t_0 years ago, such that $r_0 = ct_0$ is sufficiently small that only a relatively slight amount of radiation, from the sources in a sphere of radius r_0, could be reaching any one observer. The universe, then, would be far from a state of equilibrium between radiation and matter. But, as time goes on, the amount of radiation in space would be continuously increasing, and eventually the equilibrium point that gives a glowing background sky would be reached. With anything like the stellar densities that we know the time required might be very long indeed. E. R. Harrison[4] has pointed out that with the mean density of luminous matter which we at present observe in the universe, 10^{-30} g/cm^3, a past time of the order of 10^{23} years would be required to bring the background radiation in the sky to the intensity level of stellar surfaces. This time is far longer than the

---

[3] Although we have given Olbers' Paradox, as he did, in terms of radiation, a similar argument may be given for gravitational potential. We again assume an infinite, Euclidean universe, of average density ρ, with the only force acting on large-scale matter to be Newton's law of gravitation. The gravitational potential at a point is defined as $\sum_i Gm_i/r_i$, where m_i are various masses at distances r_i from the point in question and G is the usual gravitational constant. Then the potential at a given point resulting from all the matter in the universe is given by

$$\int_0^r \frac{4\pi G\rho r^2}{r}\, dr = G\rho \int_0^r 4\pi r\, dr.$$

We see that if $r \to \infty$, the gravitational potential becomes an indefinitely large, indeterminate quantity. The contrary fact, that we do observe determinable differences in gravitational potential at different points, argues against a simply extended universe of space and matter.

[4] *Nature*, **204**, 271 (1964). But see also D. Layzer, *Nature*, **209**, 1340 (1966), in which Harrison's stellar models are criticized as being unrealistic.

lifetimes of individual stars, and hence a static uniform universe would require some mechanism for continual formation or rejuvenation of stars.

It is certainly the case that the universe we see is one that is far from an equilibrium state between matter and radiation. Nonetheless, the hypothesis of a creation event some finite years ago, the universe that appeared being of infinite, static extension in Euclidean space and with constant density of stellar or galactic matter, is not a very credible one. The idea is reminiscent of the suggestion, sometimes given by fundamentalist Christian interpreters of the Bible, that the world was created a few thousand years ago with all its geologic and fossil evidence present in it at creation. As we shall see, the astronomical universe does in fact appear to be a developing, changing totality, and we can hope to come to some understanding of these processes of change. A simple postulation of an origin a finite number of years ago as an explanation of the darkness of the sky would be counter to attempts toward understanding the past history of the universe. Also, although a creation in the finite past is not ruled out by such information as we have, the existence of the universe for an indefinitely long past seems the better assumption, failing evidence to the contrary. We shall see that contemporary cosmology envisions possible past states for the universe much different from the present state, but always with a coherent pattern of development from those past times. A creation some finite time ago of an infinite universe, with the same average density as it has today, is a process outside of current efforts to understand the universe with the tools of scientific theory and observation. For both the reasons, then, that evidence of cosmological development does not support it, and that it is counter to the working spirit of science, we shall not further consider the hypothesis of the creation of an infinite universe, in its present state, some appropriate t_0 years ago.

If a finite past time of existence for the universe is not a likely reason for the observed darkness of the sky, it would seem that we must look to a spatial limit. The obvious possibility is that the total universe, with all its galaxies of stars and other matter, forms an island in space: incredibly vast, yet eventually thinning out on all sides into emptiness. The conception of an "hierarchial universe," with successively lower average densities as we go to larger groupings of stellar bodies, was developed (notably by C. V. L. Charlier) as a way around the Olbers' Paradox argument.[5] And yet, there are serious difficulties with this cosmological conception. If the bodies which make up the universe were relatively at rest we would expect them to tend towards each other into a single large mass under the influence of their mutual gravitational attractions. The resulting energy of motion would work against a simple coalescence into a solid mass, but the overall tendency would be towards agglomeration into a universe of increasing average density, with perhaps conversion of gravita-

[5] See F. Selety, *Annalen der Physik*, **68**, 281 (1922); also E. Finlay-Freundlich, "Cosmology," in the *International Encyclopedia of Unified Science*, edited by O. Neurath, R. Carnap, and C. Morris (Chicago, University of Chicago Press, 1938). An interesting discussion in favor of an infinite universe is given by Svante Arrhenius, in terms of the Newtonian physics of his day, in the *Monist*, April, 1911, p. 161.

tional potential energy into radiation. A way of avoiding this kind of collapse would be for the bodies to have random velocities, such that they swerve this way and that as a result of gravitational attractions but have enough kinetic energy to remain free of permanent gravitational binding among themselves. The model for the universe, then, would be something like a body of gas molecules, with perhaps an entire galaxy having the role of the individual molecule.

The conception of a gaslike finite universe of moving galaxies also, however, comes to a serious objection. In the course of time the galaxies, like the molecules of a gas, should disperse into the empty space surrounding the mass of material. That is, if the galaxies have sufficient kinetic energy to avoid both gravitational coalescence and average density increase of the stellar universe, we would expect them to fly apart; the galaxies would, as it were, evaporate away from the original group universe, however formed, and be dispersed into presumably infinite space.

It might be thought that with suitable kinds of motions for the matter in the universe a stable state, in a finite universe, could be achieved. We know, for example, that the bodies of the solar system do not all coalesce into the sun, or fly out into space; the balance between gravitational attraction and centripetal force keeps each planet in a stable orbit. A mathematical study of the possibilities with Newton's law of gravitation shows, however, that such stability is not possible for a universe of approximately uniform mass distribution. Only where the average density ρ goes to zero do the equations allow a constant density distribution of matter.[6] Modifications in the Newtonian law of gravitation which would permit a static finite universe were suggested before other possibilities recommended themselves, but these proposals were altogether without independent theoretical or empirical support and therefore carried little conviction.

The carrying of common ideas about space and matter to a cosmological scale fails, then, to lead to any solution of the cosmological problem. If we assume an infinitely extended stellar universe in space and time we are faced with a prediction of intense radiation in space that is altogether counter to the observed darkness of the night sky. If alternatively we assume a universe that is of limited spatial extent, but also without an origin at a finite past time, we have the problem that such a universe would not be expected to remain stable under gravitational forces, and would either have moved to states of higher average density or to dispersion and lower density. Conversely, though, we can say that cosmology has established an important fact about our universe; namely, that it is *not* tenable to regard the universe as consisting of stars and galaxies, in a static distribution approximately as we observe them and having so existed forever. Further, this conception of the universe is not valid, whether

---

[6] See, e.g., H. Bondi, *Cosmology*, 2nd ed. (New York, Cambridge University Press, 1960), p. 79, or E. Finlay-Freundlich, "Cosmology," in the *International Encyclopedia of Unified Science*, edited by O. Neurath, R. Carnap, and C. Morris (Chicago, University of Chicago Press, 1938), Sec. 4.4.

we assume a spatially infinite universe or one in which there is some limit to the extent of the world of stars. It is a major achievement of scientific thinking to have come to this firm conclusion, even though rather a negative one, with respect to our ideas of cosmology.

If neither a finite nor infinite stable universe fits in with physical observation and theory, it must be expected that the universe is not in a stable state. To be sure, there is the alternative that theory might be found to be wrong or inadequate (the observation of the darkness of the sky can hardly be regarded as possibly in error). It has not been the case, however, that the dilemma posed by the difficulties of a stable infinite (or finite) universe led to a convincing reconstruction of theory. This would surely eventually have occurred if such a stable world had stubbornly presented itself to us. Instead, however, it became clear around 1930 that the cosmic universe is quite strongly nonstable in its large-scale behavior; the previous arguments against a stable finite or infinite universe can therefore be seen as proper guidelines to a correct cosmological model.

2 THE EXPANDING UNIVERSE

The natural state of change on the cosmic scale which has been discovered is the remarkable and unexpected systematic expansion of the galactic universe. In 1914 the American astronomer V. M. Slipher, of the Lowell Observatory, published a list of thirteen radial velocities of galaxies which he had determined, his first measurement having been made in 1912. These values were based on the observed Doppler shifts in the spectra of the galaxies, a shift to the red (longer wavelength) for the spectral lines indicating a recessional motion of the galaxies and a shift to the blue (shorter wavelength) a relative velocity of approach for the galaxy. By 1925 Doppler shifts of some 65 galaxies had been measured, mostly by Slipher. Although both red and blue shifts were found for the nearer objects, in general a red shift was found for those which could reasonably be regarded as being far distant from our local Milky Way galaxy. Plausible interpretations of the shifts were particularly studied by the German astronomer, C. Wirtz, and he saw the possibility of their indicating a general recessional motion.

A clear indication of the significance of the galactic Doppler shifts waited, however, upon the formulation and use of criteria for distances of galaxies. Edwin Hubble of the Mt. Wilson Observatory in California first used the brightness of individual member stars as a distance indicator for galaxies, and in 1929 he found that there is a definite correlation between the distance of a galaxy and the magnitude of its red shift. The farther the galaxy, the greater the shift and hence the greater its velocity of recession. Hubble's work was extended by Milton Humason, also of Mt. Wilson, to clusters of galaxies and individual galaxies far beyond those in which individual stars could be used as distance indicators. Knowing something of the intrinsic luminosities of galaxies of various classes, Humason and Hubble were able to estimate the distance of a galaxy from its apparent size and brightness. The results fell firmly in line with what the first distance–velocity correlations had shown: the further a galaxy is from us, the faster it is receding.

Observations of galactic velocities have continued to confirm what Hubble and Humason discerned, and today the relation $V = HD$ is an established statement of the recessional galactic motion: V is the velocity of a galaxy, D is its distance, and H is an approximately constant term, known as Hubble's constant. The remarkable fact is, of course, that there should be so simple and regular a relation between distance and velocity for the galaxies well beyond our own.

The uncertainty in the assignment of a numerical value for H comes chiefly from the difficulties in estimating distance to a galaxy; for the far distant ones, the value that one infers is in fact determined even by the particular cosmological theory one accepts. Nonetheless, the general trend of linear increase of velocity with distance is definite. A current value of H is about 75 km/sec per megaparsec; or, for each million parsecs (about $3\frac{1}{4}$ million light years) of distance from the earth, a galaxy is found to have a recessional motion of 75 km/sec. Measurements have been extended to bodies which are moving from us with speeds of the order of 2×10^5 km/sec, or about two-thirds the velocity of light. On a simple extrapolation of the $V = HD$ relation as it applies to closer galaxies, a distance of about 10 billion (i.e., 10^{10}) light years would be indicated for such a galaxy. There is some evidence of a deviation from a constant H for the very distant galaxies that have been studied: these distant ones are measured as moving somewhat faster than would be expected from Hubble's relation, and, since we see distant galaxies as they were long ago, a slowing down with time of the recessional motion might be indicated. There is no certain effect, however, and the overall galactic recessional motion is unquestioned. It is also true that for galaxies that are quite close to us, some are observed to have velocities of approach and some to have recessional motion. But for these galaxies the velocities are relatively small. On a cosmic scale the relative motions of nearby galaxies are a detail, unimportant in the dominant recessional motion that is indicated.

There is, of course, no warrant other than convenience for our regarding other galaxies to be moving and our own galaxy to be at rest. The Doppler shifts which we speak of as indicating recessional motion are a consequence of relative motion, and physically it would be just as correct to speak of ourselves as moving away from a given galaxy as it is to speak of the motion of the galaxy away from us. It would, however, be awkward to choose as our reference coordinate system any one other than that in which the center of our Milky Way galaxy is at rest.

Observations have not indicated any large-scale anisotropy in the spatial distribution of galaxies. This is to say that, allowing for the obscuring effect of matter in the plane of the Milky Way, about as many galaxies are observed in one direction as in any other. Further, as is implied by the indicated constancy of H (at least out to very great distances), there is no directional dependence in the galactic expansion: the recessional motion appears to be the same for galaxies in any direction from us. We do find, then, that our observable universe is literally expanding around us, and at an enormously large rate of speed, coming even within reach of the speed of light as we go to the fastest objects that have been observed.

But even though the expansion of the universe is uniform with respect to direction, we must not think that we are at the center, with everything going out only from us. Such an assumption would be presumptious indeed. Rather, we may think that any point of observation which is taken, within the realm of the galaxies, would be one from which the expansion would appear the same in any direction, and in accordance with the $V = HD$ relation. One might think of a swarm of gnats, each initially about a centimeter from each of his neighbors. Suppose the swarm to expand, in such a way that every gnat increases the distance from each neighbor to 2 cm. During the expansion a gnat will find his nearest neighbor to be moving away through a distance of 1 cm, his neighbor next removed a distance of 2 cm, the next a distance of 3 cm, and so on. The illustration is probably not very realistic, in that I doubt that a swarm of insects would expand in this regular way. But we can easily see the required motion in one dimension by considering points on a line. Suppose that at $t = 0$ adjacent points are 1 cm apart, at $t = 1$ sec they are 2 cm apart, at 2 sec 3 cm, and so on. For *any* point a that we choose on the line, the neighboring points b will have a recessional speed of 1 cm/sec, since they must move a distance of 1 cm in 1 sec. The points c, originally twice as far away, must move away with a speed of 2 cm/sec. For d the speed with respect to a will be 3 cm/sec. (See Figure 7-1.) We see that the linear Hubble relation between distance and speed holds for the recessional motion of all points from any one point, and yet certainly no one point is preferred as a "center of motion" over any other point. In this one-dimensional model we assume either an infinitely long line, or a position sufficiently far from the end of a finite line that the "observer" does not see to the end. Our physical universe apparently corresponds to one of these two alternatives; it is infinite, or if finite, we at least

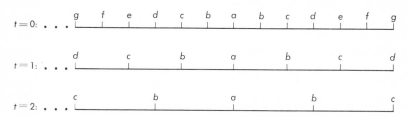

Figure 7-1.   Points on a line move so as to be separated an additional centimeter from their two nearest neighbors in each second. From a chosen point, for example a, the recessional velocity of any other point will be proportional to its distance from the chosen point.

are not now able to see through the "edge," either because of our position or for reasons arising from the structure of the universe.

The expanding universe which astronomers have discerned is surely one of the great empirical discoveries of physical science in our century. Perhaps the only other one of comparable significance for our conception of the universe is that of the wave nature of matter. With the awareness of the galactic expansion we have an altogether novel fact in cosmology, a fact which completely repudiates the concepts of static cosmological structure that had been dominant. We have seen that those concepts were not themselves without serious difficulties. With our new cosmology, those difficulties are removed by the nature of the universe. Olbers found the dark sky to be incompatible with an infinite stable universe of stars. In the expanding universe, whether finite or infinite, the problem does not arise, because if an emitting source moves from us with a speed approaching that of light, the energy content of its radiation as it reaches us approaches zero. In the limiting case of a source moving away with a relative speed equal to that of light, no radiation would reach us. In a sense, the extrapolation of the expansion to that limit does then give us a finite universe, as Olbers' argument suggests. Also, we obviously now have no problem of how a universe could remain static, for in its state of large-scale expansion the universe is most certainly not in a static condition.

This question should be mentioned: Are we certain that the observed Doppler shifts in galactic spectra actually do represent motion with respect to us? Many attempts have been made to find alternative explanations, but none have succeeded. It is clearly the case that physical theory as we now know it does not give us any cause of the observed shifts, excepting the one that is generally accepted, i.e., relative motion. The equation which describes the Doppler shift for electromagnetic radiation has been abundantly confirmed in terrestrial experiments with moving sources, and, also, there are observed Doppler shifts for astronomical bodies where relative motion clearly is the origin of the shift. Thus, the orbital motion of the earth, which has a magnitude of about 30 km/sec with respect to the sun, gives rise to Doppler shifts in our terrestrial observations of the spectra of stars. The relative velocities of distant galaxies are, of course, of immensely greater magnitude than the earth's orbital speed. Still, the velocities of some of the close-by galaxies with respect to the sun are of the same order of magnitude, and many intermediate speeds have been observed, between the slow ones and those of the distant, fast-moving galaxies. If the Doppler shift were not a kinetic effect, where would we find the dividing line, and on what basis, between those Doppler shifts which are almost certainly kinetic in origin and those which presumably have some other cause? There are no grounds for expecting a discontinuity. Finally, it may be noted that if the Doppler shift were not truly representative of motion, we would again have those problems which beset a static universe and which indicate that such a universe is not nature's way.

So, although always there is the reservation in science that future information may bring a change, we accept the mutual expansion of the galaxies as a feature of the universe. It is one of the facts, along with the dark sky, the solar system, the stars, the galaxies, the enormous magnitudes, that must enter into our cosmology. Obviously, in discerning the universe's expansion, man has not come to the answer to his questions of cosomology—instead, if anything they become more intriguing than before. Is expansion related to other physical processes? From what past state has the expansion come and what are the future states? Is the expanding universe finite or infinite? These and other questions assert themselves. Answers have been given in part, in the form of "cosmological models" for the universe. The answers are speculative, and none can have any claim to certainty. But the models are guides to further investigation, and they perhaps give some insight into what hopes we may have for eventual understanding of the overall structure of the universe.

3   THE EINSTEIN STATIC MODEL

In 1917 Albert Einstein published a paper, "Kosmologische Betrachtungen zur allgemeinen Relativitätstheorie," [7] which brought the theory of relativity to bear on the problem of cosmology. Although the specific cosmology which he proposed is now only of historic interest, Einstein's paper gave an immense advance to cosmology, and subsequent theoretical work has usually been in the framework of general relativity theory. It is in cosmology, indeed, that this theory has had its major influence on the content of physics.

The theory of relativity, we recall, requires that there be a deviation from flat space–time in association with matter, this deviation being in fact the source of the gravitational properties of matter. In considering the universe on a cosmic scale we may neglect the great reaches of virtually empty space, and regard matter as uniformly distributed, with perhaps a constant density ρ. There is, then, an overall space curvature associated with the total universe of matter, and this is superimposed on the "local" curvatures associated with individual aggregations of matter. Einstein found that he could deduce from the equations of the general theory of relativity relations that must hold between the overall space curvature and the density of matter in the universe.

At the time of Einstein's first work in cosmology there was no information that suggested anything other than a static universe, i.e., one in which the stars have comparatively small motions with respect to each other. The problem of stability that bothered those who attempted to understand such a universe in terms of Newtonian gravitational theory did not disappear with the use of relativity theory; for, the question remained, What prevents the mutual gravitational attractions between stellar bodies from bringing all matter together into a single mass? Einstein's solution was the not very satisfying one ("not

[7] *Sitzungsberichte der Preussische Akademie der Wissenschaften* (1917). English translation, "Cosmological Considerations on the General Theory of Relativity," in *The Principle of Relativity* (papers translated by W. Perrett and G. B. Jeffery) (New York, Dover, 1924), pp. 177–188.

justified by our actual knowledge of gravitation," as he put it) of inserting an additional term in the general relativity field equations. This so-called "cosmological constant," λ, was too small to give any discernible gravitational effect on a terrestrial or even galactic scale, but did introduce a small repulsive force between bodies. This force, on a cosmic scale, was sufficient to counterbalance the attractive gravitational forces that tend to bring together the stellar matter of the universe.

In his introduction of a cosmological modification of the "local" law of gravitation Einstein was only doing what others before had done in various cosmological theories. But there was a profound and liberating novelty in the concept of the cosmic space curvature. Einstein saw that with it he could achieve a finite universe, and thus remove the difficulties that arise with an infinite universe. And yet, he did not require any arbitrary boundary or "stopping point" for the spatial universe. The finite, closed universe is one that contains all the space and matter that exists, but because of the curvature of space the universe, in its spatial extension, comes back upon itself rather than extending indefinitely in any chosen direction. In Einstein's words, as translated from the German: "We finally infer that boundary conditions in spatial infinity fall away altogether, because the universal continuum in respect of its spatial dimensions is to be viewed as a self-contained continuum of finite spatial (three-dimensional) volume." [8]

It must be emphasized that the finite universe of Einstein's model is not one which exists as a world of space and stars surrounded by a more extensive Euclidean spatial universe. In comprehending the Einstein model one must divest himself of the notion that space necessarily extends as an unending "flat" Euclidean volume, and adopt the concept of a curved space that is all of space, but does not extend forever; rather, in its extension it eventually returns to any given starting point. With this model, a light ray moving in empty space is regarded as traveling in a straight line; but because of the slight curvature of space it will, if not dissipated by absorption or reflection, eventually return to its source. An analogy for the finite and yet unbounded universe is provided by the surface of a sphere. The two-dimensional surface, regarded as the totality of space, is finite and yet unbounded, for there is no place where the sphere's surface stops. The actual universe of the Einstein model, containing the three dimensions of experience, is analogically finite in that three-dimensional space nowhere stops, and yet there is only a finite amount of it. There is, of course, no "center" of the finite, three-dimensional universe, just as there is no central point on the curved two-dimensional surface of a sphere.

Einstein found that his general relativity field equations, as modified by the introduction of λ, were satisfied if the following equations between λ, ρ, and the radius R of the "spherical universe" were valid:

$$\lambda = \frac{4\pi G\rho}{c^2}, \qquad \lambda = \frac{1}{R^2}.$$

[8] *The Principle of Relativity* (papers translated by W. Perrett and G. B. Jeffery) (New York, Dover, 1924), p. 180.

G is the usual Newtonian gravitational constant and c is the speed of light, 3×10^{10} cm/sec. There is no accurately known value for the average matter density of the universe, ρ, but 10^{-30} g/cm^3 is a fair minimum estimate. Then, since $G = 6.7 \times 10^{-8}$ cm^3/g·sec^2, $\lambda \simeq 10^{-57}$ cm^{-2}. The value of R is found from the second of the two equations to be about 3×10^{28} cm, or 3×10^{10} light years. For a space with the spherical geometry which Einstein postulated, the volume is given[9] by $2\pi^2 R^3$, rather than $(4/3)\pi R^3$. The total mass of the universe was therefore expressed by Einstein as $M = 2\pi^2\rho R^3 = \pi c^3/\sqrt{16\pi G^3\rho}$. For $\rho = 10^{-30}$ g/cm^3, we find $M \simeq 10^{56}$ g.

As the term "static" implies, there is no alteration with time, on a cosmological scale, in the Einstein static model. Rather, there is the implication that the universe exists for infinite time, in the past and in the future.

The Einstein model would have been a relatively easy solution to the problem of cosmology. In fact, however, the model today is not to be seriously regarded as an adequate depiction of the natural universe. It may be noted, in the first place, that the model itself suffers from the defect that one could not expect its static quality to be maintained. Eddington showed in 1930 that the universe of the model is unstable; that the universe would begin to contract, and monotonically continue to do so, if matter began to be transformed into radiation, and, contrariwise, the universe would enter into a continuing expansion if radiation should condense into matter. Secondly, and of decisive importance, there is the fact that the observed universe is an expanding universe, as has been discussed in the preceding section. The Einstein model, then, does not at all agree with a natural world in which galaxies are found to be receding, one from another, and which is a world that suggests change and development rather than an established cosmic sameness.

We nonetheless must see Einstein's relativistic cosmology as a great achievement. In showing how relativity theory could give a guide to thinking about cosmology, it opened a new way for exploration of possibilities: there was now a method of relating the presence of matter and radiation to the cosmic structure of the universe. In contrast, Newtonian physics had given virtually no clue in this respect, since it rested on a more or less tacit assumption of an infinite Euclidean space, independent of the matter and radiation that was found to be in it. Further, as I have said, the very conception by Einstein of a curved space for the universe was a profound and imaginative innovation. This concept released cosmology from the limitations imposed by seeking solutions to its problems with only the possibilities given by an infinite Euclidean space. Indeed, in contrast with a tradition of scientific thought that for several hundred years had not considered other possibilities, Einstein's model, with its alternative to a spatial universe that simply goes on forever, seemed wonderfully appealing and comprehensible. The model is inadequate, but, happily, it was only the first in a family of proposals that were consistent with general relativity theory.

[9] See, e.g., A. S. Eddington, *Mathematical Theory of Relativity* (New York, Cambridge University Press, 1930), Sec. 67.

4   OTHER RELATIVISTIC MODELS

Shortly after Einstein presented his static cosmological model, the Dutch astronomer and mathematician, W. de Sitter, showed that the field equations of general relativity theory (with the cosmological constant λ) had a solution for the case in which there is no matter or radiation whatsoever present in the universe. In this solution, large-scale distances in the universe are to be interpreted as having the property of increasing with time. As the evidence for the expanding universe accumulated, astronomers looked to the "de Sitter universe" as one which would give a realistic description of the universe. The model suffers irreparably from the fact, however, that it is based on the assumption that the universe is empty, and the assumption is violated if one puts in even what might be regarded as the relatively small amount of stellar matter that exists in space. Although the mathematical development does not directly show the expansion in quite this way, one may consider the de Sitter model as having expansion because the term λ is present in the basic relativity equations, and this term essentially provides for expansion against attractive gravitational forces. Even, then, if no gravitating matter is present, the expansion still occurs. If matter is present the effect of λ is accordingly reduced, and if λ balances ρ as in the Einstein static model we lose expansion as an intrinsic feature of the model.

Since λ is an arbitrarily chosen constant, the existence of a solution like the de Sitter model suggests that there may be many different solutions, corresponding to various values of the cosmological constant. We shall see that such a multiplicity of possible models has in fact been found. But first we note that the de Sitter model gives a kind of limiting condition which many of the other models approach as their expansion continues indefinitely. This limiting condition is one in which each observer finds his universe to be empty. Further, the de Sitter universe is not finite in the manner of the Einstein static model. The observable universe from any one location is finite, with the de Sitter model, in that expansion carries a "test particle" which is introduced into the otherwise empty universe away from the location, with a speed that increases with distance. Radiation from the particle would therefore show a red shift, and it would be approximately linear with the distance, as in the actually observed red shift. After the particle had reached a distance R from the chosen location, light from it would no longer reach that location. This is to say that we have a "horizon" of radius R for each observer, and he would be unable to discern any event that occurred beyond that horizon. For each location there would, of course, be a different horizon, and in that sense each observer has his own closed and finite universe. But there is no limit on the extension of the entire universe, as in the first Einstein model.

Cosmological theory was given another important advance in 1922 in the work of the Russian, A. A. Fridman, who found that relativity theory could lead to explicitly nonstatic models of the universe, even with matter and radia-

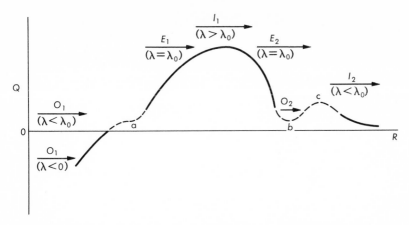

Figure 7-2.   The radius R of the model universe is plotted against the quantity $Q = 3/R^2 - 8\pi\rho$, where ρ is the average density of matter in the universe. The quantity λ is the cosmological constant, and λ_0 the value of Q at its maximum.

tion present. Fridman's work was followed by developments in relativistic cosmology at the hands of many workers: among them, G. Lemaitre in Belgium, A. S. Eddington and A. G. Walker in England, and H. P. Robertson in the United States of America. The problem of finding a model which requires expansion of the universe was now solved, for, as we shall see, all of the models other than those first ones of Einstein and de Sitter both contain matter and do have an expansion phase which could be identified with the observed expansion of the universe. Also, the work of Fridman brought out the significant fact that models could be deduced from the relativity equations without the cosmological constant (or, equivalently, with the constant set equal to zero). Einstein in particular commended this theoretical discovery. He pointed out that he had introduced the constant into the general relativity field equations with only the justification that he was thereby able to achieve a solution of the cosmological problem as it then presented itself. Since there was no other justification, he thenceforth urged that the constant be omitted from the equations. Other cosmologists (notably Eddington) have felt however that the existence of a small repulsive force as represented by the constant is not unreasonable, and that it should be retained.

We shall now present the nonstatic, matter-containing models with finite radius R, by reference to a diagram (Figure 7-2), adapted from one given by H. P. Robertson.[10] In the diagram, the radius of the universe R is plotted against a quantity $Q = 3/R^2 - 8\pi\rho$, where ρ is again the average density of matter in the universe. (I will now, in discussing the diagram, use mathe-

---

[10] *Reviews of Modern Physics*, **5**, 62 (1933). This paper gives a comprehensive and coherent survey of relativistic cosmological theory. A detailed discussion is given by Tolman, *Relativity, Thermodynamics, and Cosmology* (New York, Oxford University Press, 1934), Chap. X.

matical quantities expressed in terms of so-called "gravitational units," for which $G = 1$ and speed of light $c = 1$). The Q vs R values of the plot are deduced from the relativity equations, for a universe with positive curvature, i.e., for a universe which curves back into itself and has a finite radius. The curve is not one which can be described exactly by an equation, but, rather, is drawn on the basis of qualitative considerations. Thus, it can be shown that Q must rise asymptotically from $-\infty$ at $R = 0$ until it crosses the $Q = 0$ axis. Eventually, Q must decrease because it may be shown that its maximum value is bounded; specifically, Q cannot ever be greater than the value taken for the cosmological constant λ. With the expectation that ρ decreases as R increases, we therefore draw Q as asymptotically approaching zero as R increases without limit. The dotted lines indicate aspects of the curve, specifically, a point of inflection at a and minima and maxima as at b and c, which may be present, although we do not have information about their existence or nonexistence. The existence of a point of inflection or a minimum does require that the pressure in the universe, from radiation and matter of all kinds, increases with an increase of R; such an increase, although not to be expected with the expansion of a simple gas, is not physically inconceivable for a universe of galaxies, stars, small particles, and radiation.

The quantity Q is significant for our models because it is a consequence of the relativity equations that

$$\frac{dR}{dt} = \pm \sqrt{\frac{8\pi\rho R^2}{3} + \frac{\lambda R^2}{3} - 1}.$$

We see, then, that if $\lambda = Q = 3/R^2 - 8\pi\rho$, we have

$$\frac{dR}{dt} = \pm \sqrt{\frac{8\pi\rho R^2}{3} + 1 - \frac{8\pi\rho R^2}{3} - 1} = 0;$$

that is, for $\lambda = Q$, any motion of expansion or contraction must cease. We find that at an intersection of λ with the curve, change of R must either cease or reverse its direction. We recall that $\lambda \geqq Q$. (For $Q > \lambda$, we would have a negative quantity under the square root sign in the equation that gives the value of dR/dt; no real number, then, could be equal to dR/dt, and we presume therefore that no possible cosmological model could have $Q > \lambda$).

We are now able to describe possible models in terms of the value which we adopt for the cosmological constant λ.

(I_1) This is a model of continual expansion, with $\lambda > \lambda_0$, where λ_0 is the value of Q at its maximum. This universe may be regarded as having started from a highly condensed state, $R \simeq 0$, from which it expands indefinitely. The ultimate state, $R \to \infty$, would be a virtually empty de Sitter universe. Before the condensed state, the universe could be regarded as having been contracting (negative value of the square root in the equation for dR/dt). Calculation shows that the universe of this model spends only a finite time in expanding to any finite value of R, starting at $R \simeq 0$, but spends an unlimited amount of time in the passage from finite R to infinite R. From a simple physical point of view, we can see the characteristics of this model as arising from the high value of λ that has been assigned. This constant, we recall, in effect gives a repulsive force between material particles. The model I_1, then, expands indefinitely because of the high repulsion factor ascribed to it. If one considers the model in a contracting state, prior to its expansion from a highly condensed state, one must regard its material content as having, in the initial state considered, a large contraction-directed motion. After passage through the condensed state this motion reappears, but now it is associated with the expansion of the universe.

(E_1) This model has $\lambda = \lambda_0$, and it is found that this λ, equal to the maximum value of the Q curve, is just the value that λ must have in the static Einstein model. The expansion of the universe, then, regarded as beginning in a singular state, $R \simeq 0$, would continue until R eventually reached the radius R_E of the static Einstein model (dR/dt would be very small as $R \to R_E$). At this radius, gravitational and "λ-repulsive" forces balance; we recall, however, that the static model is not itself stable, but will tend to move to smaller or larger R.

(E_2) Increase of R from R_E, with λ still equal to λ_0, would give this model, in which expansion would continue indefinitely towards the de Sitter type universe, with $\rho \to 0$ and $R \to \infty$. The initial state of this model, then, would not be a condensed state, but that of the Einstein universe.

(I_2) If λ is less than λ_0, and R is initially greater than R_E, the universe may also begin in a noncondensed state. This could be an expanding universe, with, again, an approach to the empty de Sitter universe as time increased. There could be a prior contraction stage, with a reversal of sign of dR/dt when R contracted to the value that brought $Q = \lambda$.

(O_1) We signify by O_1 a class of models which do not increase indefinitely in size, but which instead may be characterized as oscillatory in behavior. For any value of λ less than λ_0, and with R between zero and its value at the Q curve, for the chosen λ, R is increasing or decreasing, depending on whether the $+$ or $-$ sign has been chosen for dR/dt. If, say, the universe is expanding, R will eventually intersect the Q curve, and it can be shown that the sign of dR/dt must then change (we cannot expect a stable R value). With a negative dR/dt the universe is undergoing contraction, and R decreases, presumably to some relatively small value, $R \simeq 0$. The mathematical description of the models, as gained from relativity theory, does not tell us what will happen to R in this singular state, and to gain our oscillating model we must take it purely as a hypothesis that the universe will again enter a stage of expansion, eventually to be followed by the reaching of the maximum value of R, with then again an onset of contraction, and so on.

The oscillatory model is appealing, in that it gives us a universe that can exist indefinitely, without reaching the empty de Sitter state, and without requiring a unique original state. Further, this oscillatory model allows us to take $\lambda = 0$, as was first shown by Fridman; it is in fact the only relativistic model, for a closed, homogeneous universe, for which we may have a zero value for λ. The model, then, fulfills Einstein's later recommendation, that the cosmological constant be dropped from the relativity theory equations.

(O_2) If there should be a relative maximum followed by a minimum in the Q curve, as indicated at b (Figure 7-2), we could have an oscillating model, with R varying between two finite values. The oscillation would then be without the hypothetical reversal at passage of the universe through the singular $R \simeq 0$ state. We do now require, however, as noted in our discussion of general features of the Q curve, that the pressure within the universe have the property of increasing with expansion; and, also, we require a cosmological constant $\lambda > 0$.

The relativity equations admit of solutions which require positive curvature for space, with the associated finite radius R of the closed cosmological models that we have considered. Some of these models, we have seen, move towards a de Sitter type universe, in which the radius approaches an infinite limit. If there is no matter in the universe, and there is no cosmological constant, the general relativity equations describe the flat, infinite space of Euclidean geometry. It is possible, however, to solve the equations with $\rho \neq 0$ for a negatively curved space. In this situation, the universe does not close upon itself like a sphere, to speak analogically, but rather opens out with distance, like the surface of a tuba horn. There is now in the solutions generally considered no finite value for the radius R, and we speak of the model as being open.

We will discuss two open models. First, with negative curvature and with λ equal to or greater than zero, we may have continued expansion, as in the model I_1, and with an empty de Sitter type world as the eventual state of the universe. If $\lambda = 0$, the space would be Euclidean. This open model differs from I_1, however, in that we cannot speak of the expansion in terms of the increase of R, for the radius is infinite at any time. The expansion would be discernible to a local observer, however, as a systematic increase in the distance between his galaxy and other galaxies. This increase, as in all the relativistic cosmological models, is to be interpreted as a consequence of the expansion of space, and not as a consequence of a recessional motion of galaxies in a space with a static geometry.

A second kind of open model, again with negative curvature, is obtained by setting λ less than zero. The effect of λ would now be to limit expansion rather than encourage expansion against gravitational attraction. The resulting model in the negatively curved space is found to be an oscillating model similar to O_1. Oscillation occurs between a singular state and a maximum state, but here too we cannot describe the oscillation in terms of values of the infinite R. Instead, we can say that a given volume of galaxies would expand and contract; the expansion of our observable universe would, of course, correspond to a phase of expansion in this open model.

So we find that relativistic cosmology, which began with a novel and appealing single solution in the Einstein static model, in the end gives us a variety of alternative answers to the cosmological problem. This fact tells us, as we might indeed expect, that our theory is not yet sufficiently confined by exact knowledge to lead to the deduction of a single solution. The speculative, inadequate quality of relativistic cosmology is amply indicated by the freedom of choice in the present theory for cosmological-constant and space-curvature parameters. Perhaps, at the least, we can find reassurance in the fact that the original model was theoretically in error in its property of stability, and that theory does give the possibility of an expanding universe that is in accordance with astronomical observation.

Cosmological theorists, notably E. A. Milne and W. H. McCrea in England, have found that the deductions of relativistic cosmology may be formally put into the form of Newtonian physics with the introduction of suitable parameters that modify Newtonian gravitation. It is of interest that this can be done just as, for example, the addition of a properly chosen small force term to the usual inverse-square force of Newton's law of gravity will give the correct equation for the orbit of Mercury around the sun—an orbit which is directly calculated from relativity theory without special assumption. There is, however, no basis for reverting to the conceptual world of Newtonian physics simply because the new results of relativistic physics can be reproduced in Newtonian physics in a somewhat forced and artificial manner. The great merits of relativistic cosmology are that it liberated thinking from acceptance of an infinite Euclidean space, independent of physical content of the space, and that in a direct and natural way it gives models that are in accord with the observed uniform expansion of the universe. In the Newtonian models that have been constructed these results are utilized, but without intrinsic acceptance of the relation between matter and the geometry of space. This relation is essential to the reasoning that leads to the relativistic models, and further, it is a relation that has been confirmed in the experimental tests of relativity theory.

There are many features of the various models, particularly as they relate to observed quantities, that I have not discussed. For the purposes of this book, the extent to which the cosmological models indicate the possibility of comprehension or noncomprehension of the universe are of particular interest, and I shall consider this question, along with some problems of empirical decision about the models, in the next chapter. There is first, however, one further theme in cosmological thinking which must be discussed.

5 STEADY-STATE THEORY

The expansion of the universe seems to indicate a process of cosmic change in the universe, just as astrophysical studies indicate change and development on the level of galaxy and star, and as we find geological, biological, and social change on our own planet. The relativistic models likewise indicate progressive cosmic change, except for the oscillatory models, for which there is a long time-interval periodicity. In steady-state cosmological theory an assumption is made that, in spite of the existence of expansion, the universe on a cosmic scale does remain the same in time.

A pioneer effort in steady-state cosmology was carried out in the period of about 1920, by W. D. MacMillan,[11] a mathematical astronomer at the University of Chicago. The expanding universe was of course unknown to MacMillan at this time, and he postulated that the universe exists for all time as an infinite Euclidean domain, with uniform distribution of matter on a large scale. The problem of Olbers' paradox led him to his conception of a steady-state process for the universe. Radiation, he postulated, instead of accumulating indefinitely and giving us the blazing bright sky of Olbers' calculation, is in "the depths of space" converted into matter. Hydrogen atoms, thus formed in space, eventually accumulate into clouds from which galaxies of stars are formed. These radiate, and from their radiation the new matter is formed with which the cycle may again be repeated, and so on. The conversion of radiant energy into matter accounts for the blackness of the night sky and also this conversion compensates for the inverse process, the changing of matter into energy in the energy-producing processes within the stars. The universe, then, is overall in a steady state, in accordance with MacMillan's postulate that "it does not change always in any one direction."

The steady-state idea entered contemporary cosmological speculation with the work of three British cosmologists, Hermann Bondi, Thomas Gold, and Fred Hoyle.[12] In their approach, they fully accept the expansion of the universe. It is presumed that as a result of the recessional motion of galaxies matter does eventually pass out of the universe that is observed from any one location. The observable universe does not, however, therefore become less dense as time goes on. It is postulated in the theory that new matter is formed in space, spontaneously and without reference to radiation or other forms of energy that may be present. The new matter constitutes material from which new stellar systems may be formed, and these replace those which have passed "over the horizon" of the observer's universe. The large-scale density of matter therefore remains constant in time for each observer. The universe is infinite, it is everywhere expanding, and an observer any place in the universe always sees the same large-scale distribution of matter.

---

[11] References and an account of past interest in MacMillan's work are given in a paper by R. Schlegel, *American Journal of Physics*, **26**, 601 (1958).
[12] H. Bondi and T. Gold, *Monthly Notices of the Royal Astronomical Society*, **108**, 252 (1948) ; F. Hoyle, *Monthly Notices of the Royal Astronomical Society*, **108**, 372 (1948).

At the time of the introduction of the Bondi–Gold–Hoyle steady-state theory, cosmologists had been troubled by the fact that the inferred cosmic time scale seemed in general to allow only an uncomfortably short time for the existence of the universe in anything like its present condition. An age of 3 or 4 billion years was inferred on the basis of extrapolation backwards in time, for an expanding universe, using galactic distance and velocity values; this age barely allowed for the full lifetime of the earth, as determined from radioactivity measurements in rocks. The steady-state theory, however, allowed a wide range of ages, from newly-formed to many billions of years old, for the galaxies in any one observer's universe. Since 1948, faults have been discovered in the earlier estimates, and now it is believed that an expanding universe, starting from a highly condensed state, must have been in its period of expansion for something like ten billion years. The steady-state theory, then, no longer has an advantage in its answer to the "age of the universe" problem.

Bondi and Gold have, however, claimed an interesting general support for the theory, in what they termed the "perfect cosmological principle." (Hoyle tended more to put forth the theory as simply based on a modification of the general relativity field equations in which a "creation tensor" is added to the other terms of the equation.) The assumption that the universe everywhere has the same large-scale distribution of matter and radiation is often referred to as the "cosmological principle." The stronger assumption, that this large-scale distribution does not change with time or place, is what Bondi and Gold refer to as the "perfect cosmological principle." They point out that we may expect the laws of nature to be related to the density and distribution of matter in the universe. This expectation is itself only speculative, but it does have the justification that on a cosmic scale we might think that distribution of matter-radiation and laws of nature go together: if the laws were different, the distribution would be different, for the laws are an abstraction from what does exist; and, we argue, "local" laws are affected by the total distribution of matter. Our simplest physical assumption with respect to changes in laws of nature is that they are constant in time. Failing any reason for denying that assumption, Bondi and Gold argue, we should accept it. If we also accept the intrinsic relatedness of the laws of nature and matter-energy distribution, we are then led to the uniformity of that distribution in time, i.e., to the perfect cosmological principle.

Regardless of what justification one accepts for the steady-state postulate, the theory gives an interesting and appealing possible cosmological model. The spontaneous appearance of matter in empty space which the theory requires has disturbed many physicists and astronomers; for, such a production is an outright violation of the long-established principle of conservation of mass-energy. Still, the actual amount of matter-production required is very small; about one hydrogen atom in a billion years for every liter of space will suffice to maintain a steady galactic density, assuming that there are processes in nature which will bring the atoms together into galaxies. This small rate of production could not be directly discerned, and cannot be regarded as in any way contrary to the empirical evidence which supports conservation of mass-energy. Of course, a violation even in a small degree of a principle that has been widely confirmed is not to be easily accepted. One would at least like to have some basic theoretical argument, if there is no direct empirical justification for the violation of a theoretical principle.

The apologists for the steady-state theory find theoretical argument in broad principles that are advanced as favoring the theory. In addition to the perfect cosmological principle, it is held that the theory gains support through its postulate that creation is a continuing natural process. All the relativistic models require that the matter of the universe be accepted as existing, perhaps as a result of a single "creation event" some billions of years ago. At this time there was presumably a beginning of the currently observed course of expansion, starting with a state much more condensed than the present state. In steady-state theory, in contrast, creation has proceeded throughout the infinite time that the universe has existed, just as it is proceeding at the present time. The study of creation may therefore be pursued in the same way as is that of any other natural process; and, it would be the hope of the steady-state theorist that eventually the process of the appearance of matter in space would be elucidated, just as have many other natural processes. It is hoped that the theory can thereby go a considerable way toward answering one of the great questions that man asks, How did our universe come to be?

The answer of steady-state theory would in any case require an infinite past time of existence (just as there would be an infinite future time of existence), and we shall say more about the implications of this extended period of existence in the next chapter. The theory also requires (as do many of the relativistic models) that the universe be infinite in spatial extent. Each observer sees his own universe expanding; each cubic centimeter of space in the universe eventually becomes as large as the total observable universe of any one observer, and so on. But this spatial infinity does not imply any change in dimensions of the steady-state universe, as time goes on. We have seen, in Chapter 6, that multiplication of the transfinite number $\aleph_0$ by a finite number gives no increase in the transfinite number. Or, even, we have $\aleph_0 \cdot \aleph_0 = \aleph_0$. So, the spatial universe is infinitely extended, and simply remains so as the appearance of matter and expansion of galaxies proceed.

It has been a virtue of the Bondi–Gold–Hoyle theory that it makes some definite predictions about the astronomical universe: predictions that can be tested, so that there are criteria for decision about the theory other than the general principles which are urged in its favor. One such prediction is that production of heavy elements must be a continuing process in the stars. In the cosmologies in which expansion began with the universe in a highly condensed state, it was presumed that all element formation occurred in that early state. Only then, it was assumed, would there be the conditions of temperature and density under which the nuclear reactions which give rise to the heavy elements could occur to any nontrivial extent. For the steady-state theory there is no previous condensed state, and element formation must be a continuing process.

This prediction has been amply confirmed, and must be regarded as one of the successful features of the theory. Both the detailed study of likely nuclear reactions in the stars, and direct spectroscopic identification of unstable isotopes of heavy elements, tell us that stellar element production is continuously occurring.

The production of heavy elements in the stars is in no way forbidden in the conventional relativistic cosmologies, and even though the establishing of the existence of the production gives agreement with steady-state tenets we cannot therefore conclude that steady-state theory is correct. There are, however, predictions in which steady-state and "evolutionary" relativistic models do clearly differ, and we must look to these predictions for an empirical decision with respect to the steady-state theory. The theory, for example, requires that wherever we look in space we should find the same distribution of what we judge to be "old" as against "young" galaxies (the judgment is in terms of the visual structure of the galaxies). An evolutionary, relativistic model, in contrast, predicts more young galaxies as we look billions of light years into space at what is presumably an early era of our universe. Also, the observed density of *distant* galaxies should be greater on the basis of a universe expanding from a condensed state, than for a steady-state universe. The observations that have been made on these two points have been rather strongly against the steady-state theory, so much so that many assert that the theory has been discredited empirically. It is the case, however, that at present no certain acceptance or rejection of any one cosmological model can be based on the available empirical evidence.

In 1965 one of the authors of the current steady-state theory, Hoyle, proposed a highly modified form of the theory.[13] He suggested that large-scale homogeneity, a property of the original Bondi–Gold–Hoyle theory, no longer need be assumed for the universe. Spontaneous creation of matter remains in the new Hoyle theory, but not uniformly throughout free space. Instead, creation is associated with matter already present. The theory gives an account of the concentration of matter that is necessary for the existence of galaxies, and also postulates large-scale regions that oscillate between maximum and minimum sizes. Our own observable universe would be part of one such region; other regions, beyond any possible signal exchange, might have much different average densities of matter and radiation.

I have not considered here all the cosmological models that have been presented in recent years,[14] but have discussed those which have usually been at the center of the attention of cosmological astronomers and physicists. It is next of interest that we discuss in more detail the possibilities for deciding between the models: in particular, whether or not it should be considered possible that information can be obtained which will tell us what is the overall structure of the universe.

[13] Fred Hoyle, *Galaxies, Nuclei, and Quasars* (New York, Harper & Row, 1965).
[14] The reader is referred to Bondi's book [H. Bondi, *Cosmology*, 2nd ed. (New York, Cambridge University Press, 1960)] for discussion and bibliography with respect to other models.

8

Decisions in Cosmology

SOME READERS may have a feeling that cosmological theory of the kind we have discussed is interesting, but too speculative to contribute in a substantial way to our natural knowledge. Such an attitude, however, is not justified. In some elementary ways, our cosmological knowledge is as well established as other parts of science. Many theories of the cosmos which have been held in historic times can now be definitely discarded as erroneous. Further, there are things that we know in a positive way: for example, that the universe is immensely large in contrast with our own earth, that in large-scale features one spatial region is about the same as another as far as we have been able to observe, and that the universe has been in something like its present state for at least several billion years. Also, the fact that it is expanding, and that it cannot be static and yet infinite in space and time in a uniform manner, is a reasonably firm inference from observation. Further, the most elementary of our cosmological notions are not mere adornments of our science and philosophy, but rather are working concepts which we use in the everyday thinking of life and science. There are, to cite one instance, many tacit cosmological assumptions in the concept of a world of "space" that can be explored by rockets, and, in far greater reaches, by reception of electromagnetic waves.

The great questions posed by the current cosmological models, such as whether or not the universe is infinite, and what are its past and future courses of development, are at the growing edge of physical science—somewhat, say, as were questions about the nature of the solar system in the sixteenth century. The cosmology of today has grown out of scientific theory and observation, and therefore it can be related to observations that are made of the astronomical universe. In principle we can envision the making of observations that would tell us which is the correct cosmological model. In practice, the information available is slight and uncertain; probably many surprises, as well as indications of inadequacy in the current theory, are yet to come. I shall argue, however, that there is no reason to think that the problem of cosmology, as today conceived, will not eventually be solved.

1   DIRECT ASTRONOMICAL EVIDENCE

The relativistic cosmological models, and also the Bondi–Gold–Hoyle steady-state model, each have a mathematically defined expansion (or contraction) factor associated with them. This factor gives the rate at which any two distant galaxies should be moving relative to each other at a given cosmic time (which is, in effect, the time as measured in any one galaxy, specifically, our own, projected through the entire universe). Further, the factor leads to an expression for the acceleration or deceleration of expansion at a given time. Now, our observations are not of the universe as it is during some small interval of cosmic time; rather, because of the time lag in the reception of electromagnetic waves from distant sources, we observe the universe as it has been, in various of its regions, over a period of many billions of years. The more distant a galaxy, the farther back is the time at which we see it. Since the Doppler shift in radiation from a galaxy arises from the velocity of the galaxy relative to us, we are then able to see the recessional motion at different times by observing galaxies at different distances from us. Hence, not only the velocity–distance relation, but also any variations from constancy of that relation should be discernible. Also, the nature of the scale factor that expresses the expansion or contraction of the universe is, then, a problem for empirical investigation.

In any but the steady-state model, among those that require an observable expansion, there is a variation of galactic density with time. Thus, for earlier states of the expanding universe there will be more galaxies in a given volume of space. The various models differ somewhat in their estimates for how the density has varied in past time, and the constancy of density required by steady-state theory is itself, of course, a particular estimate. By observing the galactic density at distances from us of 1, 2, 3, . . . billion light-years we could presumably determine the galactic density in the universe 1, 2, 3, . . . billion years ago. Here, then, is another way of making an empirical judgment on the validity of a particular model.

Not only the number density of galaxies in a volume of space at a given distance away, but also the average density of matter ρ in the universe is a possible empirical basis for judging between alternative models. By this latter density we mean the average amount of matter in the universe per unit volume at the present epoch. This density is taken as that which is determined from estimates of the amount of matter in a galaxy and the density of galaxies in our region of the universe; an allowance should also be made for gas and dust that are present in intergalactic space. (Estimates for the average density run from about 10^{-25} to about 10^{-30} g/cm^3.) The equations for the relativistic cosmological models give relations between the density, the distance scale-factor and its first and second time derivatives, and the cosmological constant. Information about the density constitutes, then, another set of data which must be satisfied by an acceptable model.

The curvature of the universe may be positive, zero, or negative. (In the first case, as we have seen, a finite universe is indicated, in the second and third cases an infinite universe is expected.) The value of the curvature index is also in the equations for the cosmological models, essentially as a parameter that may be arbitrarily chosen in the derivation of the equations. The same remark applies to the cosmological constant λ which, as has been discussed in the preceding chapter, leads to very different models as it takes different values. Both the curvature index (it may conveniently be reduced to either $+1$, 0, or -1) and the cosmological constant are related to the density and to the change-in-time of the distance scale factor.

In order to form a correct cosmological model, we want to know the curvature of the universe (and its radius if it is finite), the change with time of the scale factor (i.e., the expansion factor), and the value of the cosmological constant. If we knew with adequate precision the observational cosmological properties that we have discussed (that is, the intergalactic expansion and its variation with time, the variation in volume density of galaxies with increasing distance from our galaxy, and the present average density of matter in the universe) we would be in a position to make a definite choice among the various models, including the steady-state model. There are other lines of empirical evidence that may also be pursued and used; and in any event it is not the case that we have a direct, single algebraic relation between the empirical properties that I have mentioned and the quantities we need to know for selection of a model. Nonetheless, if the information desiderated were available, cosmologists could by proper choosing and fitting arrive at a unique answer to the question of what is the overall structure of the universe. (We assume that there would have been no reason, from new evidence, to doubt the assumptions on which current models are constructed.)

The observational evidence that is needed is not, however, of a kind that can be gained by a routine research program. The obtaining of the optical Doppler shifts of distant galaxies, for example, is a matter of high skill and ingenuity. For another instance, radio telescopes are utilized for studies of the number of sources, presumably galaxies, at various distances away, but the methods are new, and different research groups often come to conflicting results. But even neglecting the problems of obtaining data—problems which certainly are never properly appreciated by one who merely writes about them —there are some severe difficulties in the application of data to the cosmological problem. These may be illustrated by a discussion of the problem of cosmological distance.

We can, at the very start, raise the question of what we mean by distance over spatial intervals defined as billions of light years. A simple answer would be the distance light, traveling at a speed of 300,000 km/sec, would cover in those many years. This answer would do in a static universe, but what are we to say in one which is expanding, quite probably at a variable rate? The light which left a galaxy a billion years ago, and arrives at the Earth today, has been traveling through a space with a changing scale-factor, $R(t)$. However, the value of $R(t)$ is itself a property of the particular cosmological model which we adopt. The distance of a given galaxy (from the observation of which we may wish to gain data to help decide between cosmologies) is then itself a function of our cosmology.

The astronomer's answer to this situation is to replace distance by an observed quantity. Commonly (although not always), the distance of a galaxy is estimated in terms of its apparent luminosity (or, in practice, a cluster of galaxies is used for very distant observations, with a selected member of the cluster assumed to have the same absolute magnitude as certain chosen galaxies in our neighborhood). But eventually an interpretation in terms of distance is wanted; in this interpretation it is necessary to take into account how the apparent luminosity has been affected by the expansion of the space through which the light has traveled. The Doppler shift of the galaxy (this shift itself is of course a consequence of the expansion) must also be taken into account, since the observed luminosity decreases with increase in observed wavelength. Also, correction must be made for the effect of scattering and absorption by matter in space.

The conversion of an observed Doppler shift into a calculated recessional velocity is itself also complicated by the nonstatic nature of our spatial universe. For cosmologically relatively small Doppler shifts (with wavelength changes as high as, say, 25% of the rest wavelength) the shift may be converted into a recessional velocity by the simple procedure of multiplying the fractional wavelength shift by the speed of light c. But the expansion of space (and also the nature of its curvature) has an effect on the wavelength of light passing through it. We might say that for light from very distant galaxies or other objects the red shift has arisen from what happened to space as light passed through it, as well as from the simple recessional velocity of the source. In any event, the exact theory shows the recessional velocity to be related to the observed Doppler shift by terms that involve the particular scale-factor and curvature of a chosen model. So, as with the relation of distance to apparent luminosity, the precise kinetic interpretation of the Doppler shift for astronomical sources with motions that are a substantial fraction of the speed of light depends upon what cosmological model is employed.

In cosmology today, the evidence that is needed for decisions between alternative models is at the extreme end of the sensitivity of the observing and detection devices that are used. The information that is obtained is, therefore, often scanty and confusing; also, it is just barely from parts of the universe that are enough removed in space and time so as to give significant indication of the adequacy of one cosmological model rather than another. And, as we have discussed, the interpretation of such key observables as apparent luminosity and Doppler shift involves assumptions about cosmological models when the observed quantities are cosmologically significant.

But in spite of the paucity of the data and the explicit entanglement of speculative theory with utilization of the data, the prospect is far from hopeless. Perhaps with reasonably expected increases in information, and with hard work, the problem of what is the correct model of the universe may be solved within the next few decades. If we were led to firm grounds for holding a given value for the cosmological constant λ, and also could find clear support for a given kind of curvature, we could feel that we had progressed a long way toward knowing the overall nature of our cosmos.[1] It must be pointed out, however, that there is no guarantee that the cosmological models that arise from our present theory include the correct model. Instead, it may well be that we have only achieved some first, naive ideas in comprehension of our vast expanding universe.

The body of observational evidence which is of direct cosmological significance was enriched in the mid-1960's by the discovery of the quasistellar bodies, or "quasars" as they have come to be called. These stellar objects, first identified as strong sources of radio waves, are apparently millions of times more massive than our sun and much brighter intrinsically than most galaxies in their total emission of radiation. Yet, the quasar is small in diameter compared with a galaxy, and must be regarded as a single body rather than as a group of many stars. The quasars that have been observed all have very large red-shifts, and it is this indication of great distance which requires that they be inferred to be brighter than galaxies. Alternative interpretations for the observations have been weighed, but currently the generally preferred conclusion is that they are the kind of super-super-star that I have indicated. Another curious and puzzling feature is that a short-term variability (with a period of the order of days or months) in total emitted radiation seems to be a property of some of the quasars.

The distances of the quasars, inferred from their large observed red-shifts, are all so great that in observing them we are viewing something as it existed several billion years ago. Their discovery, then, seems to support an "evolutionary" cosmology, as against the Bondi–Gold–Hoyle steady-state theory. We presumably see in the quasars a kind of material object that does not exist today, and is a radiation "fossil" of an earlier state of the universe. In that state, it can be argued, the universe was much closer in time to a highly condensed state than at present, and the quasars are remnants or products of such a condensed state. It must certainly be granted, however, that we have much yet to learn about the quasars.

In 1965 another observational finding which may constitute a new piece of direct evidence in cosmology was obtained. Radio astronomers at the Bell Telephone Laboratories in the U.S.A. found a background, short-wavelength

[1] "The relativistic treatment of the cosmological problem promises to give in the future a definite answer to the one question which appears to be the highest prize of all efforts, namely, the question: Is the universe closed and finite?" E. Finlay-Freundlich, "Cosmology," in the *International Encyclopedia of Unified Science,* edited by O. Neurath, R. Carnap, and C. Morris (Chicago, University of Chicago Press, 1955), p. 555.

(7.4 cm) radiation coming to the earth from outer space. An extrapolation from the longer-wavelength radiation that has been observed from galaxies fails (by a factor of the order of a hundred) to account for the intensity of the observed short-wavelength radiation. It had been suggested by R. H. Dicke of Princeton University, where the new radiation is also being studied observationally, that such background radiation might be found, still present in the universe from the times of an early, highly condensed state. Calculation shows that the probability of absorption of the radiation in a volume as large as the observable universe is small, even over a period of several billion years. As yet, it cannot be denied that the newly observed radiation may simply be coming from some unknown stellar source; but if the radiation is found to have the characteristics of "blackbody radiation" (i.e., is the characteristic radiation from matter at high temperatures, even though with a general Doppler shift that could be ascribed to the expansion of the universe since the time of a relatively highly condensed state) there will then be another strong support for the hypothesis of a development of the present state of the universe from an earlier high-density state.

Even for the models that we do now have there are many obviously unanswered questions. Suppose we should find a continuously expanding model to be the correct one. What were the conditions in the "singular" state from which expansion began, and why did expansion begin? Every model that has been proposed has invited further questions of the sort, Where did the matter come from to start the universe? The possibility—one might better say, the high probability—of new discoveries that would seriously disturb the present cosmological outlook should also be kept in mind. We can only wonder whether or not something so unexpected as was the expansion of the universe will again be found: the discovery of quasars reminds us that even the more obvious features of the astronomical universe may well not yet have been altogether discerned. One might ask, too, if physical theory today encompasses all of the kinds of force fields that might be operative on a cosmological scale. The cosmological constant, if nonzero, would indicate a physical field that is not included in present theory.

With a few exceptions, the cosmological theory of recent decades has been based on an assumption of the cosmological principle, that is, on the assumption that the universe is everywhere the same in its large-scale features. Thus, we have assumed in our discussion of various models, not only that the content of stars, galaxies, dust, radiation, etc. would be about the same in every region of space (at a given cosmic time), but also that the expansion of space and the space curvature would everywhere be the same at a given time, in any chosen model. Astronomical observation has, so far, quite well substantiated the assumption of the cosmological principle. But until the time, if ever, that we have a model based on the cosmological principle and abundantly supported by observation and theory, we must be prepared for the possibility of finding cosmic nonuniformity.

2   INDIRECT METHODS

Signals from a distant part of the universe have a characteristic Doppler shift which may be expressed by the quantity z, defined as the ratio of observed wavelength to the wavelength that would be seen by an observer at rest with respect to the source. (The relativistic Doppler equation shows z to be infinite for light from a source that is receding with the speed of light). It has been suggested by W. H. McCrea[2] that our knowledge of any distant part of the universe, as measured by our ability to predict its behavior, is proportional to $1/z$. Further, McCrea argues, the resulting uncertainty in our knowledge of distant regions may be concordant with just that information which would enable us to distinguish between different cosmological models. The selection of a model on observational grounds would, then, be impossible. And, as we go toward the "horizon" in a given model, we approach regions from which the possible obtainable information is zero.[3]

It is an important fact that in our expanding universe, as we generally conceive it, there is a limit to the range of our observations of the universe. McCrea has not actually shown, however, that the information that will enable us to select a given model, and the information available, do identically decrease as $1/z$. Such existing observational evidence as we have, with respect to different models, does in fact constitute a compelling counterargument. It is true that if we had to depend only on direct perception for our knowledge of the cosmos, the horizon limit would appear as an unremovable obstacle to cosmology. Even in the observable universe, for that matter, we cannot expect to achieve direct perception of all parts of it. The answer to McCrea's argument must lie essentially in the circumstance that in cosmology, as elsewhere in science, we generalize from experience of a small domain of nature to all of nature. Such generalization is made with the guidance of theory, that is, with the complicated interplay between empirical knowledge and theoretical construction that is so characteristic of science.

We find in cosmology, for example, the phenomenon of expansion, and we generalize to the entire universe in terms of models that on grounds of mathematical consistency and physical theory put certain conditions on the expansion. The test of the resulting cosmology can come at many places; there can be direct observation, at what is in effect a far reach in space or time; but also, there may be a test in terms of the nature of some relatively local phenomenon, or perhaps by means of an altogether theoretical investigation of consistency or of relation to some other aspect of physical theory. The method

---

[2] *Nature*, **186**, 1035 (1960), and *The Monist*, **47**, 94 (1962); criticism by W. Davidson, *Nature*, **187**, 583 (1960) and by B. Balázs and Gy. Paál, *Nature*, **189**, 992 (1961).
[3] The change in possible rate of reception of information has been worked out in detail for various models by A. W. K. Metzner and Philip Morrison, "The Flow of Information in Cosmological Models," *Monthly Notices of the Royal Astronomical Society*, **119**, 657 (1959); see also G. J. Whitrow and B. D. Yallop, *Monthly Notices of the Royal Astronomical Society*, **127**, 301 (1964) and **130**, 31 (1965).

of science is one of immense fertility and ingenuity, and one can rarely fore-tell with any confidence what can or cannot be discovered.

Cosmologists do generally assume, as we have pointed out, that there is a uniformity throughout the universe in its large-scale astronomical aspects. If this uniformity should be found to be lacking, so that characterization of the universe would have to become a matter of detailed description of various super-large-scale regions, with no overall pattern amongst the regions, then we would have reason for despair with respect to ultimate success in cosmology. But since we have not as yet found such a nonuniformity, we can proceed with models based on the cosmological principle, with, of course, the reservation that further modification and specification of detail are almost certainly going to be necessary. The assumption of this uniformity allows us to use methods of relatively indirect observation in cosmology, because the uniformity implies properties that may have a variety of relations to the processes of the physical world. We shall now discuss some of these indirect methods, both for their specific results and as illustration of the possibilities that scientists may uncover for the making of cosmological decisions.

The considerations arising from Olbers' paradox may be cited as one indirect method in cosmology. We have seen how the calculation of background radiation in the sky, from a static, uniform, infinitely extended universe of galaxies, does discredit the possibility of the existence of such a universe, on account of the contradiction between the result and the actual dark night sky. The method is available for other than electromagnetic radiation (see the discussion in footnote 3, page 106). Also, when used for light in the customary manner, it gives a possible criterion for distinction between some of the alternative cosmological models.

G. J. Whitrow and B. D. Yallop[4] have investigated the question of background radiation in detail, and have come to a telling conclusion with respect to one model. They find that for an oscillating model of finite radius the background light of the sky would be infinite, assuming that the universe does not go through a zero radius singularity at the end of each expansion–contraction cycle. This result is readily understood: radiation continues to accumulate in the oscillating universe, cycle after cycle. Physically, of course, we would expect an equilibrium to be reached between radiation and matter, rather than an infinite radiation intensity. In view, however, of the observed darkness of the sky, with radiation intensity far from an equilibrium value, the result of Whitrow and Yallop tells us that the model of a finite universe whose radius simply oscillates forever between two nonzero finite values is far off the mark. Without an infinite space into which radiation may be dissipated, the oscillating, finite model gives a radiation paradox, just as Olbers found for the infinite universe whose space is everywhere filled with radiating sources. We do not necessarily have to give up the notion of an oscillating universe, but the customary oscillating model would seem to be untenable unless we can advance

[4] *Monthly Notices of the Royal Astronomical Society,* **127,** 301 (1964) and **130,** 31 (1965).

some plausible argument for destruction of radiation as the universe goes from one cycle to the next. One might, for instance, want to consider the possibility of a reversion of radiation back into matter during the highly condensed states of an oscillating universe (somewhat as suggested in MacMillan's steady-state theory). In any event, the highly contracted stage has always been a weak point in the oscillating model, because of our lack of theoretical guidance as to what would happen in that state. The Whitrow–Yallop result seems to show us that the condensed state carries the secret to the question of whether this kind of model is allowable at all in the class of tenable possibilities.[5]

With the exception of that which has been learned from meteors and meteorites, and from cosmic rays, our information about what is beyond the earth has come chiefly from electromagnetic waves (primarily and initially, of course, from those in the visible range). In the past few years, however, there have been proposals for the detection of neutrinos from extraterrestrial sources, and in particular, Steven Weinberg[6] has suggested that neutrino density measurements might be a criterion for choosing among alternative cosmological models.

The neutrino, we recall, is one of the elementary particles of nature. Its existence was first inferred from the necessity for such a particle if conservation of energy and of angular momentum were to be maintained in electron-emitting radioactive-decay processes. The existence of the neutrino has now been well established, both in connection with those decay processes and in connection with neutrino absorption processes, as proton + neutrino → positron + neutron. Two different types of neutrinos are even distinguishable, and, further, each type has its corresponding antiparticle. (It is actually an antineutrino that is absorbed in the preceding proton + neutrino reaction. Neutrino and antineutrino differ by having vector directions of spin that are parallel and antiparallel, respectively, to the direction of neutrino motion.) The neutrino is not an electromagnetic-wave particle (i.e., it is not a photon) but it is similar in that it has zero charge, apparently zero rest mass, and, presumably, a propagation speed equal to that of light.

The most remarkable property of the neutrino is the extreme smallness of its tendency to interact with other matter. The likelihood of a particle's interaction with other particles may be expressed by an "interaction cross-section" term. For the interaction of a neutron with an atomic nucleus, for example, this cross-section is typically of the order of 10^{-24} cm^2. The cross-section for a neutrino interaction with another particle is of the order of 10^{-44} cm^2. The 10^{-20} factor indicates an enormous decrease in probability of interaction, and any direct detection of neutrinos is extremely difficult.

[5] W. B. Bonnor, *Monthly Notices of the Royal Astronomical Society*, **128**, 33 (1964), has explicitly shown that in an oscillating model the light flux may be bounded, no matter how long the past time, as a consequence of absorption of radiation such that for an observer in a given cycle virtually none of the flux reaching him was emitted in a previous cycle. See also G. J. Whitrow and B. D. Yallop, *Monthly Notices of the Royal Astronomical Society*, **130**, 31 (1965).

[6] S. Weinberg, "The Neutrino Problem in Cosmology," *Nuovo Cimento*, **25**, 15 (1962); "Universal Neutrino Degeneracy," *Physical Review*, **128**, 1457 (1962).

The nuclear processes that occur in the interiors of stars are a continuing source of neutrinos, and these, because of their low interaction cross section, escape from stars into the surrounding empty space. Weinberg made a calculation of the density of these neutrinos to be expected on the basis of various cosmological models, taking into account both absorption and the effect of neutrinos already present on neutrino emission processes. He finds that in the nonoscillating, expanding relativistic models, and also in the Bondi–Gold–Hoyle steady-state model, the density of neutrinos would be relatively small: less than one neutrino per nucleon or proton. In contrast, for a universe with an infinite past history of cyclic oscillations, the neutrino density would be about 10^5 neutrinos per nuclear particle (per nucleon). These results are for neutrinos in the "ordinary" energy range. Weinberg also made calculations for neutrinos that are in the lowest energy states permitted by the mutual interference properties among neutrinos (those that are in these low-energy states are the so-called "degenerate neutrinos"). Here too he found that an oscillating cosmology requires a much higher neutrino density than is to be expected with the other cosmological models. In coming to these results, Weinberg reasoned that in an oscillating universe there must be an equilibrium between neutrino production and neutrino absorption; for, otherwise the production of neutrinos would have carried the neutrino density to a level such that neutrino absorption would suffocate all neutrino production processes. His assumption, we see, was different from that of Whitrow and Yallop: the latter authors, in calculating photon density in the oscillating universe, took no account of possible absorption of photons. The justification for the Whitrow–Yallop assumption would be that there is no evidence of equilibrium between emission and absorption of radiation (at least, not in the present epoch of our observed universe).

Weinberg also obtained an equation that relates the maximum energy of the degenerate neutrinos (that is, the highest level of those energy states which are completely filled by the low-energy neutrinos) to the ratio between the minimum radius of an oscillating finite universe and the present radius of the universe (assumed to be of that kind). His program, if successful, would then require detection of the neutrino density in the universe. If the density were low, an oscillating model for our universe could presumably be dismissed. If a high density were found, an oscillating universe would be indicated. Further, if a determination of the highest energy level of the degenerate neutrinos (this is what physicists call the "Fermi level") could be made, a calculated value for the minimum radius of the oscillating universe would be at once obtained.

The detection of neutrinos is sufficiently difficult that no significant experimental results on neutrino density have been obtained at the time of this writing (1966). Suggestions have also been put forward for detection of direct neutrino flux from the sun and from strong radio sources,[7] but here too there

[7] J. N. Bahcall, *Physical Review Letters*, **12**, 300 (1964); R. Davis, Jr., *Physical Review Letters*, **12**, 303 (1964); J. N. Bahcall and S. T. Frautschi, *Physical Review*, **135**, B788 (1964).

has not as yet been any experimental success. Nonetheless, we see in "neutrino astronomy" an imaginative new approach to observational cosmology. The relating of the minimum radius of an oscillating universe to the filled energy levels of neutrinos is, for example, only a speculative possibility today; but it is through consideration of such possibilities that science is able to infer properties of nature that are far beyond the reach of direct sense perception. The use of an ingenious chain of deduction (that is, of physical theory and mathematical calculation) has enabled scientists to go from experimental data, obtained with laboratory-size objects, to the micro-micro properties of atoms, nuclei of atoms, and constituents of nuclei. We may have some hope that observations, conjoined with theory, will likewise enable us indirectly to learn of properties of the universe that go far beyond our own human dimensions in space and time.

The wide range of approaches that may be utilized for the problems of cosmology is indicated by yet another recent speculation, one that is less firmly rooted in established physical knowledge than is Weinberg's neutrino proposal, but also, one that shows in another way how "local" evidence may conceivably be highly significant for cosmology. Electromagnetic phenomena are described by Maxwell's equations. These equations are, however, time-reversible; any phenomenon that they describe as proceeding with the passage of time could, within the content of the equations, occur equally well in a time-reversed manner. Thus, suppose an electrical disturbance (a spark discharge, say) occurs at a point A, at time $t = 0$, and that the resulting electromagnetic wave moves a charge at point B, at a time $t = d/c$ later, where d is the distance from A to B, and c the speed of propagation of the wave. The effect at B will be described by Maxwell's equations, at the time $t = d/c$. But, also, the equations describe a time-reversed process, beginning with the B effect at $t = d/c$ and terminating with the disturbance at A, at $t = 0$. Generally we neglect the "reversed" solutions of the Maxwell equations and use only the solutions that agree with the usually observed course of electromagnetic processes in time.

In 1945 Wheeler and Feynman published a theory of electromagnetic radiation[8] in which the possible solutions of Maxwell's equations for both forward and reversed directions of time were used. Radiation is not regarded, in this theory, as something to be absorbed by whatever happens to be in the space through which the radiation passes. Instead, radiation is an interaction between emitter and absorber, with the latter equally as important as the emitter in the emission process. It was postulated that the universe constitutes a total absorber for any radiation that is emitted, and both emitter and absorber are actually places of origin of electromagnetic fields. Wheeler and Feynman found that with this postulate, and with the use of both the "from the past" and the "from the future" effects that the time-symmetric Maxwell equations allow, that they could come to the ordinary "from the past" equations

[8] John A. Wheeler and Richard P. Feynman, *Reviews of Modern Physics*, **17**, 157 (1945); also, *ibid.*, **21**, 425 (1949).

that are demanded by our experience (and our usual concept of causality). Further—and this was actually the major point of their work—they found that with their theory the "self-radiation" effects[9] of a charge could be derived without the usual assumption of interaction between a charge and its own electromagnetic field.

The Wheeler–Feynman theory has been applied by J. E. Hogarth[10] to the problem of distinguishing between cosmological models. He calculated the effect of changes of the absorber with time, in accordance with the kinetics of the various models. The "future absorber" would in general be different from the "past absorber," for in an expanding universe an electromagnetic wave progressing into a future absorber undergoes a red shift. In the past absorber there is a corresponding blue shift. Hogarth calculates with a refractive index for the absorber, and since this index is a function of wavelength the wave progresses differently in the two absorbers. Also, if the density of matter diminishes because of the expansion, there will be a further variable factor in the refractive index. Taking into account these factors of difference, Hogarth finds differences in the temporal characteristics of the electromagnetic phenomena to be expected in the various cosmological models.

Hogarth found that for an expanding universe with Euclidean space the electromagnetic fields would not have their customary asymmetric, past-to-future character. Likewise, in most cases (an exceptional one was with certain prescribed values of constants in the time-dependent cosmological expansion factor) the curved, expanding models, with decreasing density of matter, did not give the electromagnetic phenomena of experience. He did find, however, that for a steady-state universe with continuous creation of matter and constant density, electromagnetic fields would have the common past-to-future behavior of experience.

Hogarth's result was, not unexpectedly, enthusiastically received by some of the supporters of steady-state theory. Hoyle and Narlikar wrote:[11] "Our opinion is that these considerations carry more weight than the rather uncertain observational attempts that have been made to distinguish between different cosmologies." It must be remembered, however, that the Wheeler–Feynman theory itself is only a speculative possibility, and not at all a part of confirmed electromagnetic theory. Also, its authors did not put it forth primarily as a solution to the question of the observed time-asymmetry of electromagnetic phenomena, but as an alternative to the concept of a self-field for charged particles. (Wheeler and Feynman seemed to accept the statistical asymmetry of initial and final conditions, just as in mechanical phenomena, as the origin of the time-asymmetry in electromagnetic phenomena.)

[9] For example, a charge e which is moving with a speed small compared with the speed of light c, and is undergoing acceleration z, emits radiation at a rate $Q = \frac{2}{3} e^2 z^2 / c^3$.
[10] *Proceedings of the Royal Society* (London), **A267**, 365 (1962); also, F. Hoyle and J. V. Narlikar, *Proceedings of the Royal Society* (London), **A277**, 1 (1964), and J. V. Narlikar, *Proceedings of the Royal Society* (London), **A270**, 553 (1963).
[11] See F. Hoyle and J. V. Narlikar, *Proceedings of the Royal Society* (London), **A277**, 1 (1964).

But, even though we cannot today accept Hogarth's results as being of decisive significance, we can see in his work an illustration of the ingenuity of the scientist's method. Someday, we can hope, the nature of the electromagnetic field will be more thoroughly understood than at present. It is not at all inconceivable that relations between electromagnetism and the total structure of the universe will then be established; possibly, even, a theory of a universal absorber of the kind envisioned by Wheeler and Feynman will be found to have been along the correct lines of thought. The linkage between large and small in the universe is too little known for us to say with any confidence where we may, or may not, find evidence that is of cosmological significance. The obvious lines of observational information seem to be apparent, but Hogarth's work reminds us that there may be overlooked wealth in domains close at hand.

3   INFINITE MATTER AND STEADY-STATE COSMOLOGY

The surest way, if possible, of eliminating a particular cosmological model is on grounds of logical inconsistency. We cannot for certain reject a physical model or theory, no matter how much at variance it is with commonly accepted physical ideas, if it may conceivably be true; but a theory which contains a contradiction is at once inadmissable. The ordinary canons of mathematics provide a check on the consistency of physical theories (if mathematically expressed), as does also, of course, the validity of the theorems or properties deduced from the theory (we recall the discussion of Sec. 3, Chapter 4). In this section I shall show how the Bondi–Gold–Hoyle steady-state model, at least in what is one common interpretation of it, does in fact entail a consequence that cannot be physically valid. In this way a cosmological decision is obtained, with respect to one particular model, without need for observation of any kind. This type of decision is relatively easy, and it would be good fortune if it could be used to eliminate many of the models that have been suggested. The type of argument that I shall use does not, however, seem to lead to a significant result for other than the continuous creation steady-state model.

Consider the creation of matter, as postulated in the Bondi–Gold–Hoyle theory, for a period of infinite time (considering that the steady-state universe has, by definition, existed through all time). We then find however, that the amount of matter which has been produced is nondenumerably infinite, and that there should therefore be an atom at every mathematical point in space. It is not possible, however, that this can be so, since physical atoms are finite in size, whereas mathematical points are without spatial extension, and may be as close together as desired. Hence, the model implies an impossible result. In presenting the argument we shall use many of the concepts of transfinite mathematics that have been introduced in Chapter 6.

The Bondi–Gold–Hoyle theory requires that new matter appear spontaneously in space, at a rate which (neglecting possible local fluctuations) is uniform throughout the universe. Further, the steady-state postulate requires that this production rate be uniform in time. The large-scale average density of matter in the universe also, of course, is a constant in space and time, in the steady-state theory. Here it is convenient to regard each atom in the universe as having associated with it that amount of space which it would have if atoms were uniformly distributed in space, with a density in accord with the average density of matter. I shall call each atom with its associated space an *atom-space*.

Since new atoms appear in space, at a defined uniform rate, each atom-space will in time give rise to a second atom. The overall expansion of the universe does, however, imply a continuing increase in distance between any two atoms, and hence the average density of matter can remain constant. Each of the two atom-spaces formed from an initial atom-space will itself eventually become two atom-spaces, giving a total of four from the initial one. Each of these four will in due course become two atom-spaces, and so on. Suppose we designate the time required for an atom-space to become two atom-spaces as τ. For convenience, we may choose time-units so as to make τ equal to unity. Then in t time units (t is an integer n) an initial atom-space will (again, neglecting local fluctuations) have become 2^n atom-spaces. Now, as long as t is finite, n and hence 2^n will be a finite number. Suppose, however, that the steady-state universe has existed for an actual infinity, $\aleph_0$, of years (or other time units), so that a one–one correspondence can be set up between the time units during which the universe has existed and the natural numbers. Then the set of all time-intervals τ through which the universe has existed will also have the cardinal number $\aleph_0$. That is, if the universe has existed for $\aleph_0$ time units, then, also, $\aleph_0 \cdot \tau = \aleph_0$. But this means that during the existence of the universe an atom-space will have been multiplied to $2^{\aleph_0}$ atom-spaces. We recall (Sec. 5, Chapter 6) that $2^{\aleph_0} = \aleph_1$.

We find, then, that in a steady-state universe which has existed through all time the set of atom-spaces must have the same cardinal number, $\aleph_1$, as the set of all mathematical points in space. It was pointed out, in Section 5 of Chapter 6, that $\aleph_1$, is the number of points in a *finite* or an *infinite* volume of space; it is, therefore, also the number of mathematical points in the universe. But, the number of atom-spaces in the universe cannot possibly be as great as the number of mathematical points, because each atom occupies a finite volume. It would, therefore, be impossible to set up a one–one correspondence between atoms and mathematical points. Alternatively,[12] it may be shown by use of an idealized counting procedure that the number of atom-spaces in an infinite universe cannot be greater than $\aleph_0$.

[12] R. Schlegel, *Nature*, **193**, 665 (1962). A complete discussion of the argument of this section against steady-state creation [including a reply to the criticism of R. R. D. Kemp, *Proceedings of the Cambridge Philosophical Society*, **60**, 176 (1964)] is given in R. Schlegel, *Philosophy of Science*, **32**, 21 (1965).

The result, that continuous creation of atom-spaces through an infinite time would lead to a set with the nondenumerable number $\aleph_1$, may also be shown by a direct analogy with Cantor's "diagonal proof" for the existence of such a set. Suppose we think of an initial atom-space becoming two atom-spaces, in time τ. We label the lines from the initial atom-space to the two that exist, after the second one appears, as "0" and "1" (see Figure 8-1). Now each of these two atom-spaces will in time τ become two atom-spaces, and we draw lines "0" and "1" to indicate again the appearance of two atom-spaces where before there had been only one. This process continues indefinitely, if we consider an initial atom-space to have existed from a time that is an infinite number of "τ" intervals in the past. Each atom-space is connected by lines "0" and "1" to two atom-spaces existing at time τ later.

We may trace "lineage paths" through the diagram, starting at a given atom-space and going through successive τ intervals. We may arbitrarily take a "0" or a "1" line at each interval, since both possibilities exist for each atom-space. In this way, if we assume creation of new atom-spaces to continue indefinitely, the lineage-paths become sequences of numbers, such as 01101100011. . . . We see that each lineage path that differs in even a single digit from every other will indicate a different atom-space from that represented by any other path. Further, our different "paths" are nonterminating sequences just as in the Cantor diagonal proof (Figure 6-3, p. 99). But also, just as in that proof, we can always form a new sequence (lineage-path) by taking a diagonal sequence and changing each "0" to "1" and each "1" to "0". Any attempt, then, to match the number of sequences, *each representing an atom-space*, with the natural numbers will fail, exactly as in the Cantor proof. We conclude, then, that if production of atom-spaces has continued forever, the number of atom-spaces cannot be $\aleph_0$, but must be $\aleph_1$. And yet, this result is physically impossible.

The contradiction which we find means that the Bondi–Gold–Hoyle theory must be rejected if the theory does require creation of matter through-

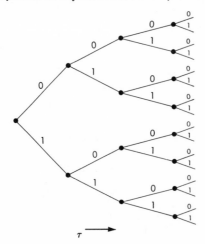

Figure 8-1. In each time unit τ a new atom-space is formed for every already existing atom space. We may think, then, of each atom-space as giving rise to two in time τ. A pair of lines, "0" and "1," connect every atom-space to two that exist after a time interval τ.

out an infinite past. Inasmuch as the theory has been closely associated with the "perfect cosmological principle," enunciated by Bondi and Gold, it is not unreasonable to ascribe such an infinite past to the steady-state universe. (The "perfect cosmological principle," it will be recalled, asserts that the universe is uniform in large-scale features throughout all time as well as all space.) A closer analysis of the concept of an infinite past time will show us a sense, however, in which we can escape the contradiction that comes with a calculation of $\aleph_1$ atom-spaces.

We recall (p. 91) that past time may be represented by the $*\omega$ sequence $\ldots, -4, -3, -2, -1$, where "-1" indicates one unit time interval in the past, "-2" two intervals, and so on. (Each unit time interval is assumed to be finite.) Any past time that is indicated in the sequence is a finite-number n intervals from the present, since every number in the $*\omega$ sequence is a finite integer. So, if by the universe having existed for an infinite past time, we mean that the origin of the universe is in the $*\omega$ sequence at some time point indefinitely far in the past, we do not have a past time of $\aleph_0$ unit intervals. Therefore we can write that the number of present atom-spaces formed from one atom-space since the time of the origin of the universe is given by $\lim_{n \to \infty} 2^n$, where n is the number of time-intervals of length τ that the universe has existed. The limit, $n \to \infty$, does not mean that n becomes the transfinite number $\aleph_0$; rather it is a mathematical specification that n may be taken to be as large a *finite* number as desired. The quantity 2^n, with this definition, will therefore never come to be the cardinal number $2^{\aleph_0} = \aleph_1$. In this connection, we recall that $\aleph_0$ is a number, but not one of the finite numbers (rather, it is the number of the set of all the finite numbers). Also, $\aleph_0$ is not defined primarily as a magnitude, but by the property that for a set of which it is the cardinal number, there is a one–one correspondence between the set and one of its proper subsets. In contrast, ∞ is not a number, or a property of a set, but, as stated, a symbol for the operation of letting a quantity increase indefinitely among the finite numbers.

In physical theory, the term "infinity" is usually taken to mean "as large as desired." Thus, if we say that a distance x becomes infinite, such that the quotient $1/x$ goes to zero, we generally write $\lim_{x \to \infty} \frac{1}{x} = 0$. We mean, then, that x becomes so large that $1/x$ is as close to zero as desired. Depending on the context, $x \to \infty$ might, for example, be satisfied by $x = 1$ mm (in an atomic problem), or by $x = 1$ light year (in an astrophysical gravitational problem). Hoyle has recently stated that the "$\to \infty$" infinity is the one which he intends in the steady-state theory. In a paper[13] published in 1963, he and Narlikar explicity disavow the perfect cosmological principle, and use the hypothesis of continuous creation in a universe which is initially in an irregular, nonuniform state. Support is found for the assertion that even though

[13] F. Hoyle and J. V. Narlikar, *Proceedings of the Royal Society* (London), **A273**, 1 (1963).

originally the universe may have been in a nonuniform "transient" state, it tends to the steady-state as $t \to \infty$. The density of matter eventually becomes constant; Hoyle and Narlikar write, "Thus in the asymptotic case creation and expansion are in exact balance—even though no such balance was initially there."

By making the assumption, then, that the steady-state universe with continuous creation of matter has its origin at some point in the past the supporters of the theory can avoid the contradiction of an atom at every mathematical point. Since the sequence of past time intervals extends indefinitely, as in the $*\omega$ sequence, the point of origin may be as far back in the past as desired; but also, every point in the $*\omega$ sequence is only a finite time in the past, and hence there will not be production of the unacceptable $\aleph_1$ atom-spaces. The steady-state universe can, therefore, have an infinite past, in accord with a definition of infinity as "as large a number as desired," or, in this case, "as long a past as desired."

However, the steady-state theory as originally presented by Bondi, Gold, and Hoyle seemed to imply a universe that was the same throughout all of time; certainly, the perfect cosmological principle seems to have this implication. If continuous creation of matter has occurred at *all* past times, then we cannot say that it *began* at some time interval in the $*\omega$ sequence, as far back as we choose; for, since the $*\omega$ sequence is endless, if continuous creation began at a time in the finite past, even though that past time may be indefinitely large, there would be an earlier time when the universe did not exist (or was not in the steady-state). There is no escape from the requirement that the steady-state universe must have existed at *every* past time point *if* it has existed through all of time. And this requirement means that the number of past unit-time intervals is the same as the number of integers in the $*\omega$ sequence, that is, $\aleph_0$. The contradiction of $\aleph_1$ atom-spaces then follows.

The difference between existence of a past time of length $t \to \infty$ for the universe and one of $t = \aleph_0$ may be put in the following way. If the universe has existed not for an achieved infinity $\aleph_0$ of past time units, but for an infinity $n \to \infty$ of time units, then its origin is in time. This is to say, its origin is somewhere in the $*\omega$ sequence of past unit time intervals. If, however, the universe has existed throughout all of the $*\omega$ sequence, during a set of unit-time intervals with cardinality $\aleph_0$, then its origin has not been "in time." For, an origin in time would be an origin in the $*\omega$ sequence of time units. Also, if the universe has existed throughout all time, one should not speak of its having had its origin "before the beginning of time," because the word "before" itself has a temporal significance. The endless $*\omega$ sequence contains all of past time, and the universe which has existed throughout the $\aleph_0$ time units of the sequence simply has no origin in time.[14]

[14] Professor R. P. McKeon has pointed out to me that in the thirteenth century St. Thomas Aquinas presented arguments against those, especially St. Bonaventura, who believed they had shown by reason that eternity was impossible and that the world had been created in time. See R. P. McKeon, *Selections from Medieval Philosophers* (New York, Scribner's, 1930), Vol. II, pp. 149–150.

The steady-state theory, with a hypothesis of continuous creation of matter, remains an interesting and plausible theory even with the restriction that the "steady" state can only have been for an indefinitely long time rather than *all* of time. And, as has been indicated, a common usage of "infinity" in physics would allow such an "indefinitely long time" as an adequate infinity. I shall take it, however, that the full meaning of "infinity" requires that the steady-state universe has existed throughout all past time. This point of view is, I believe, in accord with the mathematical concept of infinity, and also with the generally understood significance of the word "infinity." For example, if we say that the universe is spatially infinite, I do not believe that we mean its total volume is some number N of cubic meters, where N is as large as desired but still within the sequence of increasing *finite* numbers. Instead, I think we would mean that N is *not* finite, and is the transfinite number $\aleph_0$.

We accept, then, that a universe which has existed forever must have a past number of time units whose cardinal number is $\aleph_0$. It follows that we must also see continuous creation as occurring through a set of past unit-time intervals with cardinality $\aleph_0$, in the Bondi–Gold–Hoyle model of a universe which has *always* been in its steady state. But we then do have the impossible consequence that there would exist a set of atom-spaces with cardinal number $\aleph_1$. We therefore must reject this model as not giving a physically correct description of the natural world.

4 MacMILLAN'S PRINCIPLE

It is a notable feature of our consideration of various cosmological models, that we have several times found an obstacle against maintaining that a particular type of universe has existed forever. Olbers' paradox ruled out the existence of an infinite static universe through an indefinitely long past. With expansion, the paradox is removed, but the Whitrow–Yallop result shows that the infinitely existing oscillating universe is again inadmissible, on Olbers' paradox grounds (if radiation accumulates in the customary way). Finally, we have seen that a continuous-creation universe, held as existing forever, implies the production of infinitely more matter than could be physically existent. There are no other commonly considered cosmological models to which an infinite past is ascribed.

The various "evolutionary" models, which envision an origin of the present expansion of the universe ten or so billion years ago, do imply an infinite future for the universe: one in which the average density of matter gradually approaches zero. For these models, in fact, the present period of the universe, with a nonvanishing value of ρ, is an infinitely small fraction of the total time that the universe exists. In view of the theoretical difficulties associated with the models that give an infinite past, the evolutionary model, with a creation event that brought it into being, may be appealing to some, particularly to those who for reasons of a traditional religious belief would like to find the universe to have been formed in an event at some time in the finite past. We have emphasized, however, that for the scientist a postulated creation-of-the-universe is generally an arbitrary event, unrelated to other natural processes, and not amenable to investigation by the usual theoretical or observational tools of science. Also, philosophically, a single creation event poses enormous metaphysical questions (even, no doubt, as it does solve some problems). On the matter of creation, as on others, scientists should avoid dogmatism; a scientifically unexplained creation, however, must itself be supported by evidence and theory before it can be accepted into the structure of science.

Some form of steady-state theory is an appealing alternative to a cosmology that implies a creation in the finite past, because in a cosmos which has always existed there is no problem of a beginning in time. Indeed, such a universe may be regarded as atemporal. There is in it the time which we define by means of physical changes, and these may extend as far back (or forward) "in time" as we can extrapolate from our study of the physical world. But in an atemporal world time is only defined around a given set of changes or experiences, even though it be extended to billions of years. We may speak of the universe relative to those changes as being, say, a billion years older in a current state than in some previous state; but if the universe is truly atemporal it is in itself no older in any one state than in any other. In terms of the mathematical concept of infinity, the universe that is atemporal has existed for a past time that extends forever, and therefore has existed for $\aleph_0$ past time units. But $\aleph_0 + n$, where n is a finite number, is $\aleph_0$. Hence, the atemporal universe in a proper sense is no older at one time, as we judge the time of different physical states, than at another. We do *not* mean to say that time is therefore illusory, in a universe which exists always. On the contrary, time is fully as real as the progressive changes that we observe in the natural processes of the universe, including our own selves. But for the entire atemporal universe, time is without significance. That universe simply is, and time, which comes with physical change, may be thought of as an attribute of processes within it.

The obvious path from an expanding, evolutionary cosmological model with a finite past to a steady-state, atemporal model is by conversion to an oscillating model. We may refer to such a model as a steady-state one, in that it gives us a universe with no ultimate large-scale change, even though there is the grand progression through expansion and contraction. Clearly, the Whitrow–Yallop difficulty with such a model can be overcome simply by requiring that there not be a net gain of radiation in space, through the entirety of each expansion–contraction cycle. Instead, there must be a compensating process, sometime in the cycle, in which radiation is converted into some other form of energy. (In the Weinberg neutrino calculations, for example, a steady-state is achieved by assumption of a balance between production and absorption of neutrinos.)

The difficulties that we have seen in the current models that assume an infinite past suggest the great importance of MacMillan's postulate, to which we have previously referred[15]: "The universe does not change always in any one direction." Or, as MacMillan also put it, ". . . the universe does not tend constantly in any one direction." We might elevate the postulate to the status of MacMillan's Principle, in view of the difficulties that have been found to arise in models that violate the principle. A continual increase in the amount of radiation, or a continuing growth in the amount of matter, are processes that are not compatible, we have seen, with a steady-state atemporal universe. If, then, we are to have a universe whose past is not confined to a finite time, it is suggested that none of the basic processes of the universe can be unidirectional in their net effects. There must be reversals, or compensating processes, so that the universe does not change always away from some median state. Only with the operation of the principle can we envision the universe as avoiding a barrier or obstacle of an existence through infinite time.

We can also see in the purely expanding model universe an illustration of the effect of violation of the principle. If expansion continued indefinitely, we would have a universe far different from the one we know, after a finite period of time. We would fail, for this reason, then, to have any kind of steady state for the universe. But also, extrapolating backwards in time, we would come to a universe in a highly condensed state, also far different from our present one. And, if expansion were the only process of spatial change that operated, we would have little choice but to assume a creation event in the condensed state; for, expansion could hardly have brought the universe to such a state.

With a universe that does change, but with balances and compensations such that our suggested MacMillan Principle is valid, we can consider various steady-state, atemporal cosmological models. The problems of creation, and also, of "What was there before there was a universe?", are then solved by being made irrelevant. The atemporal universe has always existed, will always exist, and has no time measure of the kind that runs from start to finish of a process. For, in the atemporal universe there is no process of change that operates progressively, in a manner such that any one large-scale epoch may be distinguished from all others by its physical characteristics. Instead, we expect that at least in an approximate way any one state must be repeated, since otherwise we would have a process of change that went always in the one direction, in violation of the MacMillan Principle. And, to repeat, we have seen the difficulties that come with models that have such a process, through an infinite past.

If an atemporal, steady-state model of the kind we have been speculatively considering were actually established as being correct, one might still ask: But what are the reasons or grounds for the existence of the atemporal universe? This question would be the parallel, for that universe, to the question of creation that may be asked about a universe with a finite past. It seems,

[15] Chapter 7, p. 122.

however, that there is little that can be said at this time about why there would be an atemporal universe. The question is a form of the ancient philosophical problem of "Why is there Being?" and this appears to be one that cannot be very profitably discussed. If ever it is answered, it will probably be because it is asked in a way different from that in which it now is, in a way which allows the insight of scientific discovery and theory to bear upon it. At this time, we seem in cosmology still to be a considerable distance from ascertaining what is the correct cosmological view about our universe. When (and if) some one model has been reasonably well established as a correct one, new questions will almost certainly be occurring about the genesis or antecedents of the universe that the model describes. These questions in turn may lead to insights about the very origins of the being of the universe. We recall, from our discussion of Chapter 4, that explanatory completeness in science is relative to a given context, to a given set of axioms and terms. For our day it would be high cosmological achievement enough to comprehend the overall structure of the astronomical universe in terms of the given elements of space, matter, energy, and radiation.

5   COMPLETENESS IN COSMOLOGY

The vast spatial extent (perhaps infinite) of the universe is one apparent reason for doubting that a complete scientific account of it can ever be achieved. A second reason is the existence of the universe since the times of remote past; here too, possibly the extent is an infinite one. And yet we have seen that there is a manner in which a cosmology may comprehend the universe, even though infinite quantities are involved.

It is true that if the universe is, say, infinite in spatial extent, we could not expect specifically to describe all individual parts of it (for, as always, we assume that science is a finite body of statements). Thus, we could neither expect to list or name every galaxy in a world of infinitely many galaxies, nor could we have any expectation of observing all parts of the universe. The limitation that is imposed on science by its own finiteness, both in its content and its domain of direct observation, need not necessarily, however, be a factor that prevents cosmology from becoming a reasonably complete science. We have seen that in any science there is a limitation, such that the science does not contain all of the description that is logically possible for its domain. In cosmology, as in other sciences, generalization replaces item-by-item description, and thereby may enable even an infinite universe to be described in its general and overall properties.

If observation and theory should to a very high degree of probability indicate a universe for which no finite model would seem to be correct, we would then in an important sense have comprehended the structure of the universe. The degree of large-scale uniformity which the model indicated for the universe would probably be a significant factor in how complete the cosmology could be judged to be. If an infinite universe, in a valid model, were everywhere the same in its astronomical-scale properties, we could feel that we knew what the universe is like, even though we could in a direct sense know only a vanishingly small fraction of it. On the other hand, if the model indicated strong possibilities for variation from one region of the universe to the next, we would have to be content with a situation in which parts of the universe could exist in states very much different from our own. The mystery and unknowable quality of the universe, even in large-scale features, would then be strongly borne upon us. We would have to accept a large measure of incompleteness in our cosmology.

The establishment of a finite spatial extent of the universe would seem to be more satisfying than a discerning of infinitude. We could then have some hope of learning about all principal features of the universe (although it might be the case that even with a model which indicated a finite cosmos, its extent would be such that parts of it could never be in interaction with us through light or other signals). We might even venture the speculation that the universe is more likely to be found to be spatially finite than otherwise. For, we might expect that in any kind of spatially infinite universe there will be effects, like that of Olbers' indefinitely large amount of light in the infinitely extended static universe, which are counter to physical fact. Still, no firm support has been revealed for a general limitation on the size of the universe, and we must at present be open-minded about whether the universe is finite or infinite. Even if it is finite, it is of course quite possible that the model established for it will show it to be highly nonuniform in large-scale features. Should this be the case, there could also be for the finite universe an essential and apparently permanent incompleteness in cosmology.

We have seen that for a universe with infinite temporal extent we could nonetheless have a satisfying understanding of its past and future. Were this universe in a steady-state, or at least "quasi-steady" in its large-scale features, with some regularity of oscillation between different states, we could then see it as essentially atemporal. Time would exist for the various progressive changes which we find in the universe, but there would be no overall progressive cosmic change with which time could be associated throughout the entire, infinite past of the universe. And, of course, there would be no beginning point in time, or any significance to asking what one would be.

The universe might be found to have properties which require that it has existed always, but without the regularity in large-scale changes that would go with the "quasi-steady" universe. There would then, very probably, be essential incompleteness in our knowledge of the past of the universe. If no guiding principles for past change appeared, we could do little more than extrapolate backwards in time as far as present changes in the universe allowed. This is the situation in cosmology today, with no model established as the correct one; we can only judge the past states of the universe by a tentative backwards-in-time extrapolation from expansion, to a relatively more condensed state.

If a universe with a finite past time of existence were strongly indicated by cosmological studies, there would, as with the finite spatial universe, be a certain gain in completeness of our science of the universe; there would then be only a finite past history of the universe to describe. But, as has already been suggested, the problem of a creation event for the universe is a difficult one indeed for science. A cosmological model which rested on an unexplained creation as an axiom would have a kind of completeness, but most scientists would probably find it less satisfying than one which rested on some universal natural law, taken as an ultimate principle or axiom.

One can imaginatively consider that physical science might find principles in accordance with which the universe of space, matter, energy, and change (time) would *of itself* appear. It could well be argued, however, that the parallel in time to the spatially closed and finite universe is not the universe that has existed during only a finite past time. Rather, one might see the parallel as the atemporal universe that has existed forever. With this universe, particularly if it has a quasi-steady property, with no overall progressive change, the processes of change eventually bring the universe back in an approximate return to any given state. The universe comes back to itself in time, as analogously the space of the curved spatially finite universe comes back upon itself.

My discussion of possible degrees of incompleteness in various models for the universe emphasizes that it is in cosmology itself that we will learn how complete the science may be. Whether the universe is finite or infinite in space or time, nicely uniform in its cosmic distribution of matter and processes of change or widely fluctuating from place to place and time to time: these are questions to be answered by the work of cosmologists. I said that the answers to the questions about completeness are to a large extent determined by the natural world itself. My conclusions about completeness in cosmology well illustrate this statement. We must look to a domain of nature itself in order to learn how completely that domain may be known and understood.

As a final word on cosmology it can be pointed out that what has been found so far can leave one hopeful for a fair degree of completeness in this science. Hardly more than a start has been made, and there is promise that much important new observational data will be forthcoming within the next few decades. Radio astronomy has already provided an important supplement to optical observations. Within a few years we shall probably be getting observations from artificial satellites, beyond the earth's atmosphere. The exposure of detectors to radiation that is free from the absorption and distortion that occurs in the atmosphere may greatly increase the significant data for cosmological decisions. It is encouraging too that to date there has been no compelling indication in our observable universe of any large-scale spatial irregularity. In every direction the universe seems to be about the same, and it may well be that it does have a uniformity which justifies the kind of homogeneous model that generally has been assumed in cosmology. Temporally, to be sure, we know very little about what regularity or uniformity there may be in the overall past history of the universe, except for the highly significant expansion that we find, even for regions that we see as they were several billions of years ago.

Perhaps most important of all in our considering completeness and cosmology is the fact that no irremovable obstacles to attaining a knowledge of the large-scale structure of the universe have appeared. Cosmology is replete with speculations and alternatives, and it is attempting a task which may be far too ambitious in view of the empirical and theoretical science that man can achieve. If this is the case, if the goal of cosmology is hopeless, we should find continued failure to make progress, and clear inadequacy of information for the questions that are asked. Or, perhaps even principles would be established which show that the kind of observations we are able to make could not solve the problems that arise in cosmology. At present, however, no such barriers stand before us. Astronomical studies have given us knowledge of our universe enormously far beyond our earth, and models have been formulated, in terms of basic physical theory, which are in accord with the known properties of the universe. This fruitful interplay, between new observations on the one hand and modification and extension of theory on the other, has been characteristic of cosmology in recent decades. Such interplay is a mark of vigorous developments in a science; as long as there is no reason to see why it should stop, we can look forward to eventual achievement of completeness in cosmology.

9

The Natural Limits of Description

1   INTRODUCTION: SCALES OF MAGNITUDE

IN THE PROGRESSION of magnitudes that we are able to estimate in nature, the size of man is such that he falls considerably closer to the very small than to the very large. The largest object that we observe as having any high degree of unity in contrast with its background is the galaxy. The linear extent of a galaxy is of the order of a hundred thousand light years, or 10^{21} meters. In contrast, an atom has a diameter of about 10^{-10} m. Taking man as having dimensions that are of about 1 meter in order of magnitude, we see that the size ratio *galaxy:man* is about 10^{21}, whereas *man:atom* is about 10^{10}. This is to say, an atom would have to be multiplied ten times by a factor of ten if it were to be brought to a human dimension, but a man would have to be multiplied twenty-one times by ten, if he were to be brought to a galactic dimension.

We come to a similar result if we consider the size of man in comparison with a minimum diameter of the universe and with the smallest of physical entities. The latter are the elementary particles of nature, such as the protons, neutrons, and electrons which make up the atom. These particles have dimensions of the order of 10^{-15} m. The universe, even if finite, can hardly have an extent less than 10^{10} light years, or 10^{26} m, since galaxies are directly observed at distances which with any of the usual cosmological models must be inferred as being of the order of several billion light years. The ratio *universe : man* is then, at least of the order 10^{26}. With this ratio, in comparison with 10^{15} for *man : elementary-particle*, we again find that man is about ten factors of 10 farther from the dimension of the universe than from that of the elementary particle. Actually, of course he may be much farther than 10 factors, since we have no certain knowledge of the total extent of the universe, beyond the indication of a minimum size.

The relative closeness of man to the smallest of the natural dimensions may be a contributing element to his having come to a certain limit in the description of the very small-scale aspects of nature. This limit has been reached in the science of the twentieth century, and provides us with the one clear instance we have where natural science has brought itself to the boundary of its domain. We have seen that in cosmology we must describe the universe over immense extents in space and time, and it may well be that we shall eventually definitely learn that these dimensions are infinite. In that event, we will have to consider what limitations there are for our finite science with respect to infinite aspects of the universe. We have not yet, however, reached any definite conclusions about the space–time extent of the universe, and, it is also the case that we have not yet seen in cosmology any breakdown or inapplicability of our ordinary notions of space and time. But in the physics of atoms and elementary particles we have found that the modes of description that we use for larger objects are no longer suitable; that the atomic-level entities of the natural world cannot even be described with the same spatiotemporal concepts that we use everywhere else in science.

Until about 1925, physicists tacitly assumed that one could indefinitely extend the closeness of descriptive detail in the scientific study of any process or structure. On this belief, scientists conceived of the atomic world as being particles and radiation in space and time, just as are the matter and fields of the larger world that can be directly observed. It was expected that the same kind of physical laws, and the same kind of physical concepts of position, motion, and charge, would be valid on the atomic level as in the world of everyday experience. What we have in fact learned is that on the atomic level there is inherent in nature itself a resistance to the modes of description which we use for the objects of direct experience. Our earlier atomic concepts had been too naive, and based on too literal an extrapolation from everyday experience.

Philosophers, at least since Greek days, had debated the kind of problem that is presented in Kant's second antinomy:[1] Is matter properly to be regarded as consisting of indivisible, simple entities, or, is everything composite, and always with a possibility for further subdivision? The second of these two alternatives is based on the assumption that the physical world is continuous in the manner of mathematical space, and it is this assumption that seems generally to have been taken by physics in its expectation that there is no microscopic limit on the use of Newtonian–mechanical space–time concepts. The first alternative, which requires that there be simple entities with an associated restriction on the mathematical-point structure of space and matter, is closer to what has been found to be the way of nature with respect to the divisibility of matter.

And yet, a speculative philosopher, wishing to argue for the existence of ultimate, simple elements, would scarcely have dared to suggest that which has actually been found to be the manner in which nature does terminate the continued divisibility of space and matter. It is not just that we find the atom

[1] I. Kant, *Critique of Pure Reason*, translated by Norman Kemp Smith (London, Macmillan, 1933), p. 402.

to be a complex structure of nucleus and extranuclear electrons, with the nucleus itself a far from simple domain. It is rather that matter and radiation, in their elementary units, have properties that are contradictory and incredible when stated in the terms that we have learned to use for natural phenomena of magnitude greater than those used on the atomic level. Just as we saw in discussing cosmology that the solution to the dilemma that neither an infinite nor a finite universe seemed feasible lay in the indication of properties of curvature and expansion that are far different from the properties of a stable, Euclidean universe, so likewise we find that nature has had unexpected and even unimagined surprises for the physicists who investigated the atomic world of elementary units of matter and radiation.

The subtlety and richness of the natural world has shown us once again—and how often this must have happened in the history of man's accumulation of scientific knowledge—that we cannot with certainty extrapolate our ideas very far beyond that which is confirmed and tested in experience. It is true that it is only by extrapolation and invention and generalization that we can form the laws and constructs that make our scientific theory; but because this theory is so flexible, and can be so easily imagined as valid in nature not yet observed or discerned, it must be ever liable to modification by the information that comes with an extension of descriptive science to new domains.

Relativity theory, in this century, required modification of our concepts of the space and time variables of physical processes, because of their dependence on relative speed in an interaction or observation. Quantum theory involves an even more drastic change in our use of those concepts in the description of the entities of the atomic world. Nature has given us the answer to whether or not matter is infinitely divisible, by changing her most basic properties, and even her relation of knowability to us, when we come to the atomic domain with our question. We are, therefore, justified in saying that *in respect to scientific knowledge as men had sought it for hundreds of years past*, we have in a full and proper sense come to an end point.

Our discussion of the limit that science has reached will be centered, then, around certain key parts of the quantum theory of atomic properties of matter and radiation. We shall first consider a simple but typical physical phenomenon involving observations that cannot be explained in the terms of customary space–time description. Further sections will present the quantum-theoretic formulation of the restrictions that exist for such description, and the general limitations that are implied for our knowledge of the natural world.

2   THE WAVE-PARTICLE DUALISM

Although we have related the restrictions on atomic-level description to the problem of whether or not there are indivisible, ultimate physical entities, it would be a mistake to think that this philosophical problem in any direct way led physicists to the discovery of descriptive limits. Rather, as might be expected, it was in the course of investigating some definite physical problems that the limitations on our traditional physical concepts were discerned.

In 1900 Max Planck had found that the equation which describes the intensity of radiation emitted by a blackbody for a given wavelength at a specified temperature could be derived only with the assumption that radiation is emitted (or absorbed) in quanta or photons of magnitude $h\nu$, where ν is the frequency of the radiation and h is the quantity we now call Planck's constant. Planck also assumed that the emitted radiation had its origin in oscillatory motions of atomic charged particles, and, by the well-confirmed Maxwell theory of electricity and magnetism, such oscillators should continuously emit radiation. (We recall that according to the Maxwell theory, any particle of charge e, undergoing acceleration of magnitude a, with c the speed of light, emits electromagnetic radiation $\frac{2}{3}\, e^2 a^2/c^3$ per unit of time.) The new assumption of Planck, that radiation not be continuous but in discrete quanta, was, then, sharply at variance with a theory which had generally given correct results for observed electromagnetic phenomena.

The physical reality of the localization of energy in quanta of radiation was assumed in the photoelectric equation (1905) in which Albert Einstein, following Planck, assumed that light brings energy in packets or quanta of energy $h\nu$ to a surface. This "needle radiation," as Einstein called it, could give all its energy to an electron and send it flying off into the surrounding space. The kinetic energy of the electron, plus the work required to move it from the surface of the material in which it had been lodged, are found experimentally to be equal just to the energy $h\nu$ of the photon of the incident radiation of frequency ν. Any attempt to explain the phenomenon by means of a wave theory of light comes to failure. A wave front, even one extended over billions of atomic diameters, does not have enough energy to be equivalent to a photon of energy $h\nu$.

Further evidence for the corpuscular nature of light is given in the Compton effect: electromagnetic radiation is scattered by a free electron in matter, with some kinetic energy being given to the electron, and the radiation coming off with a reduced frequency. Here, only part of the radiation is absorbed, instead of all, as in the photoelectric effect. But the energy of the electron is found to be $h\nu_i - h\nu_s$, where ν_i is the frequency of the incident radiation and ν_s the frequency of the scattered radiation. Not only is there a correct energy balance, with the consideration of the radiation as being constituted of photons, but also the magnitude and direction of the momenta of the radiation (photons) and electron are in accord with the usual momentum laws for material particles. It is only by considering the radiation to consist of corpuscular photons, that is, with all the energy and momentum of the photon concentrated in a pointlike region, that we can correctly describe the Compton or photoelectric effects.

We find, then, that in any interaction with matter, with a transfer of energy, electromagnetic radiation behaves as a photon. This is true not only for the photoelectric and Compton effects as described, but also for the many kinds of interactions in which light excites or ionizes atoms or molecules. Thus, for example, in the exposure of a photographic film to light, the silver salts are chemically changed as a result of light-as-photons giving up its energy to molecules of the salt. (The Compton-scattering effect is readily observed only for highly energetic photons, as in x-rays. With reflection of ordinary light from a mirror, the reflecting electrons and nuclei are sufficiently massive, relative to the photon, that there is virtually no discernible wavelength change: the photons of visible light give up little energy in reflection from a chemically inert metallic surface, just as a tennis ball gives up virtually no energy in being bounced from a solid wall.)

In traveling through space, however, light does behave with both the oscillatory and spreading-out properties that we ordinarily associate with a wave. The very fact, indeed, that we calculate photon energy $h\nu$ in terms of a frequency ν indicates that light has an oscillatory nature. The dual particle-wave properties of light are nicely illustrated by an adaptation of one of the classic demonstrations of the wave properties of light, Thomas Young's double-slit interference experiment. We think of a source of light of some given wavelength as giving illumination, through a slit S, onto the parallel slits s_1 and s_2. (Figure 9-1.) Light from these reaches the film F. Here, if the slits are sufficiently narrow, we will find a series of alternate light and dark bands. The regions of maximum light, labeled m_0, m_1, . . . , are of course the locations on F where the path-length difference from slits s_1 and s_2 is an integral number of wavelengths of the light from the source. There is, then, constructive interference for the light waves reaching these strips of maximum

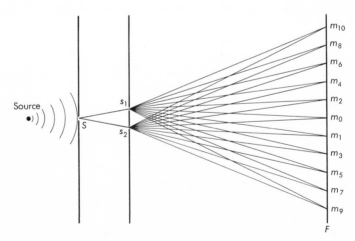

Figure 9-1.   Constructive interference between light waves from slits s_1 and s_2 gives illuminated bands m_0, m_1, m_2, . . . on the film F. Between each two adjacent light bands there is a dark region that arises from destructive interference between rays from s_1 and s_2.

illumination. Between the light strips there are strips of complete darkness on F, where the light waves from s_1 and s_2 are exactly out of phase and destructively interfere among themselves: the condition for this interference is that there be an $n + \frac{1}{2}$ wavelength difference in the paths from s_1 and s_2, where n is an integer.

There is no way in which we can understand the observed light–dark bands of a double-slit experiment except by ascribing them to constructive and destructive interference effects of light waves. Similar optical interference effects are, of course, observed in many other experiments: in the diffraction of light that has passed through small openings, in various types of diffraction gratings, and with the Michelson interferometer. Geometric analysis of the conditions for interference, taken with the observed interference effects, leads to determinations of the wavelength of light, and different types of inter- ference experiments are altogether consistent in the wavelength value they give for monochromatic light from a given source. In everyday experience, interference (as we learn in elementary physics) gives rise to the striking color patterns that we observe in light reflected from thin films, as, for example, from oil films on water.

The contrast between the wave behavior and particle properties of light is evident. In striking the film the light interacts as photons along the light strips centered on m_0, m_1, m_2, ... We could even, for example, arrange that the film F be a chemically active metallic surface, such as cesium, and we would then find photoelectrons to be emitted from the surface along the light strips, but with no emission in the dark regions. And yet, the fact that the light reaches the film or surface in alternate bands requires that there have been interference between light waves from the two slits, s_1 and s_2. This interference apparently prevents appearance of photons at locations where there is destructive interference of light waves, and allows their appearance at positions of constructive interference. Intermediate wave amplitudes, re- sulting from less than complete destructive or constructive interference, may be associated with probabilities of photon formation that are intermediate between zero and the maximum values to be found on the strip regions of greatest illumination.

The intermingling of wave and particle properties that appears in the double-slit and other interference experiments presents a hard problem to the advocate of any traditional concept of light; for, a rapid alteration from light as a physical wave to light as a corpuscle is evidently involved. And, before the light was a wave, passing through the system of slits, it must also have been a corpuscle. This we know because Planck's radiation law tells us that the light must be emitted from any source as a photon, and, also, the study of relations between atomic structure and radiation, beginning with Bohr's theory of the hydrogen atom, abundantly confirms the original Planck postulate.

Still, one might hope to understand the wave–particle behavior in terms of a basically corpuscular conception of light, with interference between oscillating photons rather than between waves. Certain further experimental evidence, however, even destroys this possibility, and virtually removes the problem beyond any solution in terms of ordinary space–time concepts. If light were basically made up of photons, and interphoton interference explained the optical interference phenomena, then there should be no such interference effects if light were sent through a double-slit apparatus only one photon at a time. Such experiments[2] have been carried out, and the result is precisely the same as if the same number of photons were sent through the apparatus in a short period of time. In other words, a lone photon is "directed" to one of the bright bands, just as if millions of photons were simultaneously passing through the apparatus.

If a double-slit apparatus is used, but with s_1 or s_2 closed, then we at once lose the interference pattern. It must be the case, then, that interference effects are a consequence of interaction between light elements that have come over the two different paths, from s_1 and s_2, as postulated in our wave description. But since we do get interference phenomena with sources so weak that only a single photon passes through the apparatus at a time, it must be the case that the photon passes through both slits. It is inescapable that interference is an intraphoton process, i.e., it occurs between different parts of the same photon (regarded as a wave). There is no possibility of regarding the photon as basic, and the wave as an effect of many photons together. Instead, we must regard the corpuscular and wave aspects as equally fundamental, with each being a true physical state of light. The manner, however, in which a photon can move and expand in space, occupying a large volume, and yet also concentrate its momentum and energy in a pointlike location, in an interaction with matter, escapes any customary space–time description of details of mechanism or process. We can scarcely do better than to say, in the words of Professor Dirac,[3] the particle and wave aspects of reality ". . . are connected in some curious manner."

We should not feel, however, that because we do not have a point-by-point spatial description of light in its wave and particle properties, that we have lost all coherent science of its behavior. We can see that in a statistical sense we have a completely reliable description or prediction of light in situations where interference occurs. That is, we are able to say what the pattern formed by many photons (or by light in a macroscopic amount) will be; thus, we can confidently expect the pattern of light and dark bands that the wavelength of light that is used will require, in a given interference apparatus, and expect as well the energy that the photons of the light will

---

[2] The experiment requires that extremely weak sources of light be used. It has been performed by G. I. Taylor [*Proceedings of the Cambridge Philosophical Society*, 15, 114 (1909)] with a double-slit interference system, and by A. J. Dempster and H. F. Batho [*Physical Review*, 30, 644 (1927)] with an echelette diffraction grating.

[3] P. A. M. Dirac, *Principles of Quantum Mechanics*, 2nd ed. (New York, Oxford University Press, 1930), p. 2.

give to electrons or atoms that absorb them. It is also worth noting that there is a nice symmetry in the wave–particle dualism between the emission and absorption of light. Light always comes from an atom (or other source) as a photon, generated at a pointlike particle with energy loss by that particle. Likewise, the photon disappears in an absorption by an atom or other charged particle—again, in a pointlike spatial region, and with energy loss. So, we have corpuscle $\rightleftarrows$ wave, with different directions for the arrows at emission and absorption. We see here a manifestation of the time reversal that is characteristic of Maxwell's wave equation for the propagation of light and also for the equations describing absorption or emission of light: the equations equally well describe a process forward or backward in time. On the microscopic level, then, light behaves according to time-reversible equations just as do particles of matter, for which the basic equations (Newton's laws, with suitable special-relativistic modifications) are time-reversible. The fact that a photon can spread out, and be partly transmitted at one slit and partly at another (or partly reflected from one plane and partly from another, in a diffraction apparatus), and yet interact as a corpuscle *anywhere* matter is placed in its path, is indeed puzzling. But it would perhaps be even more mysterious if the photon, created as a corpuscle, propagated itself through space as a wave and then continued to be a wave even in its interaction with matter. In that event nature could hardly have the ready exchange of energy between matter and radiation which we do find, and would in consequence be far more "one-way" in its processes than it actually is.

The same apparently contradictory wave and particle properties that we find for electromagnetic radiation are observed for matter. There are many phenomena of electron diffraction which establish the wave properties of matter, and they are sufficiently well-known that we shall not discuss them.[4] The wave property of matter is, of course, not unique to the electron, but is a property of all particles of matter; the wavelength λ of mass m freely moving at relative speed v is given by the de Broglie equation, $\lambda = h/mv$, where h is again Planck's constant, 6.6×10^{-27} erg·sec. De Broglie derived his equation, in fact, on the assumption that matter has a frequency v given by $E = hv$, just as do photons, where now E is the energy, mc^2, for any mass m. Besides using the relativistic $E = mc^2$ relation, he also applied the relations between space and time intervals,[5] as given by the Lorentz transformation equations of spe-

[4] The reader will find a good account of the physics of matter-waves in Max Born's *Atomic Physics*, 7th ed. (New York, Hafner Publishing Co., 1961). Or, generally any textbook of modern or atomic physics will contain a detailed presentation. The nonscientist reader will find an excellent discussion in *The New Conceptions of Matter*, by C. G. Darwin (New York, Macmillan, 1931). A brief and even less technical discussion of the wave-particle duality is given by J. R. Oppenheimer in his Reith Lectures, published as *Science and the Common Understanding* (New York, Simon and Schuster, 1955), Chaps. II–V.

[5] L. de Broglie, *Annales de Physique*, 3, 22 (1925). I have discussed the close relation between the relativistic time transformation and de Broglie waves, in accordance with de Broglie's derivation, in R. Schlegel, *Time and the Physical World* (East Lansing, Michigan, Michigan State University Press, 1961), Chap. VI.

cial relativity theory, to the energy-related frequency $\nu = E/h$, and thereby came to the $\lambda = h/mv$ equation. The Lorentz equations and the energy–mass relation would be expected to be valid for observations of any particles whatsoever, and hence the de Broglie equation should also be true for all matter, if there physically is a frequency $\nu = E/h$. Observations of de Broglie waves for protons, neutrons, and even entire molecules, such as H_2, abundantly confirm the validity of the de Broglie assumptions.

The wavelength of matter particles is too small to allow observation of interference in a double-slit apparatus of the kind that we use for light. The atomic planes in crystals do, however, provide natural diffraction gratings, with distances between planes that are comparable to the wavelengths of electrons moving at the easily achieved velocities of about 10^8 cm/sec. Electron diffraction is a commonly used probe for studying what are the orderly arrangements of atoms in crystalline substances of various kinds. And, as with photons, we must regard electron diffraction as being a consequence of interference between different parts of a given electron wave. Part of the electron wave is reflected from one plane of atoms, part from an adjoining plane, part from still the next plane, and so on. The reflected parts interfere in or out of phase (i.e., constructively or destructively), and thus determine whether or not the electron can or cannot appear at a given location as a corpuscle. As such it could convey energy and momentum to, say, a silver-salt molecule in a photographic plate, and thereby be recorded. We have, then, precisely the same situation as with the photons in the double-slit interference apparatus. The electron in motion is a wave with a wavelength given by the de Broglie equation, but in any actual interaction with matter it is a proper particle with its energy and momentum concentrated in the small spatial volume that we associate with a corpuscular electron.

Experiments[6] with the diffraction of electrons by crystals, with the use of electron beams of such a low intensity that in general only one electron would be passing through the diffracting material at a time, give the same results as when many electrons in the incident beam are simultaneously diffracted. Hence, just as for the photon, we have direct evidence that the matter particle is a corpuscle under circumstances of exchanging energy with another entity, but is a wave in its motion through space. Throughout atomic and elementary-particle physics the dual wave–particle nature of matter is now established beyond doubt, by both direct observation and the confirmed consequences of the quantum theory that is based on assumption of the dualism.

It will be useful to introduce the wave (or state) function ψ which is used in the mathematical formulation of quantum mechanics. We may regard the ψ-function as being, essentially, a mathematical expression for describing the dual wave–corpuscular properties of matter and radiation. Although ψ could be

[6] L. Biberman, N. Sushkin, and V. Fabrikant, *Doklady Academii Nauk S.S.S.R.*, **66**, 185–186 (1949). Also, M.S. Thesis, "Electron Diffraction," by John H. Muller, Michigan State University, 1954 (unpublished).

regarded, as initially introduced by Erwin Schroedinger,[7] as an amplitude function for the particle or photon wave, it does not have that direct physical significance in the later quantum mechanics which developed from the work of Schrödinger and others. We may if we like still think of ψ as a wave function, but it is not for a wave in physical, three-dimensional space, but for a wave in an abstract, mathematical space that is convenient for quantum-mechanical problems, and can be somewhat altered for each particular type of problem.

In general, ψ may be characterized as a function that describes the *state* of a physical system, and hence the term state-function is often used for it. The description that ψ gives is not, of course, the kind of detailed description that we have in prequantum mechanics, for, we have seen, such is not possible on the level of atomic events. But, ψ does indicate the probability of observing the particular effect or magnitude with which it is associated. Thus, specifically, if ψ is the state function of a particle, written as a function of space–time variables (x, y, z, t), then the probability of observing the particle at a particular set of (x, y, z, t) values is proportional to the square of the magnitude of ψ, $|\psi|^2$, at that (x, y, z, t) point. Or, in general, the probability of the system's being in a state associated with a given ψ value is proportional to $|\psi|^2$ for that state. The interpretation of $|\psi|^2$ as a measure of probability was introduced into quantum physics by Max Born in 1926; the introduction was both a penetrating insight, and a fruitful guide for the further development of the formal structure of quantum mechanics in the solution of various physical problems. (For ordinary physical waves, including electromagnetic waves, the energy of the wave is proportional to the square of its amplitude.)

We can illustrate the use of the ψ function by applying it to the double-slit interference experiment that we have discussed. The photons in the apparatus may be described by a general state function ψ. But further, since each photon passes through both slits s_1 and s_2, and may reach the film at any of many positions, m_i (see Figure 9-1), it is also convenient to regard ψ, in accordance with what is found by observing the photon effects on the film, as subdivided into ψ_i's, each ψ_i being associated with the photons that come to a given light strip m_i. (We will now take m_i as including the entire illuminated region of the ith strip.) The actual wave function would be written in a manner that entailed the path differences from s_1 and s_2 for various positions on the film F, so that the interference phenomena would de described by the state function. The evaluation of the ψ would be in accordance with Schroedinger's basic quantum mechanical equation, written in this case for photons. The form of the subdivision of ψ could be

$$\psi = a_1\psi_1 + a_2\psi_2 + a_3\psi_3 + \cdots = \sum_i a_i\psi_i.$$

The number of ψ_i's would depend on the number of light strips to be expected in an actual apparatus (in some experimental arrangements there may be many thousands of light and dark bands). The total probability $|\psi|^2$

[7] E. Schroedinger, *Collected Papers on Wave Mechanics* (Glasgow, Blackie & Son, 1928).

must be unity, this being an expression of the fact that each photon in the system interacts somewhere on the film. The probability of a photon's coming to any given strip m_i would be $|a_i|^2$. Hence, the total ψ does describe the pattern of light that is to be expected on the film. (We have given a very simple description using the assumption that we have discrete light strips m_i. One could take into account a continuous variation of observed light intensity on F and write

$$\psi = \int_0^Z a(z)\psi(z)\,dz,$$

where z is a parameter on the film, running, say, from the first illumination at the bottom, $z = 0$, to the upper edge of the illumination at $z = Z$.)

It is fundamental in quantum theory that we may consider any given ψ as a linear superposition of substate ψ's as in the equations we have just written. This superposition principle[8] permits the calculation of the interference that occurs between different wave states of the entities of the system, and, as in the ψ for photons in the double-slit experiment, the description of the entities of the system must reflect the possibilities for interference. Subject only to this limitation, and, of course a general suitability for the system, the decomposition of the state function may be made in an indefinite number of ways. We do require, however, that our ultimate expression be in terms that are related to observed quantities; thus, again, in our illustrative example, the ψ_i's refer to probabilities of observing or photographing photons at the various m_i locations. We see that the superposition principle is necessary because of what in some simple physical situations we call wavelike properties; and yet our "answer" or predicted observed quantities from a ψ function are not in terms of any kind of physical wave, but are in terms of probabilities of finding events or particles. It would seem that this must be, because we are interested in having the ψ function tell us what we can find out about the state of a system by observation, and we only make observation by some energy-exchanging physical interaction. And, we have seen, matter and radiation are corpuscular in such interactions.

3   THE UNCERTAINTY PRINCIPLE

The microscopic behavior of matter and radiation clearly does forbid the kind of unambiguous space–time description on an atomic level that we give to a macroscopic particle that is always a particle, or to a continuing wave in some material medium. It might seem, then, that we have only an inscrutable and unpredictable wave–particle at the basis of natural reality. We have already noted, however, that we are able to make predictions of results for systems of many photons or matter particles, even though we cannot describe

---

[8] See P. A. M. Dirac, *Principles of Quantum Mechanics*, 2nd ed. (New York, Oxford University Press, 1930), Chap. I.

details of process for individual entities. More than this, however, we have a definite statement of what are the limits of accuracy of our customary pre-quantum kind of description, when we wish to apply that description to systems of atomic particles (including photons). This statement is what we call the Uncertainty Principle (or, sometimes, The Principle of Indeterminacy). It was first formulated and derived by Werner Heisenberg in 1927.

The principle states the uncertainty which must exist in any possible measurements of certain pairs of the dynamical variables that are used to describe particles and photons. The most commonly used pair for which the principle is valid are position and momentum. The mathematical statement of the Uncertainty Principle for them is

$$\Delta p \cdot \Delta x \geq h/4\pi,$$

where Δp is the uncertainty in measurement of momentum in the x-direction, Δx the uncertainty in measurement of position along x, and h is again Planck's constant. We see at once that these uncertainties are negligible for objects that are substantially larger than the elements of the atomic and subatomic world, since h is of the order of 10^{-27}, in centimeter-gram-second units. But, for a very small Δx (or Δp), the uncertainty in p (or x) must become large. (The required small Δx, or Δp, could not be achieved for large-scale objects, with the use of customary large-scale measuring devices.) And, if $\Delta x \to 0$, the uncertainty in momentum must become indefinitely large, and we can say that we lose all information about the momentum. Similarly, if $\Delta p \to 0$, we are not able to know anything about the position of the particle (or photon).

In prequantum physics it was, of course, tacitly assumed that a particle could simultaneously both be localized in space and have its velocity (and hence momentum) measured, as accurately as desired. Thinking about how to do this did, to be sure, sometimes lead to disturbing difficulties. If, for example, one uses the usual definition for velocity, $v = \lim\limits_{\Delta t \to 0} \dfrac{\Delta x}{\Delta t}$, one may ask how can a velocity be physically measured at a point with $\Delta x \to 0$ as $\Delta t \to 0$. Some two thousand years ago Zeno asked this question in a very penetrating way. We recall that in his paradox of Achilles and the tortoise, Achilles must always cover $\frac{1}{2}$ of the remaining distance between himself and the tortoise. Eventually this distance, $\frac{1}{2} \times \frac{1}{2} \times \frac{1}{2} \times \ldots$, becomes as small as desired. In his paradox of the arrow Zeno carries the question of motion through such successively smaller space intervals to its logical conclusion by asking how the arrow, instantaneously occupying one given set of space points, can ever move to another set. That is, he asks how it can move at all. His conclusion is that motion is an impossibility. This result is a striking forerunner of the conclusion of quantum mechanics, that if the location of a particle is precisely known, $\Delta x = 0$, we can know nothing whatsoever about its velocity or momentum (i.e., about its motion).[9]

[9] See R. Schlegel, "Quantum Mechanics and the Paradoxes of Zeno," *American Scientist*, **36**, 396 (1948).

In the prequantum conception of motion, a particle could be regarded as a hard sphere which moved through space, with no change as a result of its motion. Detailed description of location and change of location with time seemed, then, to be as obvious and natural as for a thrown stone or orbiting satellite. But, whatever one may think of Zeno's arguments for the impossibility of motion of unvarying objects, we have found that in nature motion is not simple translation of such an entity through empty, passive space. Rather, for the elementary particles of which matter is constituted, motion is intimately associated with the wave property of the particle: one is led to say that a particle moves as a wavelike oscillation in space–time. And of course for radiation, propagation as a wave at a naturally determined single speed is its manifest and defining property. The classical way of describing matter becomes inadequate and inapplicable, then, because the particle in motion ceases to be fixed in space and time in the manner required by the classical conception of a particle. Also, the classical space–time description of radiation as a wave breaks down because the radiation, in an energy-exchanging interaction, ceases to be a wave spread out in space.

In a crude way, we can see an immediate relation between the wave–particle dualism and the uncertainty relations. If matter and radiation behave as a wave in traveling through space, then there can not be localization at a point if they are moving, because a wave is spread out in space. Also, when a particle or photon is acting as a corpuscle, in an energy exchange at a point, it cannot have the wave property that is associated with motion. These qualitative implications of wave–particle properties are found to be correct in detail when they are studied in terms of the mathematical structure of quantum theory. It is found that in order to write the equation for a wave that has an amplitude much different from zero in only a small region of space (i.e., Δx is small for the entity that is the wave) the equation must allow a possibility of many different waves, each of a different wavelength and hence, by the de Broglie equation, each corresponding to a different momentum. There is, then, a wide range of possible velocity or momentum values for a particle that is quite sharply localized. In the limiting case of $\Delta x \to 0$, an infinite range of wavelengths (momenta) must be available. Conversely, if only one wavelength is available, the particle has a sharply defined momentum. But now there is no superposition of different waves that will bring the net amplitude to nonzero in only a small space region; instead, the single-frequency wave extends indefinitely, and all locations become possible ones for the particle if there is a localization out of its wave.[10]

It is sometimes said that the position–momentum uncertainty relation arises because in any kind of measurement there must be a transfer of energy; thus, if the position of a particle is measured by reflecting a photon from it, the reflection will alter the momentum of the particle and we therefore lose

[10] The simple relation between waves, localization in space, and the uncertainty relations was given by Niels Bohr, *Nature*, **121**, 590 (1928).

exact knowledge of the momentum in making a position determination. Considerations of this kind can give illustrations of the uncertainty principle, but it is a mistake to think of the principle as coming alone from the effects of measurement interaction. With a purely classical, prequantum conception of matter and radiation we would also have disturbance of a system as a consequence of our making measurements upon it. But we would expect that we could make allowance for the disturbance, since we assume, in prequantum physics, that we can calculate the course of any interaction or other physical process with unlimited accuracy. In quantum physics we are not able to do this, because our calculations only give us probabilities for the presence of a particle or photon at a given point. The uncertainty rests, then, on what we have found to be the nature of matter and radiation, and in particular, in instances we have seen, on the transformation between wave and particle, which is not to be followed with the detail of space–time description that we could hope to give in prequantum physics. Further, because of the finite minimum quantum of energy that is established in quantum theory for any measurement-interaction exchange, we do not have the possibility (always conceivable in classical physics) of letting the effect of a measurement vanish altogether.

The mathematical derivation, in the quantum theory, of the uncertainty relations between dynamical variables utilizes the role of the state function ψ in giving calculated probabilities for the possible values of the variables. Since we cannot learn other than probabilities from ψ functions, it follows that the position–momentum uncertainty is a statistical relationship, valid for measurements on many particles (or many systems). This means, for example, that if in some manner we measure the position and momentum in a given coordinate dimension x for many particles in a given state, the distributions, Δx of position values and Δp of momentum values, will satisfy the uncertainty inequality. The uncertainty relation, as derived, does not give any information about what we may or may not observe with respect to a single particle.[11]

And yet, in presentations of the Uncertainty Principle we commonly do, for example, say that we cannot simultaneously know both the position and momentum of a particle. Also, in the "*Gedanken* experiments"[12] by which physicists illustrate their inability to devise an apparatus, even in principle, which will defeat the uncertainty restrictions, the proposed measurements are often on a single particle or photon. The two approaches to the Uncertainty Principle, first, by way of statistical results required by the mathematical theory, and second, by way of proposed physical measurements on single particles, cannot however be unrelated. If in a physical measurement of a single particle one were able to determine position and momentum such that $\Delta x \cdot \Delta p < h/4\,\pi$, it would be possible to repeat the measurement on many particles in a given state. Obviously, then, the mathematically derived uncer-

---

[11] This point is emphasized by Henry Margenau, *Philosophy of Science*, 30, 1, 138 (1963); also see Steven W. Matthysse, *American Journal of Physics*, 28, 560 (1960).

[12] W. Heisenberg, *The Physical Principles of the Quantum Theory*, translated by Carl Eckhart and Frank C. Hoyt (Chicago, University of Chicago Press, 1930), Chap. II.

tainty, for the variation in values from many observations, would have been shown to be physically wrong. Hence, we must regard the uncertainty, as it has been established for individual particle measurements, as strengthening the uncertainty which quantum theory demonstrates statistically for the description of atomic-level physical processes. Likewise, if the analysis of maximum accuracy in individual particle measurements did not indicate a close approach to the limit $\Delta x \cdot \Delta p \geqq h/4\,\pi$, we would wonder if the quantum theory properly expressed the physical restrictions on measurement. It is reassuring that the *Gedanken* experiments so far proposed have always indicated that h is approximately the minimum value for the product of the uncertainties.[13]

An indefinite number of pairs of dynamical variables could be constructed for which the product of uncertainties must $\geqq h/4\,\pi$. An important pair, for example, in addition to position and momentum, is that made up of two independent components of angular momentum of a particle or other physical system. Thus, with any given apparatus one cannot make an exact measurement of two angular momentum components, as L_x and L_y (although it is possible simultaneously to learn the value of a single component and also the value of the square $L^2 = L_x{}^2 + L_y{}^2 + L_z{}^2$). Next to that of position and momentum, the uncertainty which has probably received widest attention is the one between energy E and time t:

$$\Delta E \cdot \Delta t \geq h/4\pi.$$

If, say, the time t at which an atom emits radiation is to be measured by means of the observation of the radiation, then there will be an uncertainty Δt in the time, and also an uncertainty ΔE in the value found for the energy, with the product satisfying the uncertainty inequality. For this example, we can easily understand the necessity of the uncertainty in terms of the wave property of the emitted radiation. Exact counting of waves is required to determine frequency, and hence energy, since $E = h\nu$. The longer the time Δt of counting, the smaller is the error, because a fractional wave not counted becomes relatively less important as a contribution to error in frequency as the total counting time increases. So, what is gained in decreasing ΔE, is lost in increasing Δt.[10]

In a less obvious application of the energy–time uncertainty, we can use the fact that in general the energy of a particle or photon requires a certain time for its definition. If an electron, say, is in a stationary state in an atom, the time of its state is indefinitely long, $\Delta t \to \infty$, and the energy of the electron is sharply defined, $\Delta E \to 0$. On the other hand, for small Δt, that is, for a nonstable state, there may be variations in the energy, to be expressed by saying that ΔE is large. For very small Δt's we may have sufficiently large fluctua-

---

[13] The two approaches to the quantum-mechanical uncertainty relations have been discussed by Y. Aharonov and D. Bohm, *Physical Review*, **122**, 1649 (1961). In this paper the authors give the view of Niels Bohr (cited as a private communication): "there can be no limitation on individual measurements that cannot also be obtained from the mathematical formalism and the statistical interpretation."

tions in E to give ΔE's that allow even the momentary appearance of electrons or more massive particles (if other conditions favor the production of such particles). Over any macroscopically defined interval of time we always expect, in physics, to find the principle of conservation of energy to be rigorously true. The energy–time uncertainty does allow, however, on the atomic level, and for *very* short periods of time, the existence of energy states which are not strictly in accord with classical energy conservation. There is, however, no expectation that one could macroscopically observe any deviations from energy conservation, since the atomic level short-time energy fluctuations would cancel out in any such observation. Nonetheless, it is necessary in some instances to take these fluctuations into account, since, like the wave–particle properties of matter, they are part of the natural world.

The energy–time uncertainty is in an important way somewhat different from the uncertainty between pairs of dynamical variables, such as position and momentum. This difference has been pointed out and elucidated by Aharonov and Bohm.[14] It lies in the fact that time is not a dynamical variable, in the mathematical structure of quantum theory, in the same way as are such "mechanical" variables as position, momentum, and angular momentum. These latter variables have corresponding mathematical operators in the quantum theory, and it is in the calculation of simultaneous values for pairs of operators for a given physical system that the required distributions in values (i.e., the uncertainties) appear. The operators, in effect, correspond to an interaction between system and measuring apparatus when they are solved for an observable value. The time variable in quantum mechanics is not, however, an operator in the way that the mechanical variables are. Instead, time is a parameter, assumed to be independently given or measured. Its role in the quantum-mechanical equations is not primarily that of an instrinsic property of the system being discussed, but is rather that of a coordinate in a reference system in terms of which the system is discussed.

Because of its special role, the time in a quantum-mechanical description may be either, in the terms of Bohm and Aharonov, the "inner" time of the system, or the "clock" time of the apparatus being used for observation of the system. For the former the time-uncertainty relation must hold, but for the latter there is no necessity for an uncertainty, and the exact energy of an event may in principle be found to as accurate a time measure as is desired. Bohm and Aharonov devise an ideal experiment in which, in fact, the time of a specified energy transfer to a particle is found with arbitrarily high precision.

In order better to understand the distinction between the "inner" and apparatus-clock times, we might make an analogy with the momentum of a particle. This is a property of the particle, and although we might measure it by means of laboratory apparatus, there is nothing in the apparatus itself to

[14] *Physical Review*, **122**, 1649 (1961). Also, criticism by V. A. Fok, *Zhurnal Eksperimental'noi i Teoreticheskoi Fiziki*, **42**, 1135 (1962) ; English translation in *Soviet Physics —JETP*, **15**, 784 (1962). Reply by Y. Aharonov and D. Bohm, *Physical Review*, **134**, B1417 (1964).

provide a definition of the particle's momentum. (The apparatus, isolated, gives no measurement whatsoever of momentum.) In contrast, the time of a system that is undergoing study may be defined by our laboratory clocks, since we place all events in a matrix of a progressively increasing time variable (conventionally set up and defined by certain processes that may be conveniently accepted as uniform in time). The energy associated with an event or transition may be given by this clock time, and there is nothing in principle to limit the accuracy of the time assignment.

On the other hand, the time of a system may be measured in terms of events or processes of the system itself. Time, we recall, essentially arises from the existence of change, and it may be the changes in the system we are describing which we use for definition of time. In this case we are using "inner" time, a property of the system, just as we use the momentum of a system of particles, as given, say by their wavelength, to measure that momentum. Thus, if we are going to use the observation of electromagnetic waves from an atom as a measure for the time of emission of those waves, we are using an "inner" time (derived from a property of the atom-radiation system itself), and we can expect the energy–time uncertainty restriction to be valid. In their illustrative example of an exact time measurement of an energy transfer, Aharonov and Bohm use the position of a moving electrical capacitor as a time measure. The energy interaction to be measured is by an energy transfer between the moving capacitor and a charged particle. If the energy transferred were used in the observation of the time of transfer one would again expect the uncertainty inequality to hold; but, by using a time measure that is not in essential relation to the energy event whose time is to be measured, they do appear to be able to circumvent the inequality.

We must say, then, that even on the atomic level, we can refer the energy of an event to the "outside" time measure of our observing apparatus, with no inherent limit on the accuracy of the time measure. But because of the necessary uncertainty when the time measure is in terms of the processes of change that are associated with the energy that is being measured for a system, there remains in nature the relation for the variations between energy and time that is specified by $\Delta t \cdot \Delta E \geqq h/4\,\pi$. Hence, we get no measure of "inner" time (no process of change) for an electron moving in a fixed energy-state in an atom. And, conversely, the possibility for large fluctuations in energy of a system remains, if the system manifests these fluctuations in its own properties for time intervals that are as brief as is required by the energy–time uncertainty.

4 INDETERMINISM

The successful use of Newtonian mechanics in describing and predicting the motions of material bodies gave strong support to the concept of strict determinism among the phenomena of nature. This doctrine requires that any given state of a physical system (which may even be the entire universe) is exactly as it is as a consequence of its development or change from some preceding state in accordance with discernible and fixed natural laws. Each state or condition of a system, then, is unalterably related to any other state or condition of the system. (By a system we now mean a natural structure or organism which may be effectively described as a unit, both as regards its internal processes and its interactions with other parts of nature.) With the passage of time, a system may be described as going through states a, b, c, ... If we know the system adequately in any one of these states, then, by the doctrine of determinism, we can in principle infer what its states will be at some future time, or must have been at some past time. The future, then, is completely "determined," and for any system the passage of time merely makes manifest a succession of states whose specific characteristics have forever been unalterably set. The present is succeeded by what has been the future, but in no sense freely forms or gives rise to what succeeds it.

We may state the doctrine of determinism in explicit physical terms as follows: if the positions x_i and the momenta p_i are known for all the particles of a system, at a time $t = 0$, then we may in principle calculate these positions and momenta for all the particles of the system at any other time $t \neq 0$. It would of course be required that we understand all the interaction forces between particles, in order that the calculations could in principle be made. Since the state of a system would, presumably, be completely specified if we knew all the x_i's and p_i's for the system, their calculation for any one time would be tantamount to calculation of the state of the system at that time.

Although commonly it has been tacitly assumed as being possible, there are doubts about whether or not the complete calculation of the positions and momenta of all the atomic particles of a system is in any way feasible, even with assumption of the prequantum classical mechanics.[15] Certainly, we see, the calculation cannot be made with the restrictions which the uncertainty principle places on our knowledge of atomic particles. For, if we are unable to know a given pair of variables x_i and p_i with unlimited accuracy at an initial time $t = 0$, obviously we cannot calculate their values at other times. The doctrine of complete determinism of all events of nature is, then, contradicted by the physics that has developed with our knowledge of the quantum nature of the elementary entities and their interactions.

Niels Bohr emphasized in many writings the role of the discovery of the indivisibility of the quantum of energy or matter in our giving up of the strict deterministic doctrine of prequantum physics. We gain information about nature by observation, but since an observation always requires an interaction with what is being observed, and since the wholeness of the quantum of energy prohibits any diminution to zero of the interaction effects, there will inevitably be disturbance of the atomic level system as a result of observation. The physical behavior of quanta of matter or radiation, discussed in the preceding section, does not allow us to calculate in detail what the disturbance will be. Hence, any attempt to gain complete knowledge of an atomic-level system is

[15] See the discussion by Max Born in his *Natural Philosophy of Cause and Chance* (New York, Oxford University Press, 1949).

thwarted by the very effect of our attempt on the system. In Bohr's words,[16] "While within the scope of classical physics we are dealing with an idealization, according to which all phenomena can be arbitrarily subdivided, and the interaction between the measuring instruments and the object under observation neglected, or at any rate compensated for, . . . such interaction represents in quantum physics an integral part of the phenomena, for which no separate account can be given if the instruments shall serve the purpose of defining the conditions under which the observations are obtained."

The impossibility of gaining exact knowledge of the state of a system, even at the time of observation, is concretely manifested in the disturbing effects of measurement. But the expression of the impossibility in the uncertainty relations, as derived from the mathematical statements of the wave–particle aspects of nature, presents that impossibility as inherent in the processes of nature. It is not just that the interaction effects of measurement prevent our gaining precise descriptive knowledge, but rather, that there is in nature a lack of precise definition of, for example, the position and the momentum jointly of a particle. Because this definition is lacking, the principles of quantum physics require that measurement will not enable us to ascertain it.

The uncertainty limitations are so clearly related to what we have learned about the properties of matter and radiation that physicists generally believe them to be valid natural restrictions on the possible values of dynamical variables. It has, however, often been objected that to pass from the uncertainty relations to an argument against determinism is to change an epistemological limitation into an ontological one: even though we cannot precisely know the magnitudes of all the dynamical variables of a system, it does not follow that in nature there are no factors which are precisely determining the course of natural events. In a sense there is no answer to this objection; if one wishes to maintain a doctrine of complete determinism by recourse to unknown and unspecified factors, regardless of the possibilities for natural knowledge, any evidence from the sciences will be bootless. But in another sense one can reply that the epistemological limitation is one that comes not from any lack of skill or ingenuity on the part of scientists, but from the properties of the natural world itself. If we are to form our ideas about how nature proceeds from what we see of nature, it would then seem to follow that we should not assert a relation of strict determinism among natural events on an atomic level, for, we do not find in nature that precise definition of states which is implied by the doctrine of determinism.

Discussions yet to come will further emphasize the change that quantum theory brings in the viewpoint of classical, deterministic physics. Also, in Chapter 11 some of the objections to that change will further be discussed. It is important to realize, however, that a lack of strict determinism on the level of atomic events does not in general imply a breakdown of the *ap-*

[16] N. Bohr, *Atomic Physics and Human Knowledge* (New York, Interscience, 1963), pp. 91–92.

proximate determinism which is found in nature when magnitudes are such that Planck's constant h is a trivial quantity. The accuracy of the predictions, for example, which an astronomer can make for the behavior of the planets over a period of many thousands of years is in no way impugned by the existence of quantum-theory uncertainties. In general, the processes and events of everyday living are not of a kind for which quantum behavior is directly relevant, and we need not be concerned by the lack of determinism on the quantum level.

This difference, between a determinism for macroscopic bodies and a lack thereof for microscopic ones, does not mean that there is a disjunction in nature between the world of the very small and the rest of nature. We recall that quantum theory does enable us to calculate probabilities for the behavior of electrons, photons, and other elementary entities. Hence, when the behavior of a system of many particles is involved, a calculation which gives probable behavior of the system can be made; for systems that are macroscopic, the probability becomes virtually a certainty for behavior that is in accordance with classical prequantum predictions.

And yet, even though quantum theory does give statistical results that generally agree with those of the older and deterministic physics for the phenomena to which it had been applied, we should not therefore diminish the great significance of the change in outlook that quantum theory has brought. We are now no longer obliged to regard each successive state of the universe as formed in every detail by the preceding states. We should not expect sudden, large-scale novelty that is in violation of classical natural law; but on the quantum level there does seem to be an element of chance, of randomness, that does mean that the future is continually being born out of the present, without prior setting of every detail of the new states that are formed. The natural world, then, has something of the same quality of being fresh and new in each present state that we find in our own immediate perceptions of ourselves and our world.

In some ways, the randomness of atomic-level events can rather directly have large-scale effects. A biological organism, for example, is a system of many billions of atoms, and in general a biologist expects to find the behavior of the system to be in accordance with "deterministic" generalizations. Biological process is, however, basically on the level of atoms and photons, and a small change in an atom may have extensive large-scale effects as a consequence of the developmental influence of atomic-level constituents. Thus, the germ cells of a biological species are generally stable, but they do undergo mutations, and the consequence of a mutation may be extreme indeed for the organism which develops from that cell. We know that mutations (which are changes in molecular structure of the gene-components of the cell) can be brought about by the interaction of a photon with a cell. Such an interaction is itself a random process, in that one could not expect to calculate where a particular interaction between photon and

cell would occur as the result of an irradiation process. But further, mutations may well occur spontaneously in germ cells, and in part simply as a
consequence of quantum fluctuations in the energy of the various atomic
constituents of the cell. The constitutional changes in organisms that grew
from germ cells in which such spontaneous mutations had occurred would
be examples indeed of a process that gave some play for randomness and
novelty.

It is one of the wondrous aspects of nature, as revealed by the new
knowledge which quantum physics has brought us, that there appear to be
both the relative determinism that classical physics found for large-scale
objects, and an element of chance in behavior on the atomic level. In-
geniously, one is tempted to say, Nature arranges large-scale behavior in
accordance with pattern and law, and yet, on the base level of elementary
particles there is the openness of process which allows the novelty and
change that give a sense of time, of a future different from the past. For
mankind there can be hope and a sense of participation in a development
that is not without purpose and end. (But we know nothing of what influences
there might be, if any, that could give ultimate direction within the freedom
from rigorous determinism that is found in the quantum domain.)

The question of human freedom of the will has been closely associated
with the doctrine of rigorous determinism in nature. It is inviting to assert
that since quantum theory has shown us that we do not have rigorous
determinism in nature, there obviously is the possibility for self-determination
by human beings. I think that in an important way this is a valid assertion.
As long as nature was believed to be completely deterministic it was difficult
to see how one could regard a biological organism as having any genuine
choice with respect to its future behavior (at least, difficult as long as one
maintained a naturalistic view of living organisms and their behavior). But
if it were found that there was a break in the complete determination of
states of a system by its previous states, there would be an opening for
shaping the future with what happens in the present state. Quantum physics
does show us that there is such a break, and we therefore need not regard
all behavior of an organism as inexorably determined.

But, one may point out that the existence of elementary processes which
can only be described in terms of probability is hardly in itself an assurance
of freedom of choice. The fact, say, that the individual paths of electrons
that serve to conduct current through a nerve cell cannot be predicted with
complete precision would seem to be an indication of possible lack of
control rather than of the decision-making with respect to behavior that is
implied in freedom of the will. Clearly, if there is a role of quantum-physical
considerations in thought and choice, our understanding of it waits upon
detailed knowledge that physiologists and neurologists have not yet achieved.
Also, it would seem that to a considerable degree human behavior is determined by prior behavior (and inherent physiological–psychological characteristics), just as large-scale behavior of inanimate objects is apparently

determined by prior states. One could pretty well predict from human constitutional studies how high, say, various people would be able to jump, or even what types of food they might choose from a buffet. More subtle aspects of behavior may also be predicted by the astute observer or clinician.

Nonetheless, the wonderful possibility for unexpected behavior does remain. There is the choice, say, that constitutes an act of heroism, or of extreme unselfishness; and there is creation in the arts and sciences. We can do much to explain unusual behavior in terms of "conditioning" and genetic inheritance, but in a physical world which appears not itself to be completely determined by prior events, it would seem unreasonable to argue that biological behavior may not in some measure be determined from moment to moment by purely psychological factors (which are of course in some manner related to the sum of constitution and experience of the organism).

One final point remains. Even though we do not at all understand the quantum physics of the physical–biological processes associated with thought and will, there is a relatively simple way in which we can envision quantum indeterminism as affecting biological behavior. It has often been pointed out that freedom of the will does itself require determinism, since once a course of action has been elected by an organism, it is presumed that his bodily processes will operate in a deterministic way in carrying out that election. Thus, if a man chooses to attempt a street-crossing, it is assumed that once he has made the choice his body will deterministically respond to it. Now, since biological processes are, at root, processes on a level of atomic particles, the indeterminism of quantum physics does suggest that there may be deviations from customary behavior of these processes. Hence, chance could sometimes be the factor that prevented a person from doing what he had chosen to do. The skilled athlete, for example, may wish to catch a thrown ball, and yet, as a consequence of some chance fluctuation in his nervous system, he might not move in just that exact manner which would ensure that he catch it. So, there would be the one-in-a-thousand-times error. Actually, this same possibility for fluctuation from customary behavior, on an atomic level, would exist in the framework of prequantum physics; but there it would have to be taken, on the customary tacit assumption of complete determination of events, that the fluctuation was not chance but was inevitable and inherent in the workings of the natural world.

5   COMPLEMENTARITY

The limitations on description of nature that are stated in the uncertainty relations have also been given a somewhat different expression in the Principle of Complementarity of Niels Bohr. This principle is not a mathematical equation, but is rather an assertion of restrictions on the completeness of knowledge to be gained in a given experimental or observational situation. In Bohr's words,[17] ". . . the fundamental postulate of the indivisibility of the quantum is itself, from the classical point of view, an irrational element which inevitably requires us to forego a causal mode of description and which, because of the coupling between phenomena and their observation, forces us to adopt a new mode of description designated as complementary in the sense that any given application of classical concepts precludes the simultaneous use of other classical concepts which in a different connection are equally necessary for the elucidation of the phenomena."

We find, thus, that an apparatus by which we are able accurately to measure the wavelength of a beam of electrons that have been accelerated to a given energy will not also allow us to determine the spatial coordinates of the electrons. Knowing the wavelength, we can calculate the momentum of the electrons, using the de Broglie equation. Hence, we can describe the electrons in energy–momentum terms. But the application of these classical concepts "precludes the simultaneous use of other classical concepts"; that is, we cannot describe the electron in space–time terms. (The uncertainty relations would, of course, have given us this same restriction.) But with a different kind of apparatus, perhaps one involving clock-driven shutters and photographic film, we could gain space–time descriptions, but now without knowledge of energy–momentum magnitudes. The two kinds of description are, in Bohr's sense, complementary.

Or, we could in more general terms say that the description of radiation, or of matter, in terms of its particle behavior is complementary to the description in terms of wave behavior. With a given kind of apparatus we gain one kind of description with no possibility of the other, and vice versa with another kind of apparatus. We could also speak of the knowledge of the spectral radiation emissions of a group of atoms as being complementary to exact knowledge of orbital motions of electrons in the atoms. The term "complementary" is generally applied to observations of any of the pairs of variables for which the uncertainty principle restrictions of quantum theory hold.

Bohr believed that complementarity is the key to the resolution of the apparent paradox of photon and particle behavior on the quantum level; that we must renounce the expectation of gaining comprehensive knowledge of matter or radiation in terms of any one set of concepts, or with any one type of measurement. But, by taking complementary kinds of knowledge together, we exhaust the possibilities for descriptive knowledge of a given kind of entity. Bohr's statement[18] in this respect is: "Likewise we must be prepared that evidence, obtained by different, mutually exclusive experimental arrangements, may exhibit unprecedented contrast and even at first sight appear contradictory. It is in this situation that the notion of complementarity is called for to provide a frame wide enough to embrace the

[17] N. Bohr, *Atomic Theory and the Description of Nature* (New York, Cambridge University Press, 1934), p. 10.
[18] See *Atomic Physics and Human Knowledge* (New York, Interscience, 1963), pp. 11–12.

account of fundamental regularities of nature which cannot be comprehended within a single picture. Indeed, evidence obtained under well-defined experimental conditions—and expressed by adequate use of elementary physical concepts—exhausts in its entirety all information about the atomic object which can be communicated in ordinary language."

Bohr, and others, have extended the complementarity notion to other than pairs of physical variables. The physical and chemical methods used in the observation of a living organism may preclude, for example, just the activity which it is desirable to observe; thus, the isolation of a cell for observation may preclude that functioning in a normal environment for which observation is wanted. Or, in psychology, ". . . in an inquiry into a person's emotions, the mere fact that the inquiry is made creates an emotional reaction, so that the intervention of the observer modifies the effects of his observation." [19] And certainly in the social sciences there is complementarity between description and behavior: the very statement, for example, that a society is entering a period of economic decline can have an effect on its economic activity. The suggestion of complementarity restrictions in fields other than physics is of high interest, but of course it is not supported by the rigorously correct Uncertainty Principle. The examples that have been given, outside of physics, should perhaps be regarded as possibilities or instances rather than as absolute restrictions.

We have found in the principles of uncertainty and complementarity a domain where we have carried the search for knowledge as far as we can with our traditional expectations of what we can learn in science. Atomic phenomena cannot be described in the same manner as can be those of the world of direct sense experience, and the behavior of atomic entities must be regarded as different, in a radical way, from that of larger-scale objects. Science does properly seem, in the light of the development of quantum physics, to have reached a limit of the understanding that came in the form of complete description with the usual variables of space, time, velocity, and energy. To repeat and continue the first-page quotation of this book, "They had found the boundary to our knowledge; some things would remain unknown forever; one of the results of this new representation of matter was to tell us what we could not know as well as what we could. We were in sight of the end. It seemed incredible to me, brought up in the tradition of limitless searching, mystery beyond mystery, the agoraphobia of the infinite. I resented leaving it. . . . *We were in sight of the end.*" [20]

And yet, of course, physicists still find things to learn in the domain of the elementary particles of nature. Within the restrictions of the complementarity of description, there can be a seeking for knowledge of the properties of particles, the nature of interactions, and the kinds of forces that operate. In part, the old ideal of detailed, mechanistic, space–time

[19] Lord Brain, "Science and Behavior" (B.A.A.S. Presidential Address), *Nature*, **203**, 946 (1964).
[20] C. P. Snow, *The Search* (New York, Scribner, 1958), p. 169.

description has been replaced by appropriately different ideals: principles of invariance, of what is unchanging in structure and form in nature's elementary processes; and principles of symmetry, of what is independent and what is dependent with respect to directions in space, in time, or alteration in electrical charge or in energy. The satisfactory understanding of the basic physical field will, it appears, have to be at least partly in terms of concepts such as these, with no concern (because it would be hopeless to have it) for gaining the kind of knowledge that we found in prequantum physics for the macroscopic world.

I cannot, however, simply state the restrictions on natural description, as physicists have discovered them, and say no more. The discovery and elucidation of the restrictions is the key point in the statement of the limits on atomic-level scientific knowledge, and, taken with the indivisibility of the quantum and with the wave–particle properties with which they are associated, the restrictions have been of major importance in the successes of atomic and nuclear physics. But, there are essential matters for our problem of completeness of science that come along with the consideration of the quantum restrictions. The role of observation in quantum physics is such that we must regard the relation of scientist to nature far differently than in prequantum physics. Further, the inevitable quantum-interaction of the measuring device with that which is being measured is analogous to situations that we have met in discussing logical restrictions on scientific description. The discussion of measurement in the next chapter will lead us to a certain unity in logical and natural limitations on knowledge.

10

The Observer in Quantum Physics

WERNER HEISENBERG has written[1]: "The old division of the world into objective processes in space and time and the mind in which these processes are mirrored—in other words, the Cartesian difference between *res cogitans* and *res extensa*—is no longer a suitable starting point for our understanding of modern science. Science, we find, is now focused on the network of relationships between man and nature. . . . Science no longer confronts nature as an objective observer, but sees itself as an actor in this interplay between man and nature. The scientific method of analyzing, explaining, and classifying has become conscious of its limitations, which arise out of the fact that by its intervention science alters and refashions the object of investigation. In other words, method and object can no longer be separated."

A person's gaining of knowledge with respect to the macroscopic everyday objects about him seems to have no effect on the existence of these objects: the furniture of my house, for example, has its various properties of color, shape, and strength, regardless of my knowledge of these properties, and the properties are not changed simply as a result of my coming to know them. This attitude, that the way of the world is independent of the knower's relation to it, was carried over into the classical, prequantum physics. The scientist, then, could explore and describe nature, with no concern for what role he himself might be playing in the nature he studied. But now, Heisenberg's statement emphatically tells us, we no longer can maintain the complete independence of nature from the scientist. In any kind of physics the knowledge we gain is of course dependent upon our carrying out studies of nature, but in quantum physics what nature is, in a specific investigation, can be dependent upon the very act of investigation.

We have already seen an indication of the effect of the investigator on nature in our discussion of uncertainty and complementarity: whether,

[1] W. Heisenberg, *The Physicist's Conception of Nature*, translated by A. J. Pomerans (New York, Harcourt, Brace & World, 1958), p. 29.

for example, a physical entity appears as a particle or wave depends upon the kind of apparatus that is used in the observation. We have discussed, too, the importance of the quantization of energy in the dependence of an observed quantity on the act of the observation; for, the act always requires an interaction which disturbs the very object under observation.

The detailed dependence of natural knowledge on the action of the observer may be illustrated in another obvious way. Suppose a radioactive atom has been localized and identified on an absorbing material (the identification might have been made by observation of the radioactive emission that is known to convert a predecessor nucleus into the atom of interest). We now wish to know whether the atom decays during a certain time interval Δt, which may be a fraction of a second or many years. There is no way of determining whether or not the decay occurs except by observing an apparatus which is able to record the decay during the interval Δt. In other words, our knowledge of the decay's occurring in Δt is absolutely dependent on the decay's being observed during that time (or, of course, on the observation of some physical consequence from which the decay may be inferred). The decay is a quantum effect, and there is not the possibility in quantum physics of calculating from prior known conditions whether or not it will occur in the interval Δt. In contrast, in classical physics we are able to calculate the passage, say, of the planet Saturn through a certain point on the celestial sphere at a specified time, and give all the authority of science to the statement that the passage will occur, or has occurred. Barring some disturbing event (whose effects could also be calculated, according to the tenets of classical physics), no one would doubt the occurrence of the passage.

It is true that if we had many, many radioactive atoms of a specified type, we could confidently state what fraction would decay within a given time interval. Excepting for allowed statistical fluctuations, we would confidently believe that the decay of this fraction did occur in accordance with prediction, even if not in any way observed. This means, as we have indicated, that with ensembles of a great many quantum-level events we approach the predictable behavior of macroscopic systems. But for individual quantum events there is the striking dependence on observation for knowledge of the events. In the words of E. T. Jaynes, present quantum theory ". . . can predict the relative time decay of two Co^{60} nuclei only with a probable error of about five years, but the experimentalist can measure this interval to a microsecond." [2]

The various features of quantum physics which lead to a conception of our relation-to-nature-as-known that is so very different from the conception held in classical physics are brought to a focus in what is referred to as the problem of measurement in quantum mechanics. There is no generally satisfactory and accepted answer to the problem, but, without attempting any novel solution, we shall be able further to see how extensively quantum physics is intertwined with the object–knower relationship.

[2] E. T. Jaynes, *American Journal of Physics*, 30, 659 (1962).

1 PURE STATES AND MIXTURES

The most notable characteristic of quantum-mechanical measurement, at least for our purposes, is that it involves a disjunction between causal, mathematically described behavior, and an undescribed, discontinuous kind of behavior that is associated with the actual coming into existence of a measurement for an observer.[3] Suppose a physical system to be described by a wave function ψ. The time-dependent Schroedinger equation then describes the system at any time by its specification of $\psi(t)$. The description of ψ is similar to that given for a classical-mechanical system by its equation of motion. However, when a measurement is made in which a particular value of a variable of which ψ is a function is determined, the Schroedinger equation no longer describes what happens. Instead, a definite state of the system, associated with the variable in question, "presents itself" to the observer. The wave function gives a measure of the probability that the system will be in the state characterized by the given value of the variable, but it tells us nothing about how the system will get into that state; nor, does the Schroedinger equation for the wave function tell us anything about how the system arrives at the particular state. The state function changes, then, in two ways: (1) as described by the Schroedinger equation, and (2) in the discontinuous, "irrational" manner that carries it into a function for a specific, *observed* state.

The second of the two preceding ways in which ψ may change is often referred to as the "reduction of the wave packet"; this in reference to the fact that a wave packet (ψ-function) containing many possible values for, say, the wavelength and position of a particle might on measurement be reduced to a function giving only one position (or, alternatively one wavelength) value for the particle. The wave function may be descriptive of many other properties besides position and momentum; it might, for example, refer to the $(+)$ or $(-)$ value of the spin of a particle along a given direction. For whatever property is being described, we in general have the same quantum-theory requirement of a sharp change with measurement—a change from a state that is characterized by a ψ that specifies probabilities for the different quantum-mechanically allowed measured values of the property to a state characterized by the definite value obtained in a measurement.

In order better to understand the effect of measurement in a quantum system we will further consider the simple two-slit optical interference apparatus which we discussed in Section 2 of Chapter 9. We first want to write

---

[3] This disjunctive property of the quantum theory of measurement was explicitly enunciated in 1932 by J. von Neumann, *Mathematical Principles of Quantum Theory*, translated by Robert T. Beyer (Princeton, New Jersey, Princeton University Press, 1955), Chap. V. Two recommended journal discussions are E. P. Wigner, "The Problem of Measurement," *American Journal of Physics*, 31, 6 (1963), and Abner Shimony, "Role of the Observer in Quantum Theory," *American Journal of Physics*, 31, 755 (1963).

a wave function for the photons in the apparatus. This we could write as follows:

$$\psi(z) = Ae^{[i\omega t + (L\sec\theta/\lambda)]} + Ae^{[i\omega t + (L\sec\theta + d\sin\theta)/\lambda]} \tag{1}$$

In this equation, A is an amplitude factor, ω the angular frequency and λ the wavelength of the photon, and L and d are dimensions of the apparatus as indicated in Fig. 10-1. The two exponential factors give the variations in amplitudes to be expected on a screen a distance $x = L$ from the slits as a result of waves transmitted through the two slits. The angle θ varies, of course, with the chosen z point, which may be anywhere between the limits $+z_0$ and $-z_0$ of the interference pattern. By the quantum-mechanical principle of superposition and the proportionality between wave amplitude and photon density for electromagnetic waves, we are confident that the $\psi(z)$ as written does give us the probability of a photon's reaching a given light band $m_i(z)$.

We may regard the $\psi(z)$ wave function of Eq. (1) as describing a pure state of electromagnetic radiation in the two-slit apparatus. And, taking the

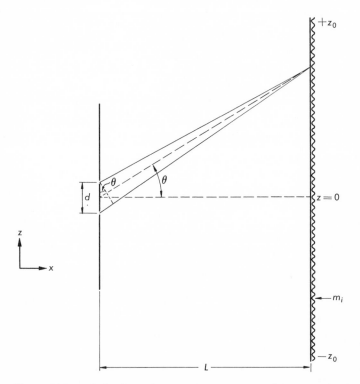

Figure 10-1.   Light from the two slits, separation d between them, forms an interference pattern on a film at a distance L from the plane of the slits. The various light bands on the screen are denoted as $m_i(z)$.

$\psi(z)$ as applying to photons, we can use it to calculate the probability of a photon's reaching any given band $m_i(z)$. We may do this whether we are concerned with the apparatus as containing only one photon or many billions of photons. Also, the Schroedinger equation, written with the $\psi(z)$, would in a very simple way be a differential equation for the variation of ψ with $z(\theta)$ and t (in effect, our $\psi(z)$ is a solution of that equation, with assumption of a steady "standing wave" radiation density in the apparatus). There is, of course, nothing in the pure state described by $\psi(z)$ to tell us about any particular photon; for, only probability (associated with amplitude) is defined by $\psi(z)$, and it is defined over the entire apparatus, i.e., for any z value, or also, should one want to regard L as variable, for any $L = x$ value. (We note that $\theta = \tan^{-1} z/x$.)

But now suppose we make a measurement of photon density, as a function of z, by observing the light bands $m_i(z)$ on the film or screen. As we said in our earlier discussion of the two-slit interference experiment, the wave function may be regarded as an expression of what we will observe. Each m_i has a substate ψ_i associated with it, reflecting the fact that the position variable, z, takes different values for the different photon groups that give the bands $m_i(z)$. So, we may write,

$$\psi = \sum_i a_i\psi_i. \tag{2}$$

The function ψ, as given by (1), may be used to evaluate the coefficients a_i of Eq. (2). They are probability coefficients, such that the probability of a photon's coming to a given band m_i is proportional to $|a_i|^2$.

As given by Eq. (2), ψ may be interpreted as descriptive of a mixture of states; that is, it describes the substates $\psi_i(z)$, each one of which is associated with a particular value z of the position coordinate of a group of photons that are observed as $m_i(z)$. The ψ of (1) described a pure state, in which the photon-wave contributions from the two slits were superimposed at each space point. Evidently, since the mixed state is equivalent to a description of what is observed on the screen, the act of observation or measurement brought a conversion from the pure state to the mixed state. Symbolically we may write:

$$O \times \psi(z) \rightarrow \sum_i a_i\psi_i,$$

where O indicates the act of observation.

The difference between a mixed state and a pure state is crucial, for it is the pure state which is characteristic of the quantum-mechanical behavior of physical systems. Considered as a mixture of states, ψ_i, the photons in the double-slit apparatus do not present the "measurement problem" that they do when they are taken as being in a pure state before measurement. For, we could regard each substate ψ_i of the mixture as describing the photons throughout their course of passage in the apparatus. Thus, we might say that even in entering the slits, a given photon is in a certain substate, described by ψ_i, and is headed for a corresponding light band m_i. Measurement, then, is no more than a matter of observing the photons of the various substates, ψ_i, as they go to their appropriate locations on the screen. But the difficulty with this view of ψ as a "mixture of states" is, as the reader will at once perceive, that it violates the superposition principle of quantum mechanics: the various contributions of electromagnetic radiation from the two slits must be superimposed throughout the apparatus and give the interference effects which are characteristic of the waves—or, mathematically, the wave function—of quantum-mechanical systems.

We know from direct experiment that each photon in the double-slit apparatus must be described as a pure state, with all possibilities for z-coordinate values on the screen taken into account. And also, for quantum-mechanical description generally, the superposition principle of quantum mechanics forbids that the ψ function of the Schroedinger equation be for a mixture of states.[4]

The difference between a pure state and a mixture may be further emphasized by means of a fantasy given by Nathan Rosen.[5] A particle enters a magnetic field, and has equal probabilities of its spin direction being parallel or antiparallel to the field direction (the state of the particle is a "pure" one, a linear combination of the parallel and antiparallel states, with equal coefficients for each). It is arranged that the particle enters an ionization chamber A or B, depending on the direction of its spin. Further, the impulse set up when the particle enters either chamber is fed into a relay device, such that particle-in-A results in an unmanned electric locomotive traveling 100 km to the north, whereas if the particle goes into B the locomotive travels an equal distance to the south. Now—and it is only here that the element of fantasy enters—we assume that the entire system, including the locomotive, obeys the laws of quantum mechanics. We then should not regard the locomotive as existing in one of two states, i.e., either in a state of traveling to the north or in a state of traveling to the south (for this would be what we call a mixture of states). Instead, in accordance with quantum theory we must regard the state of the locomotive as a "pure state" that is formed by a linear superposition of the states of traveling north and south, with equal probabilities for each; there would be no warrant for concluding from the ψ function of this state that the locomotive was actually in either the state of traveling north or the state of traveling south. And yet, if a measurement were made, as by people looking at the tracks to see where the locomotive

[4] A mathematical proof of the inconsistency between decomposition of the state function into a mixture and the linear superposition of quantum theory is given by E. P. Wigner, "The Problem of Measurement," *American Journal of Physics*, **31**, 6 (1963).

[5] "The Relation Between Classical and Quantum Mechanics," *American Journal of Physics*, **32**, 597 (1964).

was, there would then be a "reduction of the wave packet," and we could now say in which direction the locomotive was traveling. The ψ function for the "pure" state of the locomotive would have been discontinuously changed, in a manner for which we have no equations, by the act of measurement of its position.

Returning to the photons in the double-slit apparatus, we might want to say that once we had made an observation of the light bands, we henceforth could regard the state of the photons as a mixture rather than as a pure state (assuming they had not been destroyed in the observing procedures). But to describe their state as that of a mixture would in fact be no more valid for behavior after the measurement than for that before. Thus, suppose the photons were observed at each $m_i(z)$ band by virtue of the scattering of a small fraction of those reaching any one band. (The scattering might be by a translucent glass plate, placed at the screen position $x = L$.) The nonscattered photons would be propagated in space from each m_i band, and their properties could only be correctly described by a ψ-function descriptive of them in a pure state. So, in general, quantum mechanics as a description of physical systems must be of pure states of the systems, with due account taken of the interference between different contributing components of the system. And yet, in measurements by which we learn of actual states and events of systems, the pure state changes to one or more of a mixture of the definite physical states that give observational data, like spots on a photographic film, or positions of an instrument pointer (or the sights and sounds of Rosen's locomotive on only one of the tracks, north or south).

2   QUANTUM-MECHANICAL MEASUREMENT

The requirement of a "collapse" of the photon waves when they are registered or "measured" on a photographic film in the double-slit apparatus can be removed in the following way. We could, in principle at least, write a total ψ function for the system, photons in the apparatus *plus* the molecules of the film with which the photons interact. This function, then, could be descriptive of a pure state. It would not, therefore, describe the blackened light bands, $m_i(z)$, of the photographic film; for, in accordance with the superposition principle, as a function for a pure state the function would describe the various contributions to the bands, but not the photons + molecules in that state in which superposition has been replaced by one or more of a mixture of the states that actually correspond to observation. We would then perhaps say that only in observing the developed photographic film did we bring about the discontinuous change from a pure state to the physically measured state. If one accepts, however, that any physical system may be quantum-mechanically described, one could avoid the change from a pure state in the act of optical observation of the film by describing the system of double-slit apparatus, photons, photographic film, photons from film to observer, and eye and nervous system of observer with a single, comprehensive wave function. The whole system, including the observer looking at the film, would then be in a pure state. Now, however, we would require that the change to the physically observed state from the superpositions of the pure state must occur as a consequence of the process of awareness itself in the observer. This process would be the only part of the measurement act not described by the Schroedinger equation as written for the ψ function of the entire system, including the observer.

By the tenets of the standard quantum theory of measurement as enunciated by von Neumann, there is an inevitable role for the observer in the formation of the measured physical state. We see, in the example of the double-slit apparatus, that there is a choice about where the observer plays that role. The "reduction of the wave packet" may be regarded as occurring in the first measuring apparatus applied to the object under study (in the photographic film that registers the photons in our illustrative example), or it may be put into the quantum-theoretic description as occurring "closer" to the observer, in, for example, his own physical acts of observation. But, *somewhere* along the chain of interactions between object and awareness of the measurement data we must have the indescribable, discontinuous change from pure quantum state to the well-defined physically observed state. It is this change that gives rise to an observed event.

In prequantum physics, of course, the observer played a key role in our knowledge of nature; for first, knowledge is a property of observers, and, second, observation is basic to our gaining knowledge. But in quantum theory we have the major added factor that it is only by involving the observer that we can include the occurrence of events in our account of nature. In contrast, in the earlier classical physics events were describable, and were assumed to occur independently of their interaction with the observer.

The rather extreme philosophical subjectivism which the conventional quantum theory of measurement entails is not in the spirit of traditional scientific realism, and probably is not wholeheartedly accepted by most physicists. But there is no obvious way to avoid such a subjectivism within the present framework of quantum mechanics. For example, one might wish to say, with respect to the double-slit interference phenomenon, that the reduction of the wave packet is best regarded as a physical occurrence associated with the interaction of the electromagnetic radiation with the screen on which the light bands are observed. In this instance, however, it is the case that many, many photons are involved. The fact that the light bands $m_i(z)$ will be be formed is a statistically safe prediction if many photons are present, and is an occurrence in the realm where an ensemble of many quantum-level entities behaves effectively as a macroscopic system of the prequantum physics. But if we think of the behavior of a single photon (at which of the possible $m_i(z)$ bands will it give a developed grain in a photographic film?), or of the decay of a single atom (at which time instant?) we directly see how close is the dependence between events and observer. The principles of quantum mechanics require that physical systems behave as pure states, but physical measurements are of one or more of a mixture of observed states. The observer must bring about the transition from the pure states which give the interference effects of nature to the states in which the events and systems of nature are empirically measured.

We may well summarize the dependency of the natural world, as given by the quantum theory of physics, with a statement by Margenau and Wigner[6]: "Let us just repeat . . . a fact which appears to us so remarkable and which, we fear, is not yet fully appreciated. This fact can be stated as: 'present quantum mechanical theory does not recognize any reality independent of an observer.' The formulation of the laws of quantum mechanics either deal only with results of observations . . . , or, alternatively, they are given in terms of a quantity, the state vector [the ψ-function], the changes of which cannot be completely described by the equations of the theory and contain a statistical element unalterably. We do not say that quantum mechanics is the ultimate physical theory and that all future theories will have a similar character. We do not even maintain that we are glad that the present theory does have this character. However, it does."

The implications of the standard doctrine of quantum-mechanical measurement do indeed seem to lead physics to an epistemological position in which consciousness has a central role in natural reality. The implication that an *esse is percipi* doctrine is thereby supported has not escaped attention, and it is noteworthy that one of the very foremost physicists of our day, E. P. Wigner, has been a leader in pointing out the full epistemological content of quantum physics.[7] Indeed, the metaphysical idealism which is implied goes even beyond the assertion of an equivalence of reality with the content of consciousness; rather, an actual formative role of consciousness in structure of inanimate nature has been suggested, as a consequence of the wave-packet reduction required in theory of measurement. This is an idealism–subjectivism more radical than envisioned by either Berkeley or Kant.

There are in the current literature, as would be expected, counter discussions which attempt to avoid the subjectivist epistemology that is indicated by the orthodox quantum measurement theory. Wigner, and also G. Ludwig,[8] have pointed out that a revision in the principles of quantum mechanics might allow description of physically observed states without the disjunction

[6] Henry Margenau and Eugene P. Wigner, *Philosophy of Science*, 31, 7 (1964).
[7] In his paper, "Two Kinds of Reality," *The Monist*, 48, 248 (1964), Wigner uses the measurement situation in quantum mechanics in supporting an epistemological-metaphysical argument that the content of the individual person's consciousness is the only absolute reality.
[8] For references see E. P. Wigner, "The Problem of Measurement," *American Journal of Physics*, 31, 6 (1963).

between pure states and mixture that is now required. Margenau[9] has suggested that measurement be regarded as a selection of a "latent observable" from among various possibilities in the object system. He concedes that a noncausal process, not describable within the ordinary framework of quantum-mechanical description of changes of a system, does occur in the act of measurement. But, he further argues that there is then no warranty for introducing noncausal interference by an observer or by the human consciousness; that if a physical measurement be performed, and its result recorded but hidden from any sort of intelligence, this lack of a conscious observer in no way alters the physical situation. Most scientists would probably have sympathy with the point of view that Margenau presents. And yet, the objection could be made that we are not interested in the cases where there is no physical knowledge (i.e., no conscious observer), and that an analysis of the epistemology of physics, in the terms of quantum mechanics as now developed, does lead to the conclusion that the observer's participation is necessary for the existence of the properties of nature that we do find. The quotation of page 183 shows, of course, that Margenau himself appreciates this point.

There have been other suggestions for removal of the major role of the observer in the physical world of quantum mechanics. James Albertson,[10] for example, has defined a measurement operator which gives statistical results (average values and dispersion of values) for physical quantities, just prior to the measurement, without requiring the characteristic reduction of the wave-packet (or, equivalently, the indescribable change in wave-function that is associated with observation). One then forms a statistical or phenomenological kind of quantum mechanics which in many instances is sufficient. However, information about individual events is then lost, for, in the words of Arthur Komar, another writer on measurement in quantum physics, the mathematical formalism of the theory ". . . appears to have no mechanism for accounting for the fact that events do in fact occur." [11] The extent to which physicists who are concerned with quantum-mechanical measurement are willing to consider ideas that traditionally have been far outside of physics is indicated by the fact that Komar, in the paper cited, suggests that fluctuations from statistical norms in physical behavior might be governed by volition, with implication of teleological forces. Komar alternatively suggests that quantum mechanics is not complete, and that perhaps a modification of the linearity of the superposition principle must be introduced to account for the fact that we do observe events.

[9] Henry Margenau, *Philosophy of Science*, **30**, 1, 138 (1963), and *Annals of Physics*, **23**, 469 (1963). The reader may look to the latter paper for an extensive bibliography on quantum-mechanical measurement. A view somewhat similar to that of Margenau, although independent of his, and couched in quite different terms, has been put forth by J. M. Jauch, *Helvetica Physica Acta*, **37**, 293 (1964).

[10] *Physical Review*, **129**, 940 (1963).

[11] A. Komar, "Indeterminate Character of the Reduction of the Wave Packet in Quantum Theory," *Physical Review*, **126**, 365 (1962).

3 LARGE AND SMALL IN QUANTUM THEORY

The great success of quantum theory in explaining atomic and elementary-particle phenomena does, of course, place a strong constraint on proposals for its modification. Rather than consider further any possibilities for change, we shall next discuss an aspect of the theory, in its present form, which seems helpful in coming to terms with the epistemological implications of quantum-mechanical measurement.

We recall that before physicists developed that concern with atomic-level phenomena which led to quantum theory, the role of the observer in science seemed to be one of note-taker, and certainly also of selector and organizer, but not of disturber or creator. Even since the advent of quantum theory, this view seems to be amply justified for much of physics. The observation, say, of the planet Jupiter must give results that are independent of the observer: the progress of the planet around its orbit, or the changes in the red-spot phenomenon, are surely independent of our making observations by means of absorbing a miniscule fraction of the radiation reflected or emitted from the planet. The situation changes when, say, we observe the path of an electron, and must use primary detection elements that are themselves of the order of magnitude of the electron. But prequantum physics was (and is) an accurate and adequate science of a wide range of macroscopic phenomena, with no need for a substantival role of the observer's consciousness in the reality of these phenomena.

It would seem strange indeed, that there should be a discontinuity in the role of awareness as one goes from the world of macroscopic objects to that of atomic-level objects. Indeed, there is an outright inconsistency. The large-scale objects of nature are composed, we know, of atomic particles. If the observer were "in" nature, on the atomic level, to an extent such that his awareness is actually a necessary element for nature, then the same should likewise be true for the larger objects of nature. In view of this inconsistency, it would seem that the natural realism about the world which we gain from our experience could far better be extended to the physical entities of the microscopic level, rather than be eroded by an extrapolation of the epistemological subjectivism of quantum theory upwards from the microscopic level. The quantum theory of measurement is, after all, a novel and tenuous construction when compared with the immense richness of experience that gives us constructs of a natural world that is independent of our awareness of it.

We shall return to the epistemological problems of measurement on the atomic level in the next section. We can now point out, however, that there are in fact indications in physics itself of a separation in quantum theory, and hence in interpretation of measurement, between the small-scale and large-scale objects of quantum and classical physics, respectively. Hence, there are grounds for our at least being able to remove the physics of the macroscopic world from the difficulties attendant on the interpretation of observation in quantum theory. The separation has been delineated in a paper by Peres and Rosen,[12] in which they emphasize that quantum theory is required to take account of interference effects of various kinds that are observed. The superposition principle is the element of quantum theory which enables it adequately to describe these effects, and we have seen that the superposition of various components is characteristic of the "pure state" of a system. Peres and Rosen suggest that since interference is not observed for macroscopic bodies, there is no need to maintain the superposition principle in the description of these bodies. Macroscopic objects may, therefore, properly be described by wave functions which are for mixtures of observable states, rather than by wave functions which are for pure states. There is, then, no "reduction of the wave packet" in an observation of macroscopic objects. Measurement, in this view, involves a selection of a particular state, characterized by ψ_n, of the states described by the total wave function $\psi = \sum_n c_n \psi_n$. The probability of the state ψ_n occurring would still be $|c_n|^2$, but we would think that the system described by ψ was a mixture of the states ψ_n, with each state always well-defined in itself, and *not* discontinuously formed from a superposition at the time of observation.

One wants of course to ask, "Where in nature does the line of demarcation exist between systems that are mixtures and those that are pure states?" The answer that Peres and Rosen give is a very reasonable one: the fineness of one's observation determines whether a system is to be regarded as a mixture of states or as a pure superposition. For very small objects, interference effects are obviously present, and hence the function must be for a pure state. As larger entities are considered interference effects generally become less obvious, and more effort is required for the discerning of them. When we come to systems for which the primary components in our analysis are, say, as large as the smallest visible objects of our world, then the expectation of finding any interference (superposition) effects is virtually nil, by any techniques whatsoever. The description of the system would then surely be as a mixture of states. Commonly, the system would be in a single state; Rosen's railroad example (Sec. 1 of this chapter) would be an instance of a mixture of two states, each with equal probability, but now with no consideration of superposition of the two states, since we regard that as only necessary if interference effects would be present.

The separation between physical systems which may be regarded as pure states and those which may be taken as mixtures has, it would appear, a certain arbitrary quality if the choice rests on how closely we search for interference effects. And yet, we can argue that the situation is no different from any other case of scientific decision. If observation shows a pure case to be required, then in a physical sense superposition of states must be

[12] Asher Peres and Nathan Rosen, "Macroscopic Bodies in Quantum Theory," *Physical Review*, **135**, B1486 (1964).

present and giving rise to the observed interference effects. This is the situation with photons or electrons in any "interference" experiment. If interference effects are not present, superposition is not necessary, and it is incorrect to carry the superposition formalism of quantum theory into the description of the system or phenomenon. There are intermediate cases, we would expect, where close investigation is required if the extent to which superposition occurs is to be determined and adequately reflected in the descriptive state function.

In a paper[13] already referred to, Rosen finds a mathematical basis for an essential difference between quantum and classical physics. He changes the form of the conventional Schroedinger equation,

$$i\hbar \frac{\partial \psi}{\partial t} = - \frac{\hbar^2}{2m} \nabla^2 \psi + V\psi, \tag{1}$$

by making the substitution $\psi = Re^{iS/\hbar}$, where R and S are real functions. The separation of (1) into real and imaginary parts, after the substitution, leads to the equations,

$$-\frac{\partial S}{\partial t} = \frac{1}{2m}(\nabla S)^2 + V - \frac{\hbar^2}{2m}\frac{\nabla^2 R}{R} \tag{2}$$

and

$$\frac{\partial \rho}{\partial t} = -\left(\frac{1}{m}\right)\nabla \cdot (\rho \nabla S), \tag{3}$$

where $\rho = R^2$.

Now, if we assume that $\hbar \to 0$, and that $(\hbar^2/2m)$ $(\nabla^2 R/R) \to 0$, Eq. (2) becomes

$$-\frac{\partial S}{\partial t} = \frac{1}{2m}(\nabla S)^2 + V. \tag{4}$$

Equation (4) is the Hamilton–Jacobi equation, which may be taken as a basic expression of classical mechanics. It would appear from this appearance of (4) that we have a continuous transition from quantum to classical mechanics: that if $\hbar = 0$, as in prequantum mechanics, we find quantum theory to reduce to classical theory.

Rosen shows, however, that the term $(\hbar^2/2m)$ $(\nabla^2 R/R)$ does not necessarily vanish in a mechanical problem, even with $\hbar \to 0$. He considers as an example a free particle of momentum p in one-dimensional motion. A solution of (1) for this particle is

$$\psi_1 = Ae^{\{(i/\hbar)[px - (p^2/2m)t]\}}, \tag{5}$$

[13] "The Relation between Classical and Quantum Mechanics," *American Journal of Physics*, **32**, 597 (1964).

where A and p are real constants, x is the dimension in which motion occurs, and t is the time. For this case,

$$R_1 = A, \qquad S_1 = px - (p^2/2m)t, \tag{5a}$$

and these satisfy (2) and (4), since the potential energy $V = 0$, and $(\nabla S)^2 = p^2$. A second solution,

$$\psi_2 = A e^{\{-(i/\hbar)[px + (p^2/2m)t]\}} \tag{6}$$

likewise satisfies equations (2) and (4). However, we now do what we normally would not do in classical mechanics, and take as a solution (for the Schroedinger equation) the superposition,

$$\psi_3 = \frac{1}{\sqrt{2}}(\psi_1 + \psi_2) = \sqrt{2}A \cos(px/\hbar)e^{-(i/\hbar)(p^2/2m)t}. \tag{7}$$

For this solution,

$$R_3 = \sqrt{2}A \cos(px/\hbar), \qquad S_3 = -(p^2/2m)t. \tag{7a}$$

We find, then, that

$$-(\hbar^2/2m)(\nabla^2 R/R) = -(\hbar^2/2m)(-p^2/\hbar^2) = p^2/2m.$$

Hence, even if $\hbar \to 0$, $(\hbar^2/2m)(\nabla^2 R/R)$ does not vanish. Equation (2) is still satisfied, in harmony with the superposition principle of quantum mechanics, but the Hamilton–Jacobi equation (4) is not satisfied by the solution ψ_3. As Rosen points out, the Hamilton–Jacobi equation is nonlinear, and it therefore is to be expected that it would not admit a superposition of solutions as a new solution.

Classical mechanics, then, is clearly different from quantum mechanics in its property of not allowing different states of physical systems to have simultaneous, congruent existence. And, classical mechanics clearly is not just the mechanics that results when the Planck constant is hypothetically allowed to vanish in quantum theory. There is, we see, a strong and basic difference in the manner in which classical mechanics represents natural phenomena, as contrasted with the manner utilized in quantum theory, and the difference is such that classical mechanics does not require any discontinous change, as a result of measurement, in the physical systems it describes. It therefore seems altogether correct that we have no problem of wave-packet reduction and associated dependence on awareness when considering the macroscopic objects of classical mechanics. The further fact which is needed to justify this separation of macroscopic phenomena from the epistemological problems of quantum mechanics is the well-established one that classical mechanics does itself generally give an adequate and correct account of the behavior of large-scale physical objects.

And yet, the problem of measurement remains for atomic-level physical entities. Further, these are ultimate constituents of macroscopic phenomena, and our understanding of the latter cannot stand apart from quantum theory. We may justifiably maintain independence of awareness for macroscopic phenomena, as well as the limited physical determinism that we know obtains for large-scale processes as a statistical consequence of the aggregate behavior of many individual atomic processes. But why is there such a radical change in the form which physical theory must take, and in the expectations that we have for the theory as an account of nature, as we move from the large-scale to the atomic level? We shall try to answer this question in the terms of a general feature of quantum physics.

4   OBJECT AND INTERACTION IN QUANTUM PHYSICS

In his writings on the quantum theory, Niels Bohr stressed that the observer has an effect on the atomic-level phenomena which he studies, this effect being a consequence of the interaction between observer and object of study. Further, Bohr emphasized that as a result of the indivisibility of the quantum, the interaction cannot be made to vanish. Because of the statistical nature of quantum physics, the interaction effect is unpredictable and uncontrollable in individual quantum-level processes. Bohr's oft-repeated conclusion was that man as a scientist has become a constituitive part of the nature he studies; that he cannot be a spectator alone, but is of necessity also partly an actor "in the great drama of existence."

It is the case then, as Bohr pointed out, that we cannot define or measure an objective nature, independent of our relation to it. We are able with apparatus, described in the space–time terms of classical physics, to observe certain features of nature, but the features found with one kind of apparatus are complementary to (or exclusive of) the features found with another kind. Nature clearly awaits our description, but the behavior of nature that we observe and describe depends on our apparatus and techniques as well as on the nature with which we interact.

We can see in the quantum theory of measurement a restatement of Bohr's expression of the epistemological significance of quantum physics. Where Bohr spoke of the unpredictable interaction between object and observer, the theory of measurement refers to the discontinuous, noncausal change that occurs in the wave packet on measurement. In both ways of speaking, the observer is a factor that has an effect on the natural description that is obtained. Also, in the quantum theory of measurement there is no possibility of an observed occurrence unless the observer brings about the abrupt change from pure state to mixture; likewise, for Bohr there can be no observation without the transfer of the indivisible quanta of energy between object and observer. Finally, just as for Bohr there is no natural world that may be defined independently of its relation to an observer, so in the quantum theory of measurement we have a dependence of events on the observer's awareness of them. For Bohr there is a certain flexibility about what can be objectively defined in nature and what cannot be, the flexibility depending on the choice of what apparatus is used and hence on the aspects of classical description which are obtained. We have a somewhat parallel flexibility in quantum-measurement theory, in that it is arbitrary at which point between object and awareness we say that there occurs the wave-packet reduction that leads to a specific measured event or state of a system.

The key element in the epistemological revision that accompanies the change from classical to quantum mechanics seems for Bohr to have been the transfer of the indivisible quantum of energy in any observation; for it is this transfer that introduces the scientist's disturbance of the nature he is describing, and *also*, that is necessary for his gaining descriptive information about nature. In contrast, in the recent quantum-measurement theory discussions, it is the necessity of description by pure states, embodying the use of the superposition principle, that requires the unpredictable wave-packet reduction that is associated with observation. It might seem strange that two such apparently different factors should lead to similar epistemological implications for quantum theory. The two factors are not, however, unrelated. It is because of interference effects—and it is these which require the superposition principle —that the effect of energy transfer in an observation cannot be exactly calculated. (Thus, we cannot know the precise momentum of an electron as it passes through a small opening that fixes its position, because the electron is diffracted in passing through the opening and therefore takes on various possible momentum values.) Likewise, *it is because an energy transfer is necessary* that there must in a measurement be a delivery of energy or momentum at some specific point, and hence a wave-packet reduction. The need for quantum-mechanical description, with reduction on measurement, and the indivisibility of the quantum, as stressed by Bohr, are both elements in a complete account of why quantum theory breaks so strongly with the simple epistemological realism of classical mechanics. Alternatively, we might say that the necessity of transfer of quanta of energy on observation, and the widely diffused dualism of nature, such as appears in the wave–particle aspects of matter and radiation, are the factors that lead to the indissoluble relation between object and observer in quantum theory.

But why was the constitutive role of the observer in natural science so generally neglected in prequantum physics? In classical physics, emphasis was entirely on the object being studied, and the information about the object came through entities that were altogether different from the object. The motions of material bodies, in Newtonian mechanics, could be observed by light rays that had negligible influence on those bodies. Changes of state, the effects of pressure or strain, the influence of heat: these and other kinds of behavior were all investigated for aggregates of many, many millions of atoms, with equipment that could be relatively independent of the process being studied. Investigations of electrical and magnetic phenomena were of large numbers of charges, such that macroscopic meters could give pointer changes on a scale. Even in the subtleties of experiments with electromagnetic waves, as in the Michelson interferometer or the propagation of Hertzian waves, the apparatus and measurements involved systems of many photons. In contrast, in the atomic-level phenomena of quantum mechanics we are concerned with objects which are of the same magnitude of spatial dimension and energy as are the physical entities which give us information about the objects. In many instances it is the object itself which interacts with our apparatus.

In order to learn of the trajectory of a missile we can arrange to receive light or radar signals that will trace the path. But if we wish to know of a photon's path in a diffraction apparatus we can only arrange an interaction with the photon; there is nothing "smaller" that we can bounce off the photon as it is propagated through the apparatus. Or, how shall we learn of an electron's orbit in an atom, except by radiation from it as it changes energy level (a method that cannot give a detailed space–time path of the electron), or by having the electron interact with some other particle—and here again we meet the problem that there is no particle "smaller" than an electron. How else can we learn of the radioactive decay of a nucleus, except by using the decay particle itself as the entity which signals the decay: for there are no subentities by means of which we can more closely follow the process of decay of a nucleus.

Symbolically, we might say that the object or system O is known by entities I which (i) interact with O, and, (ii) thence in a second interaction bring information to the observer or his apparatus A. Our representation of the epistemological situation in prequantum physics would be $O \to I \to A$. It is with the information that is brought to A that we are able to establish and become aware of those constructs which, our science tells us, make up the natural world. There is, by the presumptions of classical physics, no dependence of O on I, and we envision a nature that stands apart from our investigation of it.

In quantum physics, O and I may be the same entity, and we must then symbolize the gaining of information as $(OI) \to A$. Or, I may be different from O, but in interacting with O it substantially affects O's physical properties, as well as being itself affected. We then have: $(OI) \to I \to A$. In either case the object of our study is OI, not O; we gain information about O as an I or in interaction with I, not about an O independent of the effect of the information-bringing interaction. In specific atomic detail the universe changes from a nature that man studies, without influencing it, to a nature that at least in part is formed by the act of man's studying it.

We have discussed the limitations on knowledge of nature which arise when we come in our physical investigations to the quantum level, and must therefore regard OI rather than O as the source of what we find: the limitations on accuracy of measurement as given by the uncertainty principle, the exclusion of certain kinds of physical description, and the inability to maintain rigorous microscopic determinism, including a lack of predictive description for the occurrence of individual events. We have also seen, in our discussion of Gödel's theorem, that it is possible to construct arithmetic propositions referring to their own provability, whose truth or falsity cannot be decided in the system in which they are constructed. In broader languages, as a natural language like English, we saw that there are statements that refer to themselves, like the Paradox of the Liar, which are undecidable because they make contradictory assertions of both truth and falsity about themselves. An obvious similarity in the physical and logical–linguistic conditions that lead to incompleteness presents itself. Physically, we come to strong and hitherto unknown limitations on our knowledge of nature when the object of investigation and the physical entities by which we study the object become the same. Literally, the incompleteness arises when we find that the elements of nature with which we investigate nature are the same as the elements which we are investigating. In language and in logic, we come to intrinsic incompleteness—to necessarily undecidable assertions—when we work with propositions whose object or reference is their own validity.

In neither the physical nor the linguistic case is the limitation on knowledge only a destructive one. There is much that we can learn about the atomic-level physical world, but also, we have seen, there is a sensitivity to the dynamic interactions necessary for descriptive knowledge which rules out much that could be obtained on the larger scale of prequantum physics. Likewise, we can easily construct sentences that make meaningful, decidable assertions about themselves: for example, "This sentence contains 27 letters." But the Gödelian sentences show us that we can come to an unbreakable pattern of undecidability when we construct sentences that speak of their own provability. In brief, we find that both in the natural world and in language there are limitations on completeness of knowledge when the describing tool, be it elementary particle or logical proposition, becomes the same as that which we are describing.

It should not be thought that the convergence of O and I in quantum physics is alone and itself the origin of the peculiar characteristics of quantum theory as contrasted with classical physics. The need for a superposition principle in describing the microscopic phenomena of the atomic world is, we have seen, an essential element in the formulation of the theory; this element seems to be independent of the "self-reference" that we find for the entities with which the observer's apparatus interacts in studies of quantum-level phenomena. In order better to understand what is the contribution of the O–I convergence, we shall now try to see what limitations on knowledge would arise with hypothetical atomic-level description in a world in which the laws of classical physics would everywhere be valid.

In our discussion of descriptive science in Chapter 3, we saw clearly that there is an inevitable "singularity of ignorance" in description, since we have an infinite regress of description of that which describes (e.g., the books of science are themselves part of the world and must be described in a complete description; but then that description of the books must itself be described, and so on). We of course come to this same singularity in any attempt to give a complete description of a classical-model universe, if (as we should do) we include the describing mechanism. Suppose the universe consists of very tiny particles, such that all the known "elementary particles" are constituted of these particles, and, likewise, that radiation be shown to consist of these ultimate particles. We assume, too, that the laws of mechanics, with suitable relativistic modification, are valid for the ultimate particles, and that the forces existing between the particles may be known. It would now be the case that when investigation of the physical world was carried out on the level of smallest entities, that of the hypothetical tiny particles, there would be no deviations from that behavior of particles which is envisioned in classical physics. Specifically, there would be no wave aspect of matter, and hence no diffraction effects as particles interact with each other or move through small passages. Likewise, radiation could be consistently described as the behavior of pointlike particles of a certain kind. The quantum-mechanical changes from classical physics would, then, not appear; presumably, even on the atomic level we could give a deterministic account of nature, with complete space–time description and prediction for all events.

The "scientist" who created a description of our hypothetical nonquantum world might, in the first instance, be a very clever experimenter-sensor-computer. But this machine must be described, and so on. Eventually, if we do have science (which is a human product that necessarily involves awareness of that which is described) we must come to human beings. They too must be described. The infinite regress of description of description of description, etc., is perhaps not itself very important, for we have seen that science in any event presents only a limited number of the possible descriptive facts about a natural domain. But, the expectation of achieving an adequate description of a sentient human being, a description of awareness, in a purely mechanical and materialistic natural world is hardly very realistic. Some kind of psycho-physical parallelism would, it appears, have to be invoked.[14] Indeed, in the heyday of classical physics, in the late nineteenth century, the biophysicist Emil du Bois-Reymond emphatically stated that the problem of consciousness was one that was forever beyond the ken of natural science.

It appears, then, that the study of the microscopic domain of nature, where object and means of investigation come together, does not *logically* entail the

[14] Abner Shimony [*American Journal of Physics*, **31**, 755 (1963)] has pointed out the neglect, in classical physics, of the problem of how the mental recognition and construction of the physical world was achieved. M. Capek, in the final chapter of his account of the breakdown of classical physics, *The Philosophical Impact of Contemporary Physics* (Princeton, New Jersey, Van Nostrand, 1961), discusses indications of unification of physical and psychical aspects of experience in the post-classical physics. The later writings of Alfred North Whitehead, even though Whitehead seems not to have been explicitly influenced by the new quantum theory that developed in the mid-1920's, are particularly suggestive in this respect. Whitehead stressed the philosophical difficulties of the psycho-physical dualism that was tacit in classical physics, and proposed an alternative metaphysical point of view for natural science.

characteristic features of quantum physics. Nature could conceivably be as envisioned in prequantum physics, even on the atomic level, and there would then be no need for the changes from our prequantum concept of nature. But then we would have the problem of a deterministic–materialistic world, in principle everywhere completely described and understood, except with no place for the scientist whose thoughts bring about the description.

In actual fact, however, we have found, in coming to the domain of nature where our means of interacting with what we study are the same kind of entities as that which we study, that nature has surprising qualities that are incomprehensible in the terms of the older, classical physics. Perhaps we should be pleased that this is so; it can be argued that the prequantum physics, for all its tidy elegance, was leading us to a situation in which science would have to give up in despair at ever understanding biological awareness and response in terms of the properties that physics had found for its ultimate entities.

We of course have not at once come to an understanding of the traditionally nonphysical aspects of the world simply by our development of quantum theory. But we have found in studying the microscopic entities of matter and radiation which make up the world that we too must be part of that world, that we do not stand apart from it as a creature outside of nature; it seems to be an advance that our science does now incorporate this fact, when we draw a contrast with the complete lack of any place for the sentient scientist in the scheme of nature implied by classical physics. The very fact that consciousness has a key role in the present orthodox theory of quantum-mechanical measurement is an indication of a radical change in physics from the prequantum, Cartesian view of a separation of all psychic attributes from physical properties and processes. The present measurement theory is hardly satisfactory, and we have indicated reasons for maintaining something like the classical point of view when we are concerned with the large-scale systems for which classical physics was developed. But, biological and psychological processes are not, it would seem, primarily a matter of classical behavior of large-scale systems of matter; rather, they are basically processes occurring at the level of atoms and molecules and photons, and it is at this level that the quantum-theory view of nature is now mandatory in physics. The incompleteness of description of nature that is in this physics, and further, the mystery that is presented by the necessary wave-mechanical formulation of physical change, are unsatisfactory indeed from the standpoint of classical physics. But these new features of the basic physical entities offer possibilities for understanding that go far beyond the contrastingly narrow physics that was developed for the macroscopic mechanical world.

In summary, then, physicists have found that when their interacting probes for investigating nature, and the nature they are investigating, come to be the same microscopic entities, the world does not present itself as the objectively defined, rigorously determined machinelike universe of classical physics. This discovery came in part because the quantum probes inevitably disturbed the similar quantum entities under investigation, but also in part because nature does have newly discovered properties of mutual influence between various possible physical states, as well as the associated property of alternation between wave and particle that is seen in events of interaction and measurement. As we would expect, because physics is not logic alone, an empirical element, to be ascertained only by experience, showed us what nature is when we study her at the quantum level where our very observation must inevitably be a disturbance.

5   INCOMPLETENESS IN PHYSICS AND LOGIC

Even though the analogy between the undecidability of sentences which refer to their own validity, and the incompleteness of physical description when O and I come to be the same, is only a partial one, let us pursue it somewhat farther. We recall that in the final section of Chapter 5 we postulated a hypothetical machine that is able to formulate correct descriptions of various aspects of nature, the machine's own activity being one of those aspects. We noted that the machine would have a limitation upon its range of description in that it could not describe its own nonactivity, since the very act of describing would be in contradiction to its not being in a state of activity (describing). The machine illustrated, we asserted, the general fact that an activity or process cannot display a property which is explicitly forbidden by the activity or process. Analogously, we saw, a language cannot consistently speak of the validity of statements when the statements themselves have properties which contradict that validity. (The reader may find it helpful at this point again to go over Section 6 of Chapter 5.)

We can see the self-describing machine as a concrete example of the complementarity between actor and observer which Bohr generalized from the complementarity that arises in quantum theory as a consequence of the convergence of O and I on the atomic level. The machine as "actor" operates in the world, as a part of all nature, and as "spectator" it describes the world. The complementarity arises when the part of the world it describes is its own self, for then it is unable completely to play both roles: it cannot describe itself in a resting, nondescribing state.

In the actual physical world, complementarity arises when O and I converge, and description of all of object O's various physical properties can no longer be obtained through interaction with entities I. Instead, I now interacts with O sufficiently to disturb it, or may even be the same as O, and, experimental arrangements that give information of one set of properties of O cannot also give information about another. Since in any experiment O is disturbed by I, it is OI about which we learn, as has already been emphasized. O alone would be "actor" and I would be "spectator"; but, in investigations on the quantum level, the two are conjoined. It is the case in nature, as with our hypothetical machine, and, to repeat Bohr's reference to actor and specta-tor, as with people in living experiences, that there are situations in which atomic-level entities cannot present all of their O properties in their OI be-havior. The fact that they are OI's places a mutual exclusion, a complemen-tarity, among some of their natural O properties.

We can easily illustrate the limitation on observation of quantum-level objects that we find when the objects must also be interaction entities: must, that is, be their own "spectators." Suppose the z-component of the intrinsic spin of a particle is to be measured, a process which involves the interaction of the particle with a z-direction magnetic field in the measuring apparatus. Here the particle is both O and I, and, in the process of bringing information about its spin s_z it excludes the possibility of at the same time interacting with another field so as to give exact information about its spin, say s_y, in another direction. If the particle were a macroscopic sphere, considerably larger in diameter than the wavelength of radiation which could be reflected from it without disturbing it, we could easily devise an apparatus for observing its z and y spin components simultaneously. But because the microscopic particle must "report on itself," its interaction that gives information about s_z excludes that activity (interaction) which would give information about s_y. The angu-lar momenta, L_z and L_y, associated with the spins s_z and s_y, must obey the un-certainty principle, which in this case would be $\Delta L_z \cdot \Delta L_y \geqq h/4\pi$, where ΔL_z and ΔL_y are the dispersions in measurements of L_z and L_y, respectively. If L_z were precisely measured, the principles of quantum mechanics would require (and there is physical support for this type of inference) that L_y could fluctuate through an indefinitely large range while the particle was in the state of the L_z measurement.[15]

Perhaps an even simpler illustration is provided by attempts to study material particles or photons in order to learn whether they are corpuscles or waves. We might return to our double-slit apparatus for interference of light. With both slits open to a light source the screen displays a pattern which tells us that the photons are waves, and must so spread and propagate through the apparatus. The pattern of light and dark bands, taken with the geometric properties of the apparatus, enables us to calculate a wavelength for the light. Now, it is true that the interaction of the light with the screen material presents the light as consisting of particles; but we would find if we closely investigated the interaction of the light with the granules of screen material that in this interaction the light, now a photon (corpuscular), would be changed in its wavelength, if not absorbed entirely. So, at the one place in the apparatus where the light clearly behaves as a corpuscle, it loses the particular wave property (the particular wavelength) that it had in the apparatus.

[15] There is a quantum-mechanical limitation even on the measurement of s_z alone, but this limitation need not concern us here. The limitation, first pointed out by E. P. Wigner, would tend to be negligible as a sufficiently large measuring apparatus were used. For discussion and references see M. M. Yanase, *American Journal of Physics*, 32, 208 (1964) ; *Physical Review*, 123, 666 (1961).

Likewise, any attempt to learn more about the corpuscular property of having a definite trajectory in space, for the light going through the apparatus, would lead to loss of information about wave properties. Thus, if we closed one slit, we could say that we know the path of the photons at least to the extent of knowing what slit they pass through. But we would now lose the interference pattern, on the screen, which tells us the wavelength of the light (and thereby gives evidence of the light's wave properties). If we make the one open slit very narrow, we diffract the light, and get a pattern on the screen which indicates a new uncertainty for the direction of propagation of the light. In all of these hypothetical experiments the uncertainty principle tells us, of course, the limiting values on the precision of measurement of location (particle) and momentum (wave) properties. The light, interacting with our apparatus, is subject to a complementarity such that when it displays itself as a wave it cannot manifest itself as a particle, and we have the converse situation when the light is in an apparatus with which it interacts so as to show its particle properties. Or, we could say that the wave activity of light prevents its displaying its own nonwave (corpuscular) activity, etc. We would of course find the same kind of restriction with an apparatus for showing the wave *or* particle property of an electron, or any other atomic particle.

Let us now retrace the steps that show us a similar source of incompleteness in logic and in physical knowledge. There are sentences which are contradictory because they assert a content which is incompatible with their own validity; Gödel's theorem shows that mathematical propositions which discuss their own provability may be constructed in arithmetic, in a manner such that they are undecidable if the arithmetic is consistent. There is an analogous limitation in scientific description, in that a scientist or machine cannot make certain correct descriptive statements about his or its own activity. In both the logical proposition and the descriptive statement, limitation centers around self-reference: content is in conflict with the assertion or activity. Passing on to quantum physics, we see that for atomic particles and for radiation, we can only gain information by having these entities themselves (or comparable ones) interact with our apparatus. The light or matter that comes to the apparatus, and eventually brings information to the scientist, does not refer to other, macroscopic objects, as in classical physics, but refers to itself. And the particle or photon that is giving complete information about one aspect of itself, e.g., corpuscular, cannot in the same apparatus give information about a contradictory (complementary) aspect of itself, e.g., wavelike. Again, we have a kind of self-reference.

Our progression is: the sentence that talks about itself, the mathematical equation that refers to its own validity, the machine that describes its own activity, the atomic particle or photon that is giving information about itself or a similar entity with which it has interacted. In each of these cases there is a limitation which arises in association with the self-reference. The "liar paradox" type of sentence tells us that we are able to construct ordinary language sentences which are not decidable because they admit both of a proof for being true and one for being false (and hence are contradictory). Gödel's construction has the immense effect of changing previous conceptions about the completeness of a mathematical system; for it had previously been believed that every proposition of a consistent logic-mathematics could be shown to be either true or false. The descriptive machine that we postulated is highly contrived, and of slight scientific importance; but it illustrates the existence of a "singularity" limitation in descriptive science, when the science refers to the scientific activity itself. Then, finally, we find that when the microscopic natural entities which make up the world, and which normally are the interaction entities by which we learn of the macroscopic nature, are themselves studied, we have limitations on our knowledge: we cannot describe or predict in the complete way that we can for the macroscopic world.

So, there is a change in possibilities for completeness, in logic or in physics, if the sentence, or the physical probe, is to be both actor and spectator, or, more technically, both assertion and referent. The limitations on descriptive science which we discussed in Chapter 3 indicated that nature could not completely describe itself, could not be entirely self-aware. In a detailed and subtle way, quantum mechanics has shown us how nature's properties do in fact make manifest this limitation. In classical physics, the indicated limitation was at the domain of consciousness, or perhaps even with the biological phenomena of spontaneity and progressive, evolutionary change among organisms; for, these are aspects of nature that seem outside the scope of the deterministic materialism of nineteenth century physics. But with the advance of physics to the study of nature's ultimate quanta of mass and radiation, a study that had to be by use of those same entities, the limitation was found to be on the classical physics itself. It was in its long-established categories of detailed space-description of every event, of rigorous determinism of all processes, of definable, permanent properties of corpuscle or wave, that physics had to give way. The classical concepts, useful and significant as they are for macroscopic nature, were found to be inapplicable to nature's basic process and structure.[16]

In losing the prequantum outlook, we have also lost the seeming anomaly of life and awareness in a world that could presumably be exhaustively described in terms of indestructible particles and the forces between them. And, the quantum physics that we have gained in place of the classical physics has, of course, been wonderfully rewarding in its explanatory power. The structure of the atom, the origin of radiation, radioactive decay, the interactions between nuclei, the forces of chemical bonding, the stability of molecules, the conditions for chemical reactions, the thermal and electromagnetic properties of solids—the list of aspects of nature that are understood by means of quantum theory could go on almost indefinitely, because quantum and not classical

[16] J. Bronowski has proposed that self-reference puts limitations on science, and has suggested relations between these limitations and creative imagination in science and in literature; see his paper, "The Logic of the Mind," in *American Scientist,* **54,** 1 (1966) and in *Nature,* **209,** 1171 (1966).

mechanics is the correct physics of the microscopic elements of the natural world. Whether or not biochemistry and biophysics, using quantum theory, will be able to achieve as successful an explanation of biological organisms as has been obtained for a wide range of inanimate phenomena remains to be seen. But surely it is the case that, even though there has been an apparent loss of simplicity in going from classical to quantum physics, there has been a great gain in adequacy of our physics. And, although self-reference brings certain limitations both in logic and in physics, it is proper to point out that also in both activities there has been immense gain in understanding as a result of study of the tools that are used. The logical study and analysis of our language as such has enormously enriched our understanding of logic and the empirical sciences. The limitations that arise in certain situations of self-reference in language are only a small aspect of the great gains resulting from the logician's "self-study," i.e., from his study (by means of language and symbols) of the language and symbols that he uses. Analogously, even though certain limitations have appeared, the physicist has vastly widened his understanding of nature by investigating the very entities by which the world is experienced and known.

We can view the quantum limitations on classical description of the physical world as indicating a partial completion of the particular physics that arises from experience with the relatively large-scale bodies that may be directly perceived by our senses. The concepts of classical physics have been strongly modified by the developments in relativity theory, but without essential change in possibilities for deterministic, space–time description. And, there remains an openness for relativistic classical physics at the very large-scale level; we have seen in previous chapters how much about the cosmological features of nature is speculative and unknown. But, on the microscopic side, the exploration of the basic entities of nature has carried us to the end of the domain of the classical concepts of physics.

In reaching the physics of those entities that are basic in nature, and for which there are no tools for observation other than their own selves, we find aspects of nature that would be disturbing from the point of view of the prequantum physics. The new emphasis on the act of observation in natural knowledge, the inability to predict specific natural occurrences, the superposition interference (between different possible states) that is inexplicable in terms of point-by-point space–time description, the alternation between wave and particle behavior: these are properties that describe a nature that has elements which are out of keeping with a world that was to be describable by means of models that could be visualized and had an understandable machine-like structure and process. It seems, indeed, that in coming to the very ground of natural being we come to elements of the irrational; that nature shows us, in the entities that exist in themselves and are not products of aggregation and interaction of many entities, both a resistance to the description and explanation that had seemed so universally reasonable and successful, and also a freedom of being that will not be caught in any of the deterministic rules that are valid in the domain of larger objects. For the basic entities, existence is obviously not simply a matter of the mechanical laws of physics. And yet, a different set of laws may be formed, in accordance with nature's ways. The success of the new quantum physics assures us that in coming to the limit of the domain where classical physics was applicable, physics did not exhaust itself. Instead, it may be hoped that what we have learned, as compared with older physics, gives a much better basis of natural knowledge for understanding not only the nonliving aspects of nature, but biological, psychological, and even social phenomena, which also are part of the physical world.

11

Criticisms of Quantum Theory

1 INTRODUCTION

IT is hardly to be expected that the radical change in natural philosophy that accompanied the development of quantum mechanics would be accepted by all physicists without counterarguments in defense of the established assumptions that served physics so well from Descartes and Newton until the time of Bohr and Heisenberg. The giving up of a rigorous determinism for the events of the physical world, the loss of space–time description for the details of atomic processes, the new emphasis on the role of the observer in microphysics: to some, these changes seem to be an unhappy retrogression for physics, and attempts have been made to repudiate the conceptual framework of quantum physics.

We should, however, place what has recently happened in physics in the perspective of its history from times before the development of the mechanical, Newtonian point of view. The physics of the late mediaeval period was essentially qualitative, and did not use constructs of the degree of abstraction from direct sense experience that were required for the new Newtonian physics. We recall that the separation of primary (physically important) qualities from secondary (subjective and physically unimportant qualities) was a prime factor in the new natural philosophy of the sixteenth and seventeenth centuries. Also, although it is true that ideas of determinism were present in physics at least from the times of the Greek atomists, a dominating concept of machine-like, *calculable* determinism seems only to have come into physics with Descartes (who strongly influenced Newton). Earlier, nature was viewed as designed for life rather than as machinelike. The mediaeval cosmology, as expressed, for example, in Dante's *Divine Comedy*, presents a cosmos in which the physical world is integrated with the realm of God and Heaven. It is a world, too, in which man's expectations for life after his bodily death are closely associated with the presumed other existing domains of the cosmos. The change to a physical world that was not centered on man and his hopes for an immortality that transcended earthly existence did not come at once, even with the acceptance of Copernicus' cosmology. We recall that Newton argued that the planets could not have initially had their motions from the effect of gravity alone, but rather, that God must have directly intervened and set up the motions of the bodies of the solar system.[1]

But the change to what we now call "classical physics" did occur, and nature, at least for physicists *qua* physicists, did come to be viewed as an impersonal, mechanical, deterministic manifold of immutable atoms in space (with, to be sure, also, a role for an indiscernible aether). It is this natural philosophy of mechanism–materialism that is being replaced by the philosophical assumptions required by quantum theory. We see, however, that the replacement does not mean that a philosophical position which was firmly established throughout the *entire* past development of physics is being changed by the twentieth century developments in quantum physics. There has, in fact, long been philosophical disagreement with the foundations of classical physics, even during the period when that physics seemed unquestionably triumphant, at least from a scientist's point of view.

An instance in point is provided by the doctrine of determinism, which has been widely criticized on philosophical grounds. The contemporary American philosopher, Charles Hartshorne, writes[2] that recent philosophic thought has been ". . . overwhelmingly unfavorable to faith in absolute law. One could give a long list of important original thinkers of the present generation and of the one which just preceded it who have rejected determinism. Peirce, James, Dewey, Russell, Varisco, Bergson, Whitehead may serve as examples. Some philosophers, among them Russell, regard the issue as incapable of definite solution. . . . There are at least three basic philosophical objections to determinism which do not depend on current physics: First, if determinism were true, then the concept of possibility, an indispensable category, could refer to nothing in the real world of nature and must be interpreted supernaturally or not at all; second, if determinism were true, then the concept of time, also indispensable, would become likewise empty of meaning; third, if determinism were true, then the concept of evolutionary change could not be taken as fundamental, but must be construed as a special case of a reality which in its broad features is changeless."

A. N. Whitehead, in his well-known *Science and the Modern World*, effectively criticized the doctrine of "simple location" that is implicit in an unambiguous space–time localization of atomic particles of matter. The European idealistic philosophy of the nineteenth century may be regarded, at least in part, as a refusal to accept the impersonal materialism of classical physics. Students of philosophy could readily cite many other writings that are critical

[1] Isaac Newton, *Letters to Dr. Bentley*, I, in *Isaac Newton's Papers and Letters on Natural Philosophy*, edited by I. Bernard Cohen (Cambridge, Massachusetts, Harvard University Press, 1958), pp. 280–290.
[2] In the essay, "Order in a Creative Universe," in *Beyond Humanism*, by Charles Hartshorne (Chicago, Willett, Clark and Co., 1937), pp. 128–129.

of that philosophical outlook. We should not, then, regard the acceptance of the new quantum physics as being in the face of strong philosophical opposition; rather, it is perhaps correct to say that there is philosophic welcome for developments that may improve on some of the philosophical defects of an unrelieved mechanism–materialism in physics.

Of course, philosophy presents a highly variegated array of doctrines, in a society that permits free discussion and publication. And, the arguments for one doctrine as opposed to another are not generally as clear-cut or as compelling as in scientific controversies. The issues debated in philosophy are subject to rational investigation, and to confirmation or negation by experience; but they are frequently so basic, and so diffuse in their application, that a long period of time is required for decision. Quantum theory, in contrast, is a physical theory, and its correctness and greater adequacy, as contrasted with the prequantum physics, has been unquestionably established. And, the broad physical implications of quantum theory, or what we could call its physical–philosophical bases, have been accepted by the great majority of physicists. The minority who remain critical do not, generally speaking, discuss the basic issues primarily in philosophical terms, but rather seek to show inadequacies in quantum theory as a physical theory. Nonetheless, even though the discussion is chiefly in terms of theory for explicit physical phenomena, the motivation for criticism of the accepted quantum theory is generally a philosophical one. Specifically, the critical physicists generally wish to reaffirm the basic concepts of classical physics, and to cast quantum theory into a form compatible with those concepts (but still retaining the added explanatory and descriptive powers of the theory).

The new philosophical assumptions that come with the quantum theory and that are accepted by a majority in the world of physics have come to be called, rather loosely, the Copenhagen Doctrine, or the Copenhagen Interpretation, by association with the residence city of Niels Bohr, who led the way in the development of the new natural philosophy. I shall not attempt to survey the entire controversy between the critics and defenders of the Copenhagen Interpretation,[3] but I will discuss one of the key critical papers, and briefly comment on some of the proposed alternatives to what has now come to be the orthodox view.

2   THE EINSTEIN–PODOLSKY–ROSEN PARADOX

In 1935 Albert Einstein, Boris Podolsky, and Nathan Rosen published a paper[4] which in a very penetrating way raises the question of the adequacy

[3] P. K. Feyerabend has written a good review, with full historical and bibliographical notes, in *Frontiers of Science and Philosophy*, edited by R. G. Colodny (Pittsburgh, University of Pittsburgh Press, 1962), pp. 189–283.
[4] "Can Quantum-Mechanical Description of Physical Reality be Considered Complete?," *Physical Review*, 47, 777 (1935).

of quantum theory. The paper is also of especial interest to us, by virtue of its explicit concern with the question of completeness in science. The charge which Einstein, Podolsky, and Rosen make against quantum theory is that it fails to describe significant elements of the natural reality within the domain of the theory. Hence, the quantum theory cannot be complete; for, it is asserted in the paper, "the following requirement for a complete theory seems to be a necessary one: *every element of the physical reality must have a counterpart in the physical theory.*" Specifically, the authors allege that there must be natural factors associated with simultaneous precise values of the position and momentum of a particle, in spite of the established uncertainty-principle results that such values cannot simultaneously be measured.

The criterion which Einstein, Podolsky, and Rosen take for reality in their paper is the following: *If, without in any way disturbing a system, we can predict with certainty (i.e., with probability equal to unity) the value of a physical quantity, then there exists an element of physical reality corresponding to this physical quantity.* We note (and this is important for the argument of the paper) that the criterion is "theory-dependent"; the criterion is not that a quantity be measurable, but that it be accurately predictable. The predictability does, of course, require at least some indirect relation to measurement, since it is only through observation that the certainty of prediction could be confirmed.

The paradox is formulated by reference to the following hypothetical experiment. Two systems, 1 and 2, are permitted to interact from a time $t = 0$ to a time T, after which time they no longer interact. The combined system is described by a wave function $\psi(1) \cdot \psi(2)$. Schroedinger's equation allows us to calculate the state of the total system for any time after $t = T$. Therefore, by use of the wave function and the Schroedinger equation, we may find the state of a system 2 at $t > T$, if a measurement has been made which tells us the state of the first system at this same time $t > T$. For example, the combined system may consist of two particles, (1) and (2), whose position and momentum are measured after the time T at which interaction has ceased. We might measure the momentum p_1 of (1) at a time $t > T$. The knowledge of $\psi(1) \cdot \psi(2)$, taken with the measured value of p_1, enables us to infer the momentum value p_2 for (2) at time t, without in any way making a measurement on (2). Or, we might choose to measure the position x_1 of (1) at the time t. Then, we learn x_2 for particle (2). Clearly, we are able, from our theory, to make a certain prediction of either p_2 or x_2, depending on whether we measure p_1 or x_1. But, whether we determine a value for p_2 or x_2 depends on a measurement that is made after particles (1) and (2) have ceased to interact. It therefore cannot be the case, the argument runs, that the measurement of particle (1) has any influence on the existence of p_2 or x_2. So, by the reality criterion that has been adopted, there must be an element of reality corresponding to both of these quantities. Since quantum theory specifies that p_2 and x_2 cannot be simultaneously known, Einstein, Podolsky, and Rosen conclude that quantum description is not complete, for it does not meet the requirement that "every element of the physical reality must have a counter-part in the physical theory."

The importance in the argument of measurement being made after the separation is to be emphasized. It is commonplace in quantum theory that the kind of quantity to be observed, for example, position or momentum, is determined by the kind of measurement that is made. But in the situation described by Einstein, Podolsky, and Rosen the quantity p_2 or x_2 apparently exists in particle (2) independently of what measurement is made on particle (1), because that measurement is made after the period of time during which there was interaction between the particles.

A physical experiment in which the Einstein–Podolsky–Rosen proposal is carried out might be the following. Charged atoms (ions) of a specific mass and charge come from the oven O. (See Figure 11-1.) A collimator and velocity selector form two beams of ions, such that motion is at a given speed and in two given directions. (There is no uncertainty-principle limitation on the precision of speed, and precision of location normal to the velocity direction.) The beams are made sufficiently intense that they approach and electrically repel each other in the interaction region I, the interaction being negligible outside of this region. Also, the ion velocities and charges are such that the beams are turned away from each other. Initial beam directions are set up so that for the system of both beams the total momentum in the z-direction is zero.

We do not attempt to make measurements on single particles, but instead, the shutter S is opened for a brief interval, so that a burst of ions moves in each of the beam directions. Now the burst may be taken through detector region D_1, and a momentum determination made, for example, by passing the particles through a diffraction grating. In this way the z-component of the momentum, p_z, for particles in beam (1) is determined. Since the net momentum for both beams is zero in the z-direction, we are at once able to infer what p_z is for particles in beam (2) as they move through region D_2 (even

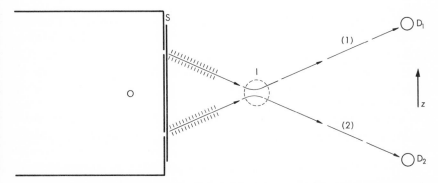

Figure 11-1.   Ions come in bursts from oven O when the shutter S is momentarily opened. The ions in the collimated beams (1) and (2) interact in region I; a measurement is made on them in detector region D_1.

though we make no measurement whatsoever in that region). Likewise, we could make a position measurement of the particles in beam (1) at some given time by putting, say, a Geiger counter and clock at D_1 which would record the z-position of a given burst of particles, t seconds after a shutter opening. Again, the Schroedinger equation for the system of bursts of particles in both beams, taken with the result found for the z-coordinate of the burst in beam (1) at the measured time t, will enable us to infer the z-coordinate of the burst in beam (2) at that time. It is seen from the simple symmetry of the experimental arrangement that a measurement of z for a burst in beam (1), at a given t, would imply a similar distance of travel in the z-direction for the burst that moves in the direction (2), since both bursts begin their travel at the same instant (during the brief period of shutter opening). The symmetry of the arrangement would, of course, be a determining element in the form that the Schroedinger equation would have for the total system.

The apparatus of Figure 11-1 would enable an experimenter to determine the momentum p_z, or the position z, for a burst of ions in the beam (2), at a given time, by means of measurements made on bursts in the other beam, at D_1. The experiment is not quite the same as that proposed by Einstein, Podolsky, and Rosen, in that we find the position of an ensemble of ions, somewhat extended spatially, rather than of a single particle. However, with high precision in the selection of ions of a given velocity (such precision is commonly achieved in mass spectrographs), and with a very brief open period for the shutter S, the extent of the burst along the beam direction could be made small. In principle then, it does seem that an ion burst in beam (2) does possess in some intrinsic manner both a position and momentum at a given time, contrary to the quantum-theory assertion that any system cannot simultaneously possess these two quantities for a given dimension. It is clear that we cannot simultaneously ever learn both p_z and z for the burst in beam (2), since to do so we would have to carry out a measurement for p_z and z simultaneously on the burst in beam (1). There is, then, no violation of the Uncertainty Principle. But since the values of p_z or z for the burst in (2) do not result physically from any measurement interaction that occurs with the burst in (1), the values are, it seems, in some latent manner simultaneously present in the burst. (It is to be granted that close analysis of the physical problems of measurement and initial conditions for the experiment suggested will soon lead to questions about the limits of accuracy for the measured or inferred p_z and z values.)

Before considering the implications of the Einstein–Podolsky–Rosen paradox, we shall present another hypothetical physical illustration[5] of the paradox that is commonly discussed. We recall that the Uncertainty Principle does not allow any two of the three spin components of a particle, s_x, s_y, s_z, to be measured simultaneously. Suppose that a diatomic molecule with net spin zero is dissociated by a force that breaks the relatively weak chemical bond of

[5] See D. R. Inglis, *Reviews of Modern Physics*, 33, 1 (1961); also, the discussion of the paradox given by D. Bohm, *Quantum Theory* (New York, Prentice-Hall, 1951), pp. 611–622.

the molecule, and that the two atoms have opposite spins (so that the initial molecule has net spin zero). Now, it is possible with present-day techniques to measure the orientation of a spin component of an atom, or nucleus, by detecting the motion of the particle in an inhomogeneous magnetic field. That is, one can determine whether the measured spin [an angular momentum of, for example, $\frac{1}{2}(h/2\pi)$] is oriented parallel or antiparallel with respect to a chosen coordinate x. But, once the coordinate on which the projection of the total spin is to be measured has been selected, then in accordance with the Uncertainty Principle the component of spin in another coordinate direction may not be simultaneously determined.

We may imagine the two atoms of our specimen diatomic molecule to be set into motion along different paths after the dissociation of the molecule. (See Figure 11-2.) Suppose the spin component of one of the two atoms is measured and found to be $s_x = +\frac{1}{2}$. Then, in view of the net spin zero of the original molecules, we must infer that the other atom has spin $-\frac{1}{2}$ in the x-direction. However, the apparatus for measuring the spin of the first atom could have been arranged so as to measure the spin component s_y. If that were found to be, say, $+\frac{1}{2}$, we could infer that the spin s_y of the second atom was $-\frac{1}{2}$. We are not able to determine s_x and s_y simultaneously for either atom, but again, as in the determination of position and momentum of a burst of ions, we are able to learn either s_x or s_y for the atom whose spin is not directly measured by means of a measurement on the other atom, the measurement being made after the two atoms have been physically separated. It does appear, then, that both spin values, s_x and s_y, must have been intrinsic in the second atom after its separation from the first atom. That is, by the criterion of reality of Einstein, Podolsky, and Rosen, the predictable spin values s_x and s_y should both have corresponding elements of physical reality. The quantum theory, however, asserts that spin values s_x and s_y cannot be simultaneously measured

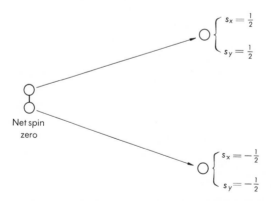

Figure 11-2.   A diatomic molecule of net spin zero is dissociated into two atoms, each of spin magnitude $\frac{1}{2}$ (in units of $h/2\pi$) along any direction that the spin is measured. If $s_x = \frac{1}{2}$ is found for one, the other atom must have $s_x = -\frac{1}{2}$; if $s_y = \frac{1}{2}$ is found for one, the other must have $s_y = -\frac{1}{2}$.

for an atom, and further, that the two values do not simultaneously exist as natural quantities.

Niels Bohr replied to Einstein, Podolsky, and Rosen in a paper[6] published a few months after their criticism appeared. He denied the charge of incompleteness in the quantum theory, even in terms of the criteria for completeness and for reality which had been used. The conditions under which measurement is made, Bohr asserted, are part of the physical reality, since they determine what it is that will be measured. It is the characteristic nature of the role of measurement in quantum theory, that only by including a description of the apparatus do we specify the physical reality that is being studied. Hence, the defender of quantum theory can argue that the experimental arrangement, including the apparatus that is used for measuring position or momentum, or for measuring s_x or s_y, is the "element of reality" which corresponds to the quantity that is inferred in the separated entities on which no measurement is made.

The following passage from Bohr's paper clearly states his counterargument. "From our point of view we now see that the wording of the . . . criterion of physical reality proposed by Einstein, Podolsky and Rosen contains an ambiguity as regards the expression 'without in any way disturbing a system'." Referring to a measurement situation of the kind we have been describing, Bohr continues: "Of course there is in a case like that just considered no question of a mechanical disturbance of the system under investigation during the last critical stages of the measuring procedure. But even at this stage there is essentially the question of *an influence on the very conditions which define the possible types of predictions regarding the future behavior of the system.* Since these conditions constitute an inherent element of the description of any phenomenon to which the term 'physical reality' can be properly attached, we see that the argumentation of the mentioned authors does not justify their conclusion that quantum-mechanical description is essentially incomplete. On the contrary this description . . . may be characterized as a rational utilization of all possibilities of unambiguous interpretation of measurements, compatible with the finite and uncontrollable interaction between the objects and the measuring instruments in the field of quantum theory."

Bohr's answer is a convincing one, in the context of quantum theory; for, corresponding to the different measured and inferred quantities there are the different experimental arrangements that constitute the appropriate corresponding elements of reality. Thus, in the first illustration which we gave of the paradox, whether position or momentum is inferred for the second group of ions depends on whether conditions are arranged for measuring z or p_z. These conditions, if inference is to be made for the unmeasured ion burst, must include assurance either that $z = 0$ at the deflection region or that total $p_z = 0$. Fulfillment of both of these initial conditions simultaneously would violate the Uncertainty Principle. Or, in the spin-measurement experiment, a requirement

[6] N. Bohr, *Physical Review*, 48, 696 (1935).

that the diatomic molecule initially have a net spin zero in more than one direction would be in violation of the principle.

The physicist who is accustomed to the kind of detailed analysis of mechanism that contributed to scientific explanation in prequantum physics will probably still have, however, a sense of dissatisfaction with the adequacy of Bohr's reply. To those brought up in the atmosphere of an acceptance of quantum theory, there may be no lingering (or initial) doubts. A young theoretical physicist, to whom I once put the question, "Do you see any problem in the Einstein–Podolsky–Rosen paradox?," lightly replied, "None at all —that's just quantum mechanics."

The measurement situation that we have been considering may be given a variation in which it perhaps presents additional understanding of the quantum-mechanical principles that are involved. Suppose a beam of atoms to have been initially accumulated by the action of an inhomogeneous magnetic field, such that only atoms of $s_z = +\frac{1}{2}$ are present in the beam. The beam is now allowed to pass through a region in which an inhomogeneous magnetic field in the x-direction separates it into two beams of atoms, with spins of $s_x = +\frac{1}{2}$ and $s_x = -\frac{1}{2}$ respectively. (See Figure 11-3.) This half-and-half separation is to be expected, since, with the preparation of the atoms as being in the $s_z = +\frac{1}{2}$ state, we must lose all information about the s_x properties (in accordance with the Uncertainty Principle). With respect to s_x, the initial state of the beam must be regarded as a *superposition* of the two equally possible s_x states, $+\frac{1}{2}$ and $-\frac{1}{2}$.

The beam of atoms with $s_x = +\frac{1}{2}$ may next be separately treated, and taken into an inhomogeneous magnetic field in the z-direction. Since we know the x-component spin of all the atoms of this beam, we can have no knowledge of the z-component. The beam must then be a superposition of the spin $s_z = +\frac{1}{2}$ and spin $s_z = -\frac{1}{2}$ states, and the decomposition effected by the z-direction magnetic field, when the total spin is projected onto it, would be

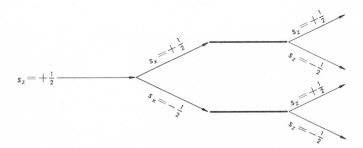

Figure 11-3. A beam initially containing only atoms with spin $s_z = +\frac{1}{2}$ is divided by an x-direction inhomogeneous magnetic field into two beams of equal intensity, one of atoms with spin $s_x = +\frac{1}{2}$ and the other of atoms with spin $s_x = -\frac{1}{2}$. Each of these beams, if passed through an inhomogeneous z-direction magnetic field, will be found to consist of as many atoms with spin $s_z = -\frac{1}{2}$ as with the original spin $s_z = +\frac{1}{2}$.

into atoms of spins $s_z = +\frac{1}{2}$ and $s_z = -\frac{1}{2}$, with equal numbers of each. The quantum-mechanical principles of uncertainty and of superposition of states have led us to the conclusion that even though the initial beam contained only atoms with spin $s_z = +\frac{1}{2}$, the effect of a loss of information about z-components has been to restore some of the $s_z = -\frac{1}{2}$ spins. This effect can be regarded as having occurred with the measurement of s_x spins; but, there is no detailed, physical way in which we can see the application of the measuring, inhomogeneous x-direction magnetic field as converting the $s_z = +\frac{1}{2}$ spins into a mixture of $s_z = +\frac{1}{2}$ and $s_z = -\frac{1}{2}$ spins. Rather, we must rest our account of what occurs on the physical principles of the quantum theory.

The hypothetical measurements just presented form a kind of anti-(Einstein–Podolsky–Rosen paradox) situation. The implication to be drawn from the paradox is that, for the first spin experiment described, the spins s_x and s_y for both atoms must have been determined from the time of separation of the two atoms. A similar conclusion would have obtained if we had proposed the experiment (and this would be much more realistic) for beams of many atoms. But the experiment that we have just discussed implies that the spin is not predetermined; for, even though the atoms were initially certain all to have spin $s_z = +\frac{1}{2}$, the quantum theory requires that there be s_z spins of both $(+)$ and $(-)$ after a measurement in which certainty about s_z spins is lost. It would seem that we cannot "predetermine" spin, except in accordance with the principles of quantum theory. A similar remark would apply, of course, for other physical variables, as momentum and position.

A physical situation that is somewhat analogous to the hypothetical spin experiment of Figure 11-3 has actually been studied.[7] One of the short-lived, unstable particles of nature is the neutral K-meson, which is designated as K°. The particle has a mass of about 975 electron masses. As with other elementary particles there is an antiparticle, $\overline{K^\circ}$, and both K° and $\overline{K^\circ}$ are formed when K particles are produced. Now, wave functions for K° and $\overline{K^\circ}$ may be superimposed in two different ways, giving rise to two different states, K_1° and K_2°. (The two ways of making the superpositions involve technical aspects of quantum theory which I shall not introduce into the discussion.) Alternatively, K° and $\overline{K^\circ}$ may be regarded as particle states formed by the two different possible superpositions of K_1° and K_2°. The relevant principles of elementary-particle physics lead to the conclusion that the "particle" (i.e., the state) K_2° should have a longer lifetime than the "particle" (state) K_1°: about 7×10^{-8} sec for K_2° as contrasted with 10^{-10} sec for K_1°. This prediction has been experimentally verified.

The physical effect of interest to us is the following. Suppose K° particles (no $\overline{K^\circ}$ present) are in a beam. After a time the K_1° component,

[7] A review discussion is given by J. J. Sakurai, in his *Invariance Principles and Elementary Particles* (Princeton, New Jersey, Princeton University Press, 1964), Sec. 10.4. I am indebted to my colleague, Dr. J. S. Kovacs, for this reference. Also, see the paper of D. R. Inglis, *Reviews of Modern Physics*, 33, 1 (1961).

which makes up one-half of the beam, dies out because of its shorter lifetime, leaving only the K_2° component. When these two components were superimposed, the $\overline{K^{\circ}}$'s present in each of the superpositions K_1° and K_2° were "cancelled out"; but now, with only K_2° present, the remaining beam consists of 50% K°'s and 50% $\overline{K^{\circ}}$'s. The K_2° beam may be passed through nuclear matter, e.g., through a lead plate. As a consequence of interactions by the K° or $\overline{K^{\circ}}$ particles with the matter, the states K_1° and K_2° are again formed. So, the K_1° state, which had died out, is regenerated from the K° and $\overline{K^{\circ}}$ states. The reappearance of the K_1° state is analogous to the appearance of spin $s_z = -\frac{1}{2}$ states in the preceding experiment.

The observed difference of stability in the states, K_1° and K_2°, formed by two different superpositions of the particles K° and $\overline{K^{\circ}}$, is a dramatic illustration of the significance of the superposition principle. Theory also indicates that there should be a very slight mass difference between the states K_1° and K_2°, arising from differences in the interaction energy for the two states. A mass difference has actually been observed.

3   CLASSICAL AND QUANTUM CONSTRUCTS

The characteristic features which distinguish classical from quantum physics may be given as the following constructs, delineated as elements of the natural world: atoms with continuous and definite localization in space and time, fields which behave unambiguously in accordance with static- or wave-form equations, continuous rather than quantum energy transfer, mechanistic processes of interaction and change which are subject to completely deterministic description. In asking for a complete theory to account for their measurement situation, Einstein, Podolsky, and Rosen appeared to be asking for a theory that was still at least in part within the framework of these constructs. If the position or momentum of the second atom is not measured and may nonetheless be inferred, depending on what one chooses to measure for the other atom, it would seem that it is possible, in classical terms, to identify some aspect of the second atom with the variable that is inferred: that the atom must continuously possess this variable after its separation from the first atom. Bohr's reply, that the act of measurement (including all relevant preparations) does itself provide the aspect of nature which determines whether it is a momentum or position variable that is known for the second particle, is an adequate one in the framework of quantum theory and the emphasis given therein to the role of measurement in determining what it is we find in nature. But how fully are we to be satisfied with the answer of quantum theory, and with an associated renunciation of the demands of classical physics? The tradition of that physics, enriched by its many successes in understanding the macroscopic world, is not readily given up in studying the atomic world.

We recall, however, that we have seen reasons for accepting the notion that there are basic differences in physical theory as we move from the macroscopic world to the quantum-level world. This difference need give us no discomfort, as indicating a discontinuity in nature. The indeterminate events of the atomic world, undescribable in terms of point-by-point space–time processes, conjoin in systems of many events to give the approximately deterministic macroscopic processes which we are able unambiguously to describe with the spatial and temporal variables that are derived from direct experience. It should be noted, too, that incompleteness, in the sense of lack of detailed space–time description of phenomena, is diffused throughout our knowledge of the atomic-level world; the Einstein–Podolsky–Rosen paradox is just one (very clearly defined) illustrative example. The wave–particle duality in its many manifestations is certainly not explicable as a process which can be followed in point-by-point detail in space–time. And, we have seen in our discussion of quantum-mechanical measurement how the super-position principle of quantum theory requires, for the occurrence of observed events, processes which are not within the purview of the explicit equations of the theory. Thus, we are able to predict that waves from a light source will give rise to photon interactions on an appropriately placed photographic plate, but there is nothing in our theory, except a probability estimate, that corresponds to the specific localizing of the photon interaction, and also, nothing that corresponds to the process of transition from a wave to the corpuscular photon.

Of course, in prequantum physics we also had obvious incompleteness, again in the sense of lack of detailed space–time description for some major aspects of nature. The Newtonian theory of gravitation provides a striking example: invoking "action at a distance" to explain gravitational attraction through a (presumably) completely passive and empty space was just giving a name to a phenomenon that defied any explanation in terms of mechanistic physics. In this instance, as has been discussed, we have the successful solution that Einstein's general theory of relativity provided in its ascription of gravitational force to the mass-associated distortions of a flat, "Euclidean" space–time. Not all facets of prequantum physics, however, have fared so well. There are, for example, phenomena of electromagnetism that are as puzzling in mechanical terms as was Newtonian gravitation. Thus, in accordance with Faraday's law of induction, an electrical potential is formed in a closed loop of wire as a consequence of a changing magnetic field within the region enclosed by the loop; the wire itself may be at locations where there is virtually no magnetic field, and yet the electric current in it will be formed in response to the changing magnetic field at interior points within the loop. Einstein's own special theory of relativity postulates changes in the characteristics of physical entities of all kinds (including a change in time rate of all physical processes) simply as a consequence of relative motion, with no hint of what might be the physical mechanism for the changes.

It is not the case, therefore, that the inexplicable aspects of quantum physics are a novelty to be contrasted with a comprehensible structure of classical physics, even though it can hardly be denied that quantum physics has brought new and basic problems that so far have defied traditional modes of understanding. Quantum theory was not developed, however, primarily as an alternative set of concepts, independent of the facts of nature that had arisen in the context of the prequantum physics. Rather it was developed (as is clear to a student of its history) because the classical constructs were found to be wrong. In the words of one of the major pioneers of quantum theory, ". . . nor do I deny that the forming of new concepts is guided to some extent by general philosophical principles. But I know from my own experience, and I could call on Heisenberg for confirmation, that the laws of quantum mechanics were found by a slow and tedious process of interpreting experimental results." [8]

We can believe that the further achievement of completeness of theory for quantum-level phenomena will come with further statement of constructs appropriate to the observations of the phenomena, not with continued attempts to find a place for quantum physics within the basic assumptions of classical, deterministic physics. Completeness of theory, as we have seen in our discussion in Chapter 4 of the relation of theory to explanation, is in any event always relative to a set of assumptions. We want, of course, that set of assumptions, or framework of physical constructs, which does give the most coherent and intelligible total account that we can find for our experience of the natural world. Quantum physics has shown defects in the constructs of classical physics, and, at least in part, given us a new intelligibility, along with new problems.

It is of interest to give some further indication of the attitude which Einstein maintained toward the change in physical philosophy that came with quantum theory. His writings leave no doubt of his opposition to the Copenhagen interpretation, and in particular, to its probabilistic, nondeterministic element. He has indicated, too, the unhappy estrangement which he felt from the great majority of his colleagues, in consequence of that opposition.[9] He did not in any way assert, however, that quantum theory, as it was developed in the 1930's, was incorrect, as far as it went. His view was rather (as we have been suggesting in the present discussion) that further development is needed to restore to physics a completeness which it lost with its extension to quantum phenomena (an extension to which he contributed in large measure). Thus, to quote from Einstein's own writings,

[8] Max Born, in his *Natural Philosophy of Cause and Chance* (New York, Oxford University Press, 1949), p. 86.

[9] In a letter to Erwin Schroedinger, written in 1937, Einstein said of his remarks on the interpretation of quantum theory as developed by Born and Bohr (I have translated from the original German): "I write to you not in the illusion that I will convince you, but solely with the intention that you may understand my viewpoint, which has led me into deep loneliness." *Briefe zur Wellenmechanik*, edited by K. Przibram (Vienna, Springer, 1963), p. 33.

he says of Heisenberg's indeterminacy-relation, ". . . the correctness of which is, from my own point of view, rightfully regarded as finally demonstrated. . . ." [10] And, he writes of quantum theory: "This theory is until now the only one which unites the corpuscular and undulatory dual character of matter in a logically satisfactory fashion: and the (testable) relations, which are contained in it, are, within the natural limits fixed by the indeterminacy-relation, *complete*. The formal relations which are given in this theory—i.e., its entire mathematical formalism—will probably have to be contained, in the form of logical inferences, in every useful future theory." [11]

But Einstein also writes, "I am, in fact, firmly convinced that the essentially statistical character of contemporary quantum theory is solely to be ascribed to the fact that this theory operates with an incomplete description of physical systems." [12] In reply to an imagined quantum-theorist who considers complete description impossible, Einstein says: "Your point of view—taken as a theoretical possibility—is incontestable. For me, however, the expectation that the adequate formulation of the universal laws involves the use of *all* conceptual elements which are necessary for a complete description, is more natural. It is furthermore not at all surprising that, by using an incomplete description, (in the main) only statistical elements can be obtained out of such description. If it should be possible to move forward to a complete description, it is likely that the laws would represent relations among all the conceptual elements of this description which, *per se*, have nothing to do with statistics." [13]

Of course, there is a tacit assumption in the view which Einstein expresses that in nature there are existing entities which correspond to the conceptual elements that he desiderates for a complete description. It is on just this point that most contemporary theoretical physicists part company with Einstein's views. They have, instead, widely accepted the doctrines put forth by Bohr, Born, and Heisenberg. What Einstein saw as an incompleteness in quantum theory is maintained as in fact representing the way nature is. There is, then, only the approximate determinism of statistical probability on the atomic level, and we cannot gain detailed knowledge of particles and waves, beyond the limitations set by the Uncertainty Principle.

Shall we be satisfied with the apparently inexplicable transformation in physical processes between wave and particle as being simply a fact of nature's behavior; or is it fruitful to search for further elucidation? Questions of this kind have led a few physicists to explore the possibilities for major variations from the general point of view characterized as the Copenhagen Interpretation. One attempt, that of Alfred Landé, has been in the direction of maintaining the statistical indeterministic character of quantum theory,

[10] Albert Einstein, "Reply to Criticisms," in *Albert Einstein: Philosopher-Scientist*, edited by P. A. Schilpp (Evanston, Illinois, Library of Living Philosophers, Inc., 1949), p. 666.
[11] *Ibid.*, pp. 666–667.
[12] *Ibid.*, p. 666.
[13] *Ibid.*, pp. 672–673.

but with an elucidation of the puzzling features of wave–particle behavior. Other attempts have been toward renunciation of the noncausal features of quantum theory, and with re-establishment of the detailed completeness and determinism of nineteenth century physics. We shall briefly comment on some of these efforts, turning first to the work of Landé.

4   SOME ALTERNATIVE INTERPRETATIONS

In his first publications[14] proposing a new basis for quantum theory Landé based the quantum postulates on a novel thermodynamic approach. He began with the fact that two macroscopic systems can have varying degrees of difference, rather than being entirely "like" or "unlike." Hence, he argued, there must be fractional degrees of likeness, based on quantum differences in fractional numbers of the atomic constituent particles of macroscopic systems. In his most recent work[15] Landé regards his thermodynamic approach as appropriate only for a special problem and instead he bases his quantum theory on certain general features of the probabilities of transitions between different states of any kind of system. Such considerations are essential to his development in either case, and he deftly shows how they lead when taken with a few general assumptions to the essential elementary formalism of quantum theory.

The statistical, probabilistic aspect of quantum theory is basic, then, in Landé's work, and he argues that in this respect the present-day theory faithfully represents natural processes. He strongly breaks with accepted quantum mechanics, however, in his statement that the wave–particle dualism is only a statistical effect. Matter, he asserts, consists of corpuscular particles, and the phenomena of matter-waves are actually statistical effects of many particles. Landé presents his case with personal conviction, and sees his point of view as being on the side of a sound physical realism, in contrast to the vagueness with respect to the nature of atomic entities that is inherent in the position of Bohr and his followers.

The fact is, however, that Landé's explanation in terms of a purely corpuscular nature of matter is not convincing for wave phenomena such as the diffraction of electrons. He uses an analysis of diffraction of matter waves, by a crystal, that was first put forth by the American physicist W. Duane in 1923, for X-ray diffraction by crystals (with the X rays taken as corpuscles). This is a possibly tenable explanation, dependent upon the entire crystal lattice taking up quantized amounts of momenta from the diffracted particles, and hence giving preferential reflection of the particles in certain directions. The

[14] For example, A. Landé, *American Journal of Physics*, **20**, 353 (1952) ; **22**, 87 (1954) ; also the book, *Foundations of Quantum Theory, A Study in Continuity and Symmetry* (New Haven, Connecticut, Yale University Press; London, Oxford University Press, 1955).

[15] *From Dualism to Unity in Quantum Physics* (New York, Cambridge University Press, 1960).

argument breaks down altogether, however, for diffraction by slits.[16] Further, Landé's "unity in quantum theory" is ineffective in explaining the corpuscular nature of light. He asserts that just as matter is actually particles, so light is actually electromagnetic waves, and photons are no more than heuristic pictorializations. But such an assertion is hardly warranted, in view of the localization-of-light phenomena, such as the photoelectric effect, which initially gave rise to the wave–particle dualism for light.

One can sympathize with the pointed criticisms that Landé and others have made with respect to the present-day standard quantum theory, and I have been concerned in these discussions with some of the problems that come with the theory; and yet, it would seem that one is brought back to the wry remark, "Everything is against quantum theory except the facts."

Erwin Schroedinger expressed dissatisfaction with the generally accepted interpretation of quantum theory, and hoped that it might be possible to regard quantum-level phenomena entirely in terms of waves. With this approach, the exchange of radiation between an emitter and an absorber can be regarded not primarily as emission and subsequent absorption of a quantum of energy, possibly corpuscular in nature, but rather as an exchange of wavelike radiation between two atomic systems which are in a coupled resonance with each other.[17] Schroedinger did not find, however, that he could formulate a general wave theory in which the properties of localization which we do observe for matter and radiation were derived from primary wave properties.

David Bohm and J. P. Vigier have proposed the introduction of a new construct which would radically change the foundations of quantum theory.[18] Bohm initially suggested that there exists a "quantum potential," different from the potentials associated with any of the usual physical fields (gravitational, electromagnetic, or nuclear). The basic Schroedinger equation of quantum theory is rewritten by Bohm with the introduction of the new potential function, and the wavelike properties of particles are found to be describable in terms of motions which are given to them by the quantum potentials. That is, Bohm, like Landé, reverts to a prequantum conception of the elementary particles as corpuscles with a definite position at all times. The goal of Bohm's work has primarily been to give a causal interpretation to quantum phenomena, and at first this was sought for simply in the writing of equations which presumably did describe the detailed behavior of atomic particles. In later papers he was joined by the French physicist, Vigier, in formulating a theory[19] of a subquantal "fluid" which is to be understood as

---

[16] Landé's explanation of wave phenomena of particles is effectively criticized by H. V. Stopes-Roe, *Nature*, **193**, 1276 (1962).

[17] See E. Schroedinger, *British Journal for the Philosophy of Science*, **3**, 109, 233 (1952).

[18] The first papers are D. Bohm, *Physical Review*, **85**, 166, 180 (1952). For bibliography of later papers, and general discussion, see Bohm's book *Causality and Chance in Modern Physics* (London, Routledge and Kegan Paul, 1957; New York, Harper Torchbooks, Harper & Row, 1961).

[19] D. Bohm and J. P. Vigier, *Physical Review*, **96**, 208 (1954).

giving rise to the "quantum-potential" fluctuations of atomic particles which we interpret as their wavelike behavior.

Bohm and Vigier, and others, have developed the theory of the basic substratum or fluid, so as to give it appropriate relativistic properties, thereby removing such nonrelativistic behavior as fluctuating motions at infinite velocity for elementary particles in Bohm's original theory. Formally, the theory can explain many quantum phenomena in terms of the postulated constructs. And yet, it has not had any general acceptance among physicists. There is a reluctance to return to a purely particle concept of matter when there is such direct evidence for wave properties, and when quantum theory in its wave-mechanical form has so enriched our understanding of the natural world. The reluctance would be overcome, to be sure, if a revised particle theory led to new understanding in terms of accepted physical ideas, or improved on the descriptive capacities of the accepted quantum theory. The Bohm–Vigier theory, although it does give an explanatory scheme of quantum phenomena in terms of particles, does also introduce new constructs that are altogether lacking any empirical confirmation; and, it does not enable us to calculate any observable quantum effect with one whit more precision, or higher degree of determinism, than with the customary probabilistic interpretation of quantum theory.

In recent years the attempt to find a detailed space–time description of atomic processes has been led by the founder of the theory of the wave properties of matter, Louis de Broglie. He has written[20] that, although he had come to accept the Copenhagen Interpretation for quantum theory, and taught it for many years, in the early 1950's he came back to his first ideas about particles and their wave properties. He has undoubtedly found encouragement in the ideas of Vigier, Bohm, and other younger theoretical physicists.

De Broglie's attitude toward the accepted view of impossibility of detailed explanation in quantum theory is perhaps indicated by the following statement, made by him about quantum transitions which accompany emission of radiation from an atom: "A long time ago Bohr said that the description of these quantum transitions has 'transcended' the framework of space–time, which is purely and simply a refusal to offer an explanation." [21] De Broglie believes that we should seek a space–time description, in what I take would be the traditional pre-Bohr manner, but at the same time he is fully aware of the problem which the observed wave–particle dualism of matter and radiation presents to whoever would offer any such description. In the terms of quantum theory, de Broglie expresses the dilemma with respect to the ψ-function. The

[20] De Broglie presents an elegant *precís* of his point of view in *The Current Interpretation of Wave Mechanics: A Critical Study* (with a chapter by J. Andrade e Silva) (Amsterdam, Elsevier, 1964). A more complete account is given in L. de Broglie, *Non-Linear Wave Mechanics: A Causal Interpretation*, translated by A. J. Knodel and J. C. Miller (Amsterdam, Elsevier, 1960).
[21] *The Current Interpretation of Wave Mechanics: A Critical Study* (Amsterdam, Elsevier, 1964), p. 23.

interpretation of the function as a measure of probability for a given state, in accordance with Born's "probability is proportional to $|\psi|^2$" prescription, is abundantly confirmed. However, the ψ-function cannot be only a subjective estimate of probability, but must also describe genuine physical waves which give matter its observed interference properties.

The two aspects of the ψ-function are reconciled, de Broglie suggests, in what he calls his Theory of the Double Solution. For this theory there is in nature a linear wave field, v, associated with a particle, and the ψ-wave is proportional to the wave field, such that $\psi = Cv$, where C is a normalization constant. The v field is responsible for the wavelike behavior of matter; it can give rise to atomic phenomena of diffraction, interference, and quantized energy states. There is also, however, a field, u_0, associated with a particle and described by a nonlinear equation. This u_0-singularity is, in effect, the corpuscular particle; the total wave–particle is described by a function $u = u_0 + v$. In de Broglie's words, "By associating the singular region with the particle, we return to the picture which I had in my early researches: the very small singular region constituting the particle is the seat of a periodic phenomenon which can be likened to a clock and which moves in the midst of the v-wave, of which it is an integral part, in such a way as to remain constantly in phase with it." [22] The v wave is envisioned as having streamlines along which the u_0-singularity (the particle) must move. But de Broglie proposes that, just as in the theory of Bohm and Vigier, the particle is subject to constant fluctuations as a result of interaction with a hidden "subquantum medium." Hence, the particle passes from one streamline to another, and thereby possesses the randomness of position that gives atomic phenomena their nondeterminate, statistical property. De Broglie emphasizes however that, "In the Theory of the Double Solution the particle occupies at every instant a position in the wave which is unknown but which exists, and hence the uncertainty Δx." [23]

De Broglie and his associates are continuing the development of his theory, many aspects of which have already been given careful mathematical formulation. With respect, however, to its acceptance by physicists, the same comments which we made about the work of Bohm and Vigier may be applied. The success of the present quantum theory in giving prediction and understanding for observed physical processes has been so great, and Niels Bohr did the work so well of leading physicists to a new conception of the natural world on its atomic level, that relatively few physicists are today concerned with possible defects in the basic assumptions of quantum theory. Indeterminism, superposition of states, complementarity of different modes of description, inability to give detailed and complete space–time description: these are taken as elements of our new knowledge of nature on the microscopic level, and in the opinion of most physicists only a striking achievement in understanding or prediction is likely to justify a change from the now-established orthodox quantum theory.

[22] *Ibid.*, p. 46.
[23] *Ibid.*, pp. 58–59.

I believe that one can with good reason maintain that quantum theory, with its currently accepted interpretation, does give us a more accurate account of the atomic level of the natural world than could be given by a physics that was developed within the conceptual framework of the classical, prequantum physics. It does not follow, however, that one should dogmatically insist, as some enthusiastic supporters seem to do, that the Copenhagen Interpretation gives us a final doctrine for quantum physics. With respect, for example, to the renunciation of detailed space–time description of atomic wave–particle phenomena, the point can be made that our very use of wave concepts and our ascription of wave properties implies a detailed space–time phenomenon; for, a wave form is indeed a particular kind of space–time form. It is hardly satisfactory, then, to say that in working with the wave–particle entities of nature we cannot have detailed space–time knowledge, and yet tacitly employ such knowledge in the inferring of wave properties for the entities.

We see another clear instance of inadequacy in current quantum theory in the discussion of observation. The indeterminism which comes with quantum physics appears to be well supported by physical knowledge, as well as by more general philosophical arguments; and, with indeterminism we of necessity must accept the dependence of our knowledge of events on the observer's measurement and awareness of events. However, we have seen in our discussion of quantum-mechanical measurement that this dependence has brought a tendency towards metaphysical subjectivism into quantum theory. The spirit of science and scientists, on the contrary, is overwhelmingly in favor of a metaphysical realism which asserts the existence of the natural world, independent of man's efforts to know it. The particular way in which our experimental study of quantum-level natural processes affects those processes does need clarification, and we can hope that possibly understanding of such interactions may lead to elucidation for problems of consciousness in living organisms. But the quantum-theory problem of the relation between observer and object should be considered without any implication, in the structure of the theory, that study of nature is the condition of the existence of nature.

It hardly seems likely, however, that improvements in the conceptual framework of quantum theory will come as a result of speculative attempts to return to a classical or quasi-classical framework. What we have already gained, with our established quantum constructs, is an immense deepening and enrichment of our understanding of nature. It would seem in the light of the historical past of physics, that yet further understanding will be built on an acceptance of changes in basic constructs for that microphysical nature which provides the interaction entities for studying the macroscopic world, and, that further developments will very likely be in a direction rather more away from than back to the constructs of prequantum physics. Also, judging again from the history of physics, one can say that quite possibly further elucidation will not come from direct efforts on the puzzling aspects of quantum theory, but rather from studies that initially appear to be on specific problems of an altogether different kind.

12

Atomic Finitude in Nature

1   HYPOTHETICAL OTHER WORLDS

THERE is a theme of speculation about nature that is centered in the idea that there is an infinite hierarchy of spatial worlds, with each elemental physical entity of one level being an effective total universe of still smaller entities. This theme is well illustrated by the following conjectures reported as having been made by the philosopher Alfred N. Whitehead: " 'Our notions of physical dimension,' assented Whitehead, 'are absurdly arbitrary. It doesn't strike one as at all impossible that the smallest pebble might contain within it a universe as complex as the one we know, and that the universe or universes which we have recently begun to apprehend may be as minute in the scale of what lies beyond as that in the pebble to the one we know; or that the vastness might be as much greater in the opposite direction—the direction of what we consider the infinitely small.' " [1] In another conversation we are told, " 'From what science has discovered about the infinitely small and the infinitely vast, the size of our bodies is almost totally irrelevant. In this little mahogany stand'— he touched it with his hand—'may be civilizations as complex and diversified in scale as our own; and up there, the heavens, with all their vastness, may be only a minute strand of tissue in the body of a being in the scale of which all our universes are as a trifle.' " [2]

Whitehead is reported as explicitly suggesting that the hierarchy of universes is an infinite one. Thus, " 'I see no reason to suppose that the air about us and heavenly spaces over us may not be peopled by intelligences, or entities, or forms of life, as unintelligible to us as we are to insects; and—who knows?—perhaps the nebulae are sentient entities and what we can see of them are their bodies . . . . My point is, that we are part of an infinite series

---

[1] *Dialogues of Alfred North Whitehead*, as recorded by Lucien Price (New York, Mentor Books, 1956), p. 278. It is to be emphasized that these are nontechnical notes made from casual conversations with Whitehead and not statements deliberately written by him.
[2] *Ibid.*, p. 294.

and since the series *is* infinite, we had better take account of that fact, and admit into our thinking these infinite possibilities.' " [3]

The notion that the complex structure of the natural world might be expected on various levels of magnitude is a quite obvious one, and perhaps it gains support in the natural similarities of pattern, as between the solar system and the atom, or between galactic "dust" clouds and terrestrial atmospheric clouds. Occasionally one finds the idea suggested in technical physics discussions.[4]

In a somewhat different manner, Isaac Newton suggested that God may have created worlds with altogether different properties than those we find in our natural world. He writes at the end of Query 31 of the *Opticks*: "And since space is divisible *in infinitum*, and Matter is not necessarily in all places, it may be also allow'd that God is able to create Particles of Matter of several Sizes and Figures, and in several Proportions to Space, and perhaps of different Densities and Forces, and thereby to vary the Laws of Nature, and make Worlds of several sorts in several Parts of the Universe. At least, I see nothing of Contradiction in all this." Newton seems to be suggesting not a hierarchy of worlds of different magnitudes each successively within another, but rather separated worlds of different compositions, within the total universe. As Sir Isaac said, there is indeed nothing unreasonable ("nothing of Contradiction") in the existence of more than one kind of natural world. To date, however, we seem to have come upon no empirical evidence whatsoever in favor of such an existence. We have found a remarkable universality of natural law in all parts of the universe that have been observed. If it were otherwise, if we should find domains of nature with differing laws of nature that could not be comprehended under some yet more general law, the hopes for a coherent view of the natural world would suffer serious diminution.

In recent years, the notion of "different worlds" has been developed by Denys H. Wilkinson, and also has been discussed by G. J. Whitrow.[5] Wilkinson proposes that the universes of different physical entities might actually interpenetrate each other, and thus exist in the same spatial regions. He argues that there might be complete noninteraction between the elements of one universe and those of any other. We, therefore, could be completely unaware of any natural world other than the one we observe and study, even though other and different worlds were intermingled within our own. Or, Wilkinson suggests, through some common but elusive interaction, we might come to discern one or more of these other interpenetrating worlds.

The possibility of "orders of nature" quite different from our own is, of course, not one that can be summarily dismissed. It seems contrary to the significance of natural science, however, that there should be an entire world altogether different from our own and yet intermingled with it. The discovery

---

[3] *Ibid.*, p. 193.
[4] For example, see J. Barnothy, *Bulletin of the American Physical Society*, 8, 536 (1963).
[5] D. H. Wilkinson, *The Listener*, 64, 96 (21 July 1960); G. J. Whitrow, *The Monist*, 47, 77 (1962).

of new physical entities and associated fields is, of course, a part of the history of science, and we may well expect that entities at present undiscovered will yet be found. But newly discovered aspects of the physical world have always been found to fit into the nature we already know: to be a part of it and continuous with it. Further, in the extreme case, to hypothesize a natural domain with which we cannot interact is to suggest a realm which is in principle unknowable, and beyond the ken of scientific investigation. We may imaginatively construct any domain of being that we like, but we are not concerning ourselves with the natural world of existing things unless we relate that domain to possible effects on our world of known (or *possibly* known) entities.

2　LIMITS ON THE INFINITELY SMALL

Let us return to the assumption of an infinite hierarchy of worlds, as expressed by Whitehead. This idea does have a certain credibility as an immediate extrapolation from experience, just because, as we have noted, there is some recurrence of pattern in nature, extending from the very largest to the very smallest known magnitudes. In our discussions of cosmology we have seen that there is no certainty of any finite spatial limit for the universe, and hence it is conceivable that there is an infinite series of worlds, of increasing scales of magnitude beyond our own. The Olbers' paradox considerations, however, do place certain limits on the hierarchy. It is a consequence of the paradox, we recall, that at least one of the following conditions obtain for the universe: (i) it is effectively finite in past time (perhaps oscillatory); (ii) it is spatially finite; (iii) it is expanding in such a way that if it is spatially infinite, radiation does not reach us from all stellar sources within it. We seem to find the expansion described in condition (iii), and hence the universe may be spatially infinite. We cannot rule out, then, the possibility that we are part of an expanding hierarchy—that is, of a total universe, of many worlds each successively larger in scale than our own, and all expanding in the required manner. We should expect eventually to find evidence, if our universe is hierarchial in this manner, that there is a continuing series of structures: that galaxies combine to form groups (there is indeed some indication of this), the groups are combined into super-groups, and so on. And, always, the hierarchy must have an expansion which prevents our being overwhelmed by the radiation from the massive amounts of matter in the worlds of higher levels of magnitude. Even a star of our world would, presumably, be no more than an atom in relative size, for the world next larger in the hierarchy. The bodies of that world would, however, apparently have to be expanding, since our galaxies, say, which presumably would be constituent elements of one of the bodies, are in mutual recessional motion (and must be, to avoid Olbers' paradox in the spatially and temporally infinite hierarchy).

If there are worlds altogether beyond our stellar universe in magnitude, it would seem that we might have had more evidence of them than has been found so far. But we shall leave the question of their existence as a speculative one that cannot be definitively settled at present. Turning to the possible existence of worlds on a smaller scale than our own, we are able to come to a much firmer conclusion. It is true that purely mathematical considerations of space would allow the possibility of an infinite series of smaller worlds, but we shall see that the established principles of quantum physics forbid such a series (or even *one* universe of a spatial magnitude much smaller than our own).

Mathematically we could argue for the existence of the infinite hierarchy as follows. Suppose our observed natural world to contain n entities e_1, as, for example, atoms; these are combined in various ways to give the complex world that we know. Next, we assume that each of these entities, e_1, in turn contains n entities e_2. The e_2 entities are assumed to be able to form a world, as complex as ours, for *each* of the e_1 entities. In accordance with the notion of an infinite series of successive smaller worlds, we further assume that each e_2 contains n entities e_3, and these form a complex universe within each e_2. The e_3 entities each contain n entities e_4, and so on. We see, then, that since there are n entities labeled e_{j+1} within each entity e_j, where $j = 1, 2, 3, \ldots$, and since j numbers continue indefinitely (since we have an infinite series of worlds), the total number of entities of all j values must be

$$n \cdot n \cdot n \cdot n \cdot n \cdot n \cdot n \cdot \cdots = n^{\aleph_0}.$$

Now, it can be shown[6] that

$$n^{\aleph_0} = 2^{\aleph_0} = \aleph_1,$$

and we recall that $\aleph_1$ is the first nondenumerable infinite number. The quantity n may be any integer greater than one, in the above equation. Even if n, the number of entities e_{j+1} in each entity e_j, is the denumerable infinity $\aleph_0$ we have the same result as for a finite n. That is, it may also be shown[6] that

$$\aleph_0^{\aleph_0} = \aleph_1.$$

The hierarchy of worlds extending infinitely through successively smaller magnitudes requires, then, that there be a set of points of cardinality $\aleph_1$. With this available number of points, we could provide sufficient entities to give the required complexity of the infinite hierarchy, assuming that an entity could be associated in one–one correspondence with each mathematical point. Our discussions of Chapter 6 have shown us that there is a set of points with cardinal number $\aleph_1$ in any finite volume of space. So, from a mathematical point of view there is no objection, apparently, to the hypothesis of the infinite hierarchy.

[6] See, e.g., A. A. Fraenkel, *Abstract Set Theory* (Amsterdam, North-Holland Publishing Co., 1961), p. 116.

But we know (as has already been emphasized in our discussion of steady-state cosmology) that physically there cannot be an atom at every mathematical point of space. We cannot even have a denumerable set of particles with cardinal number $\aleph_0$ in a finite volume, if every particle has a finite volume. This means that if the volume per particle is any number greater than zero, no matter how small, there cannot be an infinite set of particles in the volume. Mathematically we can express this fact by assigning a volume V/N to each particle in volume V. By making N a very large number, the volume per particle, $v = V/N$, can be made very small. But if the total number of particles n in V is infinite, n may always be made as large as desired. The calculated net volume of the particles, nv, is

$$nV/N = (n/N)V,$$

and since n can always be made larger than N, we calculate a volume greater than the assumed volume V. We come, therefore, to a contradiction in our assumption of an infinite number of particles.

The supporter of the existence of a hierarchy of smaller worlds might wish to answer the above argument in one of two ways. First, he might contend that entities of the worlds that are smaller than our own world could be mathematical points of zero volume. I believe, however, that in urging this argument one would have called upon a realm that goes beyond that of the natural world. The argument requires, it is to be noted, not particles of volume $v = V/N$, where v is as small as desired (and N therefore as large as desired, with V finite) ; rather, since we are not to have $n > N$, it requires that N be actually infinite, and hence $v = V/N$ be actually zero. The particles, then, have zero extension, and therefore zero content of any quantity like mass or energy which is commonly associated with a particle *or* a field. But we have no physical constructs based on experience which we can associate with the presumed zero-volume particles. It appears, then, that the hypothetical small-scale world made up of such particles is not a world that can be regarded as a continuation or extrapolation of our natural world.

The second answer to the criticism that there cannot be an infinite number of subparticles in finite volume V might be to accept the criticism, but to argue that we can still have worlds smaller than our own. We need not have an infinite hierarchy of such worlds, but still there may be a series of one or more such worlds. Since we can make N as large as we like, and still have finite particle volume $v = V/N$, if we assert the existence not of an infinite number of particles in V, but only of a very large number, n, we can by requiring that $N > n$ avoid any contradiction with respect to the net volume of all the n particles in V.

In considering the possibility that there are subworlds of smaller scale than our own, consisting not of an infinite but of a finite number of very small entities in a finite volume V, we are able to utilize the physical content of quantum physics. We recall that the Uncertainty Principle places a limit on the spatial region within which a particle may be localized, a limit that is defined in terms of the momentum available to the particle. Thus, since $\Delta x \cdot \Delta p \geqslant h/4\pi$, we have,

$$\Delta x \geq h/(4\pi \cdot \Delta p),$$

where Δp is the uncertainty in the x-component of momentum that must be associated with the extension Δx within which the particle is to be confined. Since the particle may have any momentum value within the range Δp (in the x-direction), we may regard Δp as the range of the x-component of the momentum of the particle. We see from the mathematical form of the Uncertainty Relation that if Δx is to be small, Δp must be correspondingly large, in an inverse ratio.

Now, the kinetic energy E of a mass m may be written $\frac{1}{2}mv^2 = p^2/2m$, where v is velocity, and momentum $p = mv$. Or, taking account of relativistic effects, the total energy (kinetic plus rest mass) W of a particle may be shown to be given by

$$W = \sqrt{p^2c^2 + m^2c^4},$$

where m is the rest mass of the particle, and c is the speed of light. Now, either of these equations tells us that as p becomes large the energy becomes large. Hence if we wish to limit the possible localization region of a particle to a small Δx, we must have a large available energy. If we do not have a large energy, we can have only a small Δp. With a small Δp, Δx cannot be small, by the basic uncertainty relation between Δx and Δp.

The requirement of a large possible momentum range for a closely confined particle is readily intelligible in terms of the wave nature of matter and the superposition properties of waves. A single wave has a unique wavelength, and hence, by the de Broglie equation, $\lambda = h/mv$, a single momentum associated with it. Such a wave, however, extends indefinitely along, say, a hypothetical x-axis. If waves of various λ values are superimposed we are able to form a wave packet which has nonnegligible amplitude in only a limited region. It is, then, only in this region of width Δx that the wave particle may be localized. But because a whole range of waves, of varying λ values, are required to form the packet, there must be a large range of available p values (associated with the λ's). The Uncertainty Principle is a statement of just the precise relations between Δx and Δp that come with the formation of the wave packet and its limitations on the region of possible localization of the particle.

Numerically, we find that very large momenta, and hence energies, are required for a Δx that is small by atomic standards. Thus, the smallest atomic nucleus, a single proton, has a radius of about 1.2×10^{-13} cm. Then, if we take $\Delta x = 2.4 \times 10^{-13}$ cm, $\Delta p = h/(4\pi \cdot \Delta x) \simeq 2 \times 10^{-15}$ g·cm/sec. So, any particle which is to be localized within an extent equivalent to the diameter of a proton, even in one dimension, must have an available momentum p of this amount. The particle must have an energy, then, of $pc = 2 \times 10^{-15} \times 3 \times 10^{10} = 6 \times 10^{-5}$ ergs. (We use the relativistic expression for W, with neglect of the m^2c^4 term; we assume that the mass would be small, since we are considering hypothetical particles in a sub-observable world; and also, that because the masses are small the velocities that give the required momentum would be in the relativistic region.) Now, this is a very large energy on the atomic scale; in terms of the electron volt (eV) commonly used to express elementary particle energies, it is about 4×10^7 eV. An electron, the smallest of the mass particles that we do observe, is never found to have such high energies in nuclear decay processes, and its rest-mass energy, mc^2, is only 0.51×10^6 eV. And yet, we are only considering the localization of a particle within a proton diameter, in one dimension. If, as Whitehead speculated, there is to be a subworld, as complex and diversified as our own, in a relatively small region of our world, there would have to be structure and differentiation that requires localization within diameters much smaller than 10^{-13} cm. We justify this assertion by pointing out that we know fairly well the structure of matter down to dimensions of about 10^{-13} cm; the complexities that we have found are not to be underestimated, but the patterns and structure which emerge from this complexity are just those that give us our observable world. A presumed subworld, comparable to our own, must then have its structure and complexity within the atomic entities that constitute our known world. It would be for localization and differentiation within those entities that the large momenta and energies which we calculate from the Uncertainty Principle would be required.

The energy required for confinement of a particle in a given volume has long been a standard quantum-theoretic argument against the existence of the electron as a constituent of atomic nuclei. As has been noted, the observed energies of electrons in nuclear processes are not sufficient to allow localization within a nuclear volume, even when we take into account the rest-mass energy. (Electrons are emitted from nuclei in certain radioactive processes; we believe that the electron leaves virtually as soon as it is formed in the nucleus.) Any presumed subelectron, maintaining a given position so as to contribute to a structure on a subnuclear level, would have even less rest mass than an electron; hence, even less energy would be available for the even greater energy that would be required for confinement within an even smaller volume than that of the nucleus.

The Uncertainty Principle does allow very short-time existence of particles in closely localized regions, with an increase in energy-mass of the particle as the duration of its existence is decreased. What is a "very short time" by our macroscopic measure could be "long" in a subdomain. But these "virtual particles" that exist by the grace of the quantum uncertainty relation between time and energy are, to the best of our knowledge, subject to statistical fluctuations. We know of no microscopic ordered structure among the particles, comparable to that found on the macroscopic level. If we did, we would have manifestations of that subquantum determinism for which evidence is so conspicuously lacking in quantum physics.

It might be proposed that there are stores of energy in space itself which can bring about stable localization of tiny entities into an undiscerned subworld structure. There is, however, no evidence whatsoever in favor of such a proposal. It is true that we no longer regard space as an empty, passive vessel—a simple property of pure extension in which matter moves and exerts forces, but with no interaction with the space. The facts that space supports physical fields and that particles can be produced out of these fields, taken together with the geometric variations which general relativity theory requires, give us a conception of space as an active participant in physical processes. Nonetheless, we never find occurrences in space without energy having been supplied as required by the occurrences. A gamma ray, for example, will produce an electron and a positron out of "empty" space, in the neighborhood of some other charged particle whose response can insure momentum conservation for the process. But this "pair production" will only occur if the gamma ray does itself possess energy equal to the rest-mass energy of the particles that are produced, plus any kinetic energy that is given to them or to other neighboring particles. We have never found empty space alone to possess energy.

In this connection it may be pointed out that the various short-lived elementary particles which have been discovered by physicists in recent years give no support to a proposal for a world of subentities far below the scale of magnitude of our own. The array of unstable mesons and hyperons which have been discovered have not been commonly "found" in nature, harbingers of a perhaps much richer realm of natural entities. Rather, they have been "made," in connection with interactions between atomic particles and protons or electrons that have been artificially accelerated to very high energies. The significance of these various elementary particles is not as entities dispersed throughout nature, but rather as modes of energy which may give clues to the properties of matter and the fields associated with it. The impressive magnitude of the high-energy particle accelerators which have been built for study of the various exotic elementary particles (as well as of the common constituents of atoms and radiation) is an indication of the great energy which must be given to an atomic volume of space, so to speak, if an elementary particle is to be formed there.

We can conclude that the principles of quantum mechanics forbid the existence of localized particles which could be formed into regular structures of complexity similar to the structures of our macroscopic world, but on a scale of magnitude such that 10^{-12} cm, say, would be a large dimension. There is not the energy present in nature to permit the specification of locality for entities in so small a domain; instead with the energies that are available, the hypothetical subentities would necessarily be spread out over

larger regions, and therefore could not be formed into the patterned structures of a presumed miniscule world.[7]

One might persist and argue that the entities that make up a world
that is of a magnitude different from our own are not necessarily localized
entities; that instead of forming definite, stable patterns or structures, the
constituent entities are diffuse, with relations to each other that are independent of having localization in space. Indeed, it could be argued that
very small mass (or mass-energy) could then be characteristic of these
entities, and a factor in their existing relatively undiscerned in our natural
world. With this turn in the proposal for other worlds we come again,
however, to the notion of interpenetrating natural domains, more or less
independent of each other, as discussed by Wilkinson. If the independence
is complete, then of course the proposed world is beyond our nature and
beyond our natural science. If the independence is not complete, we should
expect in some way to observe the entities, or to find evidence of their
existence in their interaction effects on our observed world.

It hardly seems credible that a complex domain of entities which have
any very considerable energy, either as particles or as waves, exists as part
of our natural world and has not been detected. In any event, if any such
entities do exist, and are in interaction with our observable natural entities,
they then are not entities that constitute a complex subworld analogous
to our own; for, we have seen, they cannot be of a scale of magnitude
smaller than that of our natural world. In a more realistic vein of speculation, it seems quite appropriate to conceive that there may be fairly low-
energy entities (and, of course, they may be "waves" or "particles", depending upon their situation) which we have not yet detected in nature. The
natural processes of biological systems, for example, including those of
highly complex nervous systems, might well involve modes of energy and
interaction that are not yet within the ken of our science. But speculations
such as these are for the natural world we study, and not for the hypothetical
other worlds.

3   AT THE END OF A SEARCH

Until a few hundred years ago, man directly perceived no more of the
world than his senses brought to him. The Greek atomists introduced speculation about a minute structure, far below the direct evidence of the senses,
and many lines of argument indicate the existence of particulate bits of

---

[7] Current work that physicists are doing on the *internal* structure of protons and neutrons
(nucleons) is not counter to the conclusions we have reached. The nucleon structure that
is inferred from observation is characterized by rapid fluctuations, with appearance and
disappearance of virtual elementary particles (as previously discussed), in accord with
the Heisenberg Uncertainty Principle. For a review discussion see L. L. Foldy, "The
Structure of Nucleons," *Physics Today*, 18, 26 (September, 1965).

matter, too small to be seen. But until the microscope came into use, there was no compelling reason to believe that there was a world of living entities different from those of ordinary unaided observation. With the microscope, however, a new order of biological existence became known to man. Nature could then be observed as being far more complex, and more extensive in its range, than had hitherto been realized. Further evidence accumulated, too, for the atomic nature of matter, and in this century we have learned how to see the paths and reflections of individual atoms. The complex world of molecular and atomic structure is smaller than that of the ordinary one-celled animals, by a difference about an order of magnitude greater than that between man and the one-celled organism.

It might naturally have been thought—and the speculations which we have been discussing show that some have so thought—that scientific work would continue to disclose new realms, with ever smaller dimensions. We have seen, however, that the quantum theory tells us that this is not to be the case. Rather, we have come to a limit of the very small in nature, and there is no yet smaller microscopic structure to be found: no further complex atoms within atoms, and no complete biological realm as small to the amoeba as the amoeba is to us. The space–time–motion–energy properties of nature, we have found, simply do not allow a continuing decrease in size, without limit, in the specific details of natural structures with the pattern of organized structures in our macroscopic world.

The limit that quantum physics has found can give us a certain re-assurance that the universe may be comprehensible. One of the hopes for a study of the completeness of science is to be able to learn whether or not scientists can in any way assert that they have learned the salient aspects of nature. We have suggested earlier that nature may be so intricate and so far-reaching that we may never be able to apprehend any limit of it. But now we know that in respect to its smallness of magnitude nature is not without end. There is a limit to its minuteness of stable structure, and we have apparently discerned that limit. The fineness of detail that does in fact exist is virtually beyond our imagination—the immense detail, say, in a single green leaf, and within it the millions of articulated living cells, again the millions of molecules in each cell, each molecule in turn a certain complex spatial structure of atoms, and then each atom with its own world of energy-ordered electrons and closely bound nuclear particles. But, we know we cannot go much farther. The atom is what it is, without another universe still in it; and space, though potentially the source and carrier of any of nature's parts, is empty when no energy is being supplied to it. Our science can be complete with respect to the extent of nature, on the microscopic level, for nature has shown herself not to be able to repeat in a series of ever-smaller magnitudes.

It may be well to repeat that physicists are far from regarding their work on the quantum level of nature as being finished. There are, of course, myriad detailed problems of nuclear, atomic, and molecular structure yet to be studied, as well as the unanswered questions about molecular biological structure. And, as we have noticed, even though we can no longer ask questions on the quantum level in the terms of classical space–time–energy description, we hope in other ways to gain understanding of quantum-level phenomena. Nature, we believe, is one: physicists hope that studies of fields and transformations by use of high-energy elementary particles, in realms where we are far from the "classical" physics of everyday observations and only quantum-relativistic theories can guide us, will give insights into basic properties of all nature, even on a cosmological scale. And yet, quantum theory has indeed taught us that certain questions need no longer be asked.

We may borrow a simile used by Heisenberg.[8] He points out that people, with notions of the world's being disk-shaped, once asked about what one would find "at the end of the world." But after the voyages of Columbus and Magellan it no longer made sense to ask such questions, even though much of the earth was still unexplored. Similarly, Heisenberg writes, we must now renounce the questions about "objective happenings in space and time" that were asked before the days of quantum theory. One must temper this suggestion by remembering that in the macroscopic world the older physics is still valid; but we can suggest that quantum theory has made questions about what is the next smaller world to be discovered as meaningless as are geographic questions about what indications there are of an "end of the earth." We can agree, too, with a suggestion by Heisenberg that quantum physics does not at all bring an end to science but gives a better basis for further science; he writes (translated from this same paper), "The hope that the whole life of man would be understood by the principles of classical physics is no more proper than the hope of the traveller that he would be able to solve all riddles when he reached the ends of the earth."

The problem of "how can the flat earth end" was solved by man's learning that in nature there is no such problem, because our spherical planet has no ends. Likewise, the solution to the problem of the infinite divisibility of matter has come with a change in basic constructs, that is, with our discerning that nature does not allow a projection of the properties of macroscopic bodies to indefinitely small magnitudes. For, when we study those very atomic entities by which the macroscopic world presents itself to us, we can use no tools other than these same or similar atomic entities, and natural behavior in their domain is not to be described in terms of the same categories of space, time, and motion that we use for bodies of larger magnitude.

Nature has solved a problem, of the composition of the entities of smallest magnitude, that seemed difficult and all but hopeless to us; but the solution came not in the terms in which we had been asking it. We can expect that it is thus with other basic scientific problems that today seem

[8] W. Heisenberg, *Naturwissenschaften*, **22**, 669 (1934).

insoluble: we have not learned the correct properties of nature in terms of which they can be solved. The new properties that we find for quantum phenomena do in their own way raise novel problems, even though the classical problems of infinite microscopic complexity melt away. How to solve the new problems is a fresh and different task. But we may rest for a time on the shore, and appreciate the limit that the abundantly confirmed ideas of quantum theory do place on patterns of increasing fineness in natural objects.

13

Completeness and Limitation in Science

WE can now look back over the various aspects of completeness that we have considered, and attempt to sum up the possibilities for completeness in knowing and understanding our natural world.

1   THE PRAGMATIC DEFINITION

Although we might in a careless way speak of knowing everything about an aspect of nature, we do in practice quickly come to appreciate the limits on the number of detailed facts that can be established and recorded. Excepting for the inherent limitations that exist on the quantum level, we always find a possibility both for refining and extending the descriptive knowledge that we have with respect to a given domain of nature. But we often deem such further knowledge as trivial. In fact, we generally do not want to know "everything," but only that which will, in the main, satisfy our curiosity about a group of phenomena, or will give the information needed for some manner of control or prediction. Hence, we may regard a branch of science as essentially complete, just because it has been carried far enough to satisfy our purposes.

I have presented the pragmatic criterion of completeness in Section 2 of Chapter 3. Much of the change in interests—one could even say in fashions— that occurs among scientists from decade to decade can be understood, I believe, in terms of this simple criterion. New techniques of experimental study and new developments of theory open up possibilities for fresh exploration and understanding: as a consequence, research workers then tend to carry out their work along the lines of those possibilities. The basic motivation may primarily be either one of advance of knowledge, or one of response to some need that can be satisfied by application of the knowledge. When the new field of study has been explored sufficiently that it no longer commands strong curiosity or interest, scientists of high creativity will tend to look to another domain of research. Those who continue to work in the field may nonetheless do useful and important work in adding various details, and among them will be those who seek information for purposes of specific application.

I have noted, too, that a field of inquiry may sometimes be discarded, as if it were effectively complete, not because there is no interest in it, but because there seems to be nothing of scientific significance that can be achieved in pursuing it. From both a theoretical and a practical point of view, for example, the gravitational attraction between bodies is of immense interest; and yet, comparatively few physicists work on the problem of gravity as such, because not very many have fruitful new ideas or methods to bring to bear on the problem. Scientists are generally pragmatic, both in the sense that we have been using, of judging practical completeness in terms of how much information is desired, and also in the sense of wishing to achieve new results as a consequence of their work. Continued discussion of problems for which there is no apparent method of solution has not been the way of science; indeed, historians of science have made the point that in their focusing of attention on solvable problems scientists have gained successes that would not have come in the philosophical tradition of sustained contemplation of all questions.

It would not be fair to scientists to characterize them as questioning only where answers are to be found, but clearly there is a desire on their part to work where new information or understanding can be gained. This pragmatic point of view has resulted in an extension of science to many aspects of inanimate and animate nature, with scientists frequently tarrying not very long at the domains they have first discerned. But even so there are continuing desires for detailed knowledge in the various special fields, and we must bear in mind that completeness of science for a natural philosopher, with respect to a given domain, may be far different from completeness, for example, for a pharmacologist or a chemical engineer, with respect to that same domain.

E. P. Wigner has discussed the question of the limits of science from what I would take to be essentially a pragmatic approach.[1] He raises the question of how far the complexity of a science serves as a barrier to further study and work in the science. Also, he asks if there may not be changes in emphasis away from science as the best way to improve the welfare of mankind, with accompanying loss of enthusiasm by people for scientific work. The discussions in the next chapter will have some relevance to this latter question, and both of the issues of Wigner's paper well deserve detailed examination.

2   IMPOSSIBILITY OF COMPLETE DESCRIPTION

Aside from the pragmatic reasons for not attempting complete description, there are inherent limitations on achieving such a description. These

[1] Eugene P. Wigner, "The Limits of Science," *Proceedings of the American Philosophical Society*, 94, 422–427 (1950).

arise both from the properties of our universe and from properties that are characteristic of the act of describing; in their general form, the limitations are independent of the particular physical constructs which we have found in nature.

Limitations arise from the properties of the universe, in that nature is so very rich and complex, possibly even infinite in its number of distinguishable entities. We find, then, that the multiplicity of facts about entities and their interrelationships is apparently endless. If the universe does contain an infinite number of entities, say, for example, a set of stars with cardinal number $\aleph_0$, then the number of facts of relations between the stars would be at least the noncountable cardinal number $\aleph_1$, since there is that number of different subsets among a set with cardinality $\aleph_0$. (The relations among the members of each subset of stars would be a fact of nature, although probably a trivial one indeed for most subsets.)

In practice we can include many, even an infinite number, of individual descriptive facts in a single statement, as, for example, "all sodium atoms in their ground state have 11 extranuclear electrons." We might, therefore, expect that by use of appropriate general statements we could in principle achieve a complete description, at least of a finite universe. But even though one could maintain that the limitation which arises from the multiplicity of actual entities, events, and relationships is not necessarily insuperable, a limitation does arise from the descriptive act itself, and this limitation is one that is logically necessary. Any description of a part of nature is itself an element of nature, and therefore forms a new aspect of nature to be described. We have seen (Chapter 3) that we therefore have an infinite regress in attempting to achieve a complete description. The process of describing always adds more constituents of the world to be described, and therefore necessarily constitutes a singularity which has escaped any projected complete description. We saw that this feature of descriptive science argues against any concept of hypothetical complete self-awareness by the universe.

In science the describer of nature is man, and man's scientific activity is itself a part of nature. We can know, from the consideration of the logical impossibility of complete description, that nature and man's relation to it as describer can never be completely described in science. It could be that this limitation is a trivial one; that we can describe nature, and man as part of nature, and that our only nondescribable singularity is the scientific description which we thereby achieve. To describe that description, and then in turn to describe the description of that description, and so on, might be a regress that is of little concern to us. We could well be content to allow scientific description just to be; for, if our science adequately described man in his relations to the nature of which he is a part, there would be little interest in making explicit description of that science, etc.

But in fact we seem to be finding that on the quantum level specific events of interaction have an effect on what we find nature to be (aside from the obvious dependence of any scientific knowledge on the existence of sentient beings who observe nature and formulate knowledge). There are in the descriptions that involve interactions among atomic-level entities *uncontrollable and unpredictable quantum energy transfers which prevent man from gaining precise and universal description of nature in the manner to be expected from studies of macroscopic phenomena.* The descriptive act itself, then, has become one of interest, and also a source of descriptive incompleteness in science, because we are not able in any significant and general way to describe that act and thereby remove the incompleteness of the quantum-level description.

Not only is each individual quantum interaction an unpredictable event, but also we have found that in quantum physics nature does not allow the infinite regress that we hypothesized as arising with the series, description of the act of description, and so forth. There is no further possibility of making a description of the quantum-level act of description, for we have no other entities than those of the quantum-level that can be used in such a description. So, although we conceptually propose a nonending chain of descriptions, we in fact find that on the atomic level we have exhausted the natural descriptive possibilities with respect to detailed events or structures. Nature seems to stop the regress by being so constituted that we have come to entities whose interaction cannot be generally described and predicted, and for which there are no additional descriptive entities. How the act of primary description does occur, such that we become aware of the entities, is perhaps a question interwoven with the question of what are the properties of the basic entities that cause them so effectively to elude our concepts of physical behavior derived from experience with macroscopic bodies.

It is to be emphasized that it is on the physical level that the chain of description stops; we find that successively more inclusive descriptions of an initial description (interaction between observer and object of description) cannot be achieved, because even the initial quantum-physics description (interaction) cannot be described with customary macroscopic completeness. One could construct an unending verbal regress with respect to large-scale aspects of a descriptive situation. Thus, I could write a description of a physicist's measuring a wavelength for radiation from a given source, and then write a description of the writing of the description, and so on. But if we wished physically to describe the initial act of description, in terms of the movements made by the physicist, and the interactions between himself, his apparatus, and the radiation, we would soon come to the quantum-level restrictions, as well as to the psycho-physical problem (relation between physical events and thought) which is basic in the problems of understanding description. Of course, the attempt to make this description would itself be material for a physical description; but, since the initial description is limited by the quantum restrictions, the description of the first describer, and his interaction with the physicist, would be doubly subject to these limitations.

I have discussed (Chapter 10, Section 4) the fact that the quantum restrictions become significant in studies where elementary physical entities bring information about themselves. We have here a kind of self-description, and we see in the relevant quantum limitation on description a physical analogue to the necessary incompleteness that remains where any scientific description of a domain has not itself been described. This motif of the incompleteness associated with the descriptive act appears also, we have seen (Chapter 5), on the formal, verbal level of logic and mathematics. Gödel's incompleteness proof shows that mathematical propositions which may be interpreted as referring to their own provability are incomplete, in that they may be neither proved nor disproved in the system in which they are constructed. The existence of these self-referring propositions is a singularity that prevents formal systems from being complete, in the sense that all of their propositions may be proved or disproved, just as analogously, the quantum-mechanical limitations on elementary atomic entities prevent our being able to gain a complete self-description by these entities of their behavior.

3   THEORY AND COMPLETENESS

Our knowledge of the natural world gains coherence and manageability through its formulation into a theoretical structure. Scientific theory is based on empirical findings, but we have also emphasized (Chapter 2) that the experimental–observational statements of science are not independent of theory. We must regard theoretical and empirical assertions as two interdependent constituents of science, even though we can focus attention on one with a partial exclusion of the other.

We can judge completeness of a theory with respect to a given kind or domain of natural phenomena. If the desired descriptive statements relevant to the phenomena may be deduced as consequences of the theory, we regard the theory as adequately complete (Chapter 4, Sections 2 and 4). The form of a theory is, ideally, that of a strict axiomatic system. Although in practice scientific theories have rarely been so presented, many parts of current science are capable of being given an axiomatic formulation, and may be referred to as latently deductive (Chapter 4, Section 2). The consistency property of a scientific theory, like that of completeness, may be judged by reference to the empirical statements in the domain of the theory; this procedure is in accordance with the canons for consistency that have been developed by logicians (Chapter 4, Section 3).

Theories in physics are usually presented and to some extent developed without a concomitant statement of a large number of the descriptive facts that are necessary consequences from the theory. An elegant and succinct description of a domain of nature, in terms of general, abstracted properties, may therefore be achieved. The theory is, at the same time, available as a description of the various specific physical situations which are within the purview of its general terms.

Probably no other feature of science is so impressive in its contribution to our understanding of nature as is a successful theory of wide application. It is here that science seems to come closest to an ideal of completeness. In physics, mechanics and electromagnetic theory, for example, are comprehensive, rigorously deductive theories, and are virtually complete for their domains (which are, to be sure, not without limits in nature). A bringing together of two theories, so that they may have a common body of basic terms and presuppositions gives an increase in coherence, and a sense that the new unified theory is giving a more basic and universal insight into the natural properties of the universe. The unification of electromagnetic and optical phenomena in Maxwell's theory is an illustrative example.

The development of new theoretical systems that unite previously disparate systems of description provides a major path for growth in the completeness of natural science. Later, in the final chapter, I shall discuss the possibility of an inclusive unification into a single complete theory.

4   LIMITS ON SCIENTIFIC EXPLANATION

Although explanation is in part description and familiarity (Chapter 4, Section 1), scientists generally feel that for the understanding of a phenomenon they must be able to see it as a consequence of natural law. That is, it must be related to the entities and processes that have been discerned as universally occurring in nature. In terms of the structure of science, an event or phenomenon has been explained when its description has been shown to be (at least in principle) a consequence of the basic terms and assumptions of an established scientific theory. We explain a part of the natural universe, then, if any chosen event of that part is covered by a confirmed physical theory, itself consistent with other established theories.

Scientific theory has been enormously successful in giving us explanations, in the manner just indicated. And, a theory which explains also predicts events within its domain, and hence is of great value in our adjusting to events of the domain, or, in many instances, to controlling them. But we must recognize two serious limitations (Chapter 4, Section 5) on the completeness of understanding which comes with scientific theory. There is, first, the fact that a theory is always concerned with what we have referred to as a domain of nature, that is, with selected aspects of the universe. Even in physics, which is concerned with the most general aspects of natural entities, we have not as yet achieved a theory that deals with all of the properties of particles of matter in a single unified scheme. For a more special aspect of nature there is immensely greater complexity of structure, and, correspondingly, many more different separate sciences. Our own species, for example, is studied in human anatomy, physiology, biochemistry, genetics, dietetics, learning theory, group dynamics, developmental psychology, educational guidance—just to name a few relevant disciplines. We study a science pertaining to mankind and come to know something of one aspect of human structure or behavior, but can hardly thereby claim to understand humanity.

Secondly, any given theory is incomplete in the explanation that it gives, because the theory always begins with a set of assumptions. The assumed axioms or first principles may themselves be unexplained; or, if explained by reference to another theory, there will eventually be an ending of the chain in a theory whose assumptions cannot be seen as consequences of some other theory. Also, each theory must have a set of primitive terms, corresponding to some constituents of nature (as, e.g., field, space–time, electrical charge). These are constructs defined with congruence between theory and experience, and some of them are, just as with the basic axioms, without explanation. Taken together, the primitive terms may be regarded as elements of a model. Usually the model properties will not be without some similarity to models (or principles) of other parts of physics, but commonly there are also novel, underived properties for the model associated with a given theory. Ultimately, then, there are unexplained elements which are given or assumed rather than derived, in any scientific theory that we have known.

The limitation that arises from the fact that a theory is concerned only with certain kinds of properties or events of nature is ameliorated when previously separated theories are unified; we then, as has been indicated in the preceding section, gain in completeness of explanation and understanding. It is also the case that with unification of theories we generally reduce the number of unexplained principles and constructs. If all the processes and structures of nature were potentially described by some one master theory, we probably would feel justified in regarding the salient features of that theory as descriptive of the essential features of the universe. In our discussion of the possibilities for a unified theory we shall consider whether such a theory still need have unexplained primary elements.

5   COMPLETENESS AND THE NATURAL WORLD

I have emphasized on several occasions in our discussions that whether or not science achieves completeness with respect to any aspect of nature must to a major degree depend on what nature is. Certain logical restrictions on completeness, it would seem, will always remain. But if an aspect of nature that is being studied is not too complex or irregular, and can be at least indirectly observed, then significant scientific description and theory can be attained for that domain. How complex the domain may be, or how indirect the method of observation must be, and still allow a successful science to be developed, is not a question that is to be answered in any general terms. The ingenuity of theoretical and experimental scientists is impressive, and one would hesitate to lay down any criteria for deciding that a part of nature was beyond scientific study. It must be remembered, too, that the goal even for partial completeness of a science (using an essentially pragmatic definition) will change with the development of the science. New and previously unknown aspects of nature may be discerned by a science, giving entirely new goals. With the discovery of extraterrestrial radio waves, for example, the astronomer had to add a large group of phenomena for which knowledge is desirable. Much of the content of a science may be presented as a statement of what we know and what we do not know about nature, at a given point in the development of the science. An account of the elements of contemporary scientific knowledge, organized just around the question of hoped-for completeness, would indeed be of interest. It is, however, beyond the scope of this book for me to attempt any such summary. But I have discussed two fields of science which seem particularly relevant to the problem of completeness, cosmology and quantum theory.

The immensity of the universe suggests that in the cosmological problem we may face an essential aspect of nature that can never be scientifically described; that, even without an interest in most of its individual bodies, we cannot achieve a completeness which would tell us in large-scale, overall terms what is the structure and history of the universe. However, the scientific work that is now underway in cosmology does not support an attitude of despair (Chapters 7 and 8). As yet, there is not very much that can be definitely asserted, but conceivably observations that may be obtained within the next decade or two will enable us to decide what is the correct model of the cosmos. The basic question (certainly of prime importance for considerations of possible completeness of science) of whether or not the universe is infinite in extent has not even yet been answered, but here too, methods in cosmology that are now in use would, in their decision for a given cosmological model, lead to a definite answer. Our optimism should, of course, be guarded. The work of astronomers and astrophysicists could also, conceivably, bring us evidence which indicated that a solution to the cosmological problem is beyond the reach of our science; that the universe is such that it is physically impossible for us to obtain the observations that will lead to a solution.

If the universe is infinite in extent we need not necessarily conclude that we are therefore blocked by incomprehensibility and essential incompleteness in our cosmological thinking. We saw (Chapter 6) that the mathematical concept of infinity has been rigorously developed, and we can associate with an infinite number certain well-defined properties. We can thereby attain a measure of understanding and information with respect to infinite quantities of any kind: atoms, stars, parsecs, or years.

The question of an infinite past time of existence for the universe particularly concerned us and we saw that there may be certain limitations (MacMillan's Principle) on the processes of change in a universe that has existed through all of an infinite past time. Such a universe (for example, one that undergoes cyclic expansion and contraction) would not have an origin at any past time, as the infinite past sequence of time units is usually conceived. Our time measure would then be properly regarded as associated with the progressive physical changes which we observe, but would be anthropomorphic in that earlier and later would only be distinguishable within a finite time extension. Thus, we could properly speak of time flow within one expansion–contraction cycle, if the universe is cyclic in that manner. There might, however, be no process that could give physical meaning to the statement that a given cycle is earlier or later than another.

At the other extreme from cosmological magnitudes scientists have come to a limit of nature with the development of the quantum theory for microscopic entities. One can view this limit (Chapter 9) as an inevitable incompleteness, arising from properties of nature which prevent our obtaining the same kind of detailed information at the atomic level as we find for larger constituents and processes of the universe. But, it is perhaps more appropriate to the role of science as descriptive of nature to take the alternative point of view, and regard the limit as a significant completeness in science. We may then conclude that we have made explorations of the structure of the world down to that microscopic level where there is a change in elementary physical properties. The possibilities for continuous space–time description of events, precise localization of entities, and calculable determinism which we had made a part of physical science are found to disappear as we come to the level of nature where magnitudes are comparable to that of Planck's quantum of action.

The particles of matter and radiation which we observe in quantum physics describe themselves, in that they interact with our observing apparatus (Chapter 10). We have not found subentities which can interact with the particles and thereby bring description of them. I have pointed out an analogy between, (i) the inability of a scientist to describe his own descriptive acts, (ii) the incompleteness (undecidability) that is found for certain propositions, propositions of formal deductive systems, which refer to themselves, and (iii) the loss by atomic-level entities of properties that may be described in macroscopic physics. The loss is associated with the fact that the interaction events by which atomic particles are observed may not themselves be further described. I do not wish to say, however, that these characteristic features of nature on the atomic level are logically necessary consequences of the physical situation of self-description. Physical properties of nature, empirically discerned, have led us to our knowledge of quantum physics. Conceivably, there is a further substructure in nature which will enable us further to describe the acts of quantum interaction–observation, and hence restore some part or all of the prequantum descriptive possibilities. Current efforts to delineate such a structure, however, are not promising, and the established quantum physics argues against these efforts (Chapter 11).

Because of the importance of interaction between object and observer (including his apparatus) in quantum physics, with no possibility for further description of the interaction events themselves, nature on the quantum level must in part at least be defined in terms of its interaction with the observer; for, interaction-event and object are closely related, and perhaps even identical. In contrast, in nonquantum physics the interaction of the observer with nature is not regarded as in itself an element in the properties of the nature that is observed. There is, I believe, no philosophical justification for suggestions that the role of the observer in quantum physics properly implies that nature is dependent upon observation for its properties of physical existence. But, the termination of the process of further detailed description that we find with quantum phenomena indicates that with them we are approaching a ground level of being where nature can yield no further description of itself. *We see in this limit the pertinence of the analogies to the necessary incompleteness in the description by a describing mechanism and to the undecidability of the self-describing Gödelian sentence.*

6   SOME ASPECTS OF COMPLETENESS

In the opening chapter of this book I quoted a variety of statements relating to the completeness of science. These were presented simply as expressions of points of view by different scientific writers. It may now be of interest briefly to consider each of these statements in the light of the approaches to completeness that I have attempted to elucidate.

Horace Lamb, we see, corrects a notion that science gives "an account of the way things go on in the world" by pointing out that it is hopeless to give a complete description of any phenomenon. His comment is in accord with our remarks on the practical impossibility of including every possible fact in a scientific description; and, also, his speaking of a complete description as useless can be understood in terms of the pragmatic criterion that selects certain facts as desirable or needed.

Robert Lindsay refers to a quite different meaning for completeness. He sees mechanics as a successful theory because it does give, from a few principles, a general description of large-scale (i.e., mechanical) features of all matter. His reference, clearly, is to completeness as embodied in science as a deductive system. (Lindsay's statement should not be interpreted as intending to mean, however, that all large-scale, cosmological features of the universe have been deduced from mechanics; or that a specific system of masses, the solar system, for example, can be deductively described without specification of initial conditions).

Condon and Shortley are also concerned with completeness as measured by the capacity of a theory to give description of a given kind of phenomena. Specifically, they are concerned with atomic radiation at discrete wavelengths.

It is interesting that they speak of the theory as an interpretation and specify that it is in terms of a given model, with quantum-mechanical treatment. The justification given for regarding the theory as satisfactory is that it explains "at least semiquantitatively" all the known features of atomic spectra. This statement reflects the close relation, to a scientist, between a phenomenon's being explained and its description being deductively a part of a theory.

Slater's quotation is directed not to the theory of a certain group of entities, that is, atoms and their radiation, but to the quantum theory generally. But, like Condon and Shortley, he is concerned with the ability of the theory to give description. The wide range of phenomena covered is given as impressive evidence for the correctness of the quantum theory. We notice that Slater explicitly refers to the relation of mathematical deduction that exists between the theory and its descriptive consequences.

In the comment by Meggers in his review we see a scientist's interest in extending completeness, in the sense of bringing a maximum number of principles into a single deductive system. Extension of completeness in this way is extension of scientific explanation. And yet, we know that any deductive system must have primitive, underived elements. The Pauli exclusion principle, and the antisymmetric property of wavefunctions for the ordinary elementary particles of matter, are so intimately a part of quantum mechanics that one would like to see them as deduced consequences. And, perhaps some day they will be shown to follow from still more general properties of nature. But then that deduction will be in a theory which has its own elementary terms and postulates.

The requirements in the statement by Harnwell and Stephens that an adequate theory be universal and precise are not to be questioned, although these are not properties of theories that we have explicitly discussed. Universality is expected because we have found it possible to formulate scientific descriptions and theories which do not vary from time to time or place to place—that is, we have found that there are significant invariants in the natural world. Precision is wanted because we do work, particularly in the physical sciences, with quantitatively measured variables. The specification of simplicity by Harnwell and Stephens forbids theories which because of their complexity do not give a sense of understanding or do not allow calculation of consequences. In our processes of abstraction and selection in the construction of a physical theory we neglect aspects of nature which would make a theory forbiddingly complex. The fact that we can form a successful theory with the partial aspects that we use is itself a significant feature of nature. It seems to indicate, again, that there are invariants relating universal, determining elements of nature. Thus, mass and gravitational field can be abstracted from matter and space, and related in a theory which does universally describe interactions of matter in space (if electromagnetic and nuclear-force effects may be neglected). For description (for which Harnwell and Stephens also state their requirements) simplicity does of course mean selection of properties which are relevant for a theory, or for other purposes. We see again an indication that not all possible facts are wanted in descriptive science.

Darrow's statement very well tells us of the descriptive limitations of science, even for "a restricted field of nature." The pragmatic criteria for guidance of choice in description are also indicated. In the latter part of the statement we have again a reference to simplicity: to the method that we follow in science of trying to discern those constructs which will lead to an adequate theory ("model") which is simple enough to be comprehensible.

The definition of a complete theory given by Einstein, Podolsky, and Rosen can only acquire meaning after we accept an adequate explication of the phrase, "element of physical reality." This might be taken to mean any possibly observed property or relation, and in that case a complete theory would have to lead to derived consequences parallel to all the possible descriptive statements that can be made. With this interpretation the Einstein–Podolsky–Rosen definition seems to put a strong requirement indeed on a complete theory. If, however, the theory is viewed as applying to a certain set or kind of natural phenomena, and "any possibly observed property or relation" changed to one for which description is desired or obtained, we would then have a criterion for completeness of a theory similar to the one that we have suggested.

We recall from our discussion of their paradox that Einstein, Podolsky, and Rosen actually defined an element of physical reality in terms of prediction (p. 204): if the value of a physical quantity can be predicted with certainty, then there is an element of reality corresponding to the quantity. This definition gives an appearance of circularity; the theory is complete if it contains a counterpart of each element of physical reality, and physical reality is that for which the theory can make predictions with certainty (and for which it therefore has a counterpart). There is a break in the circle of reasoning, however, in connection with the making of predictions. These can be tested, and it is only if they are confirmed that we can judge the theory to be descriptive of nature. We may therefore regard "predict with certainty" as implicitly requiring descriptive statements (even though perhaps not directly in confirmation of a given prediction). The condition that the theory contain counterparts of elements of reality does then become equivalent to its containing propositions that are in agreement with descriptive statements. It was, of course, an alleged lack of counterpart corresponding to certain predicted quantities that Einstein, Podolsky, and Rosen put forth as an incompleteness in quantum theory.

Florence Moog leads us in her comment to an aspect of science that we have not as yet considered. She takes it that science is completed, in that we know what it will do; and, that what it will do for man is not enough. The role of science as a total philosophy is a topic that is rather different from the technical aspects of completeness that we have discussed. But I shall a little later have some remarks to make on this important question.

7   A HUNDRED YEARS AGO: DU BOIS-REYMOND

The best known statement by a scientist about the possibilities for complete understanding from science is probably that made by Emil du Bois-Reymond, in his celebrated lecture on the natural limits of knowledge. Du Bois-Reymond (1818–1896), of Swiss and Huguenot descent, was a German physicist and physiologist, professor at Berlin from 1848 until his death. He did important scientific work in problems of electrical aspects of muscular action and nerve conduction. The lecture, *Über die Grenzen des Naturerkennens*, was delivered to the Versammlung Deutscher Naturforscher und Ärzte in Leipzig, August 14, 1872.[2]

Du Bois-Reymond lived at a time when a completely mechanical atomism was little questioned by physicists. In his lecture he accepted Laplace's assertion that a sufficiently able mathematical mind, given a set of boundary conditions, could calculate all past and future states of the universe (Mechanics, du Bois-Reymond said, has the same apodictic certainty as does mathematics.) Our science, he tells us, is as yet far from achieving all that it can, working as a Laplacian mind. Mechanically, we can look forward to such devices as ships that will navigate themselves from port to port. He gives physiological evidence for the postulate that the properties associated with, for example, sound and light are not intrinsic qualities in nature, but are results of responses of nerves. The objective, mechanical outlook, he states, gives us a world which has only motion of a propertyless, here ponderable, there unponderable, matter. Even the origin of life can eventually be understood as a process in which materials first came together to form living things. It is, we are told, a misunderstanding to see something supernatural, something other than a very difficult mechanical problem, in the first appearance of life on earth or on any other world body.

The knowledge to be obtained by the Laplacian mind is for du Bois-Reymond the highest possible reach of our natural knowledge, and we therefore find the limits of our science (of our much less able minds) by studying the limits of Laplace's idealized intelligence. There are two places where, we find, its endeavors to advance are fruitless, and it is here that science has its insuperable limits. One of these places is in the question of the nature of the atoms of which matter is composed. At the time of his lecture physicists and chemists knew very little of the structure of the atom, and du Bois-Reymond presents queries about it which seemed unanswerable. The physical atom is supposed to be an element of matter, and therefore is divisible, and yet is supposed to be indivisible. Also, it is required that forces emanate from atoms, through empty space, and this is an absurdity. If the atom occupies space

---

[2] There are many published editions; I have used one by Verlag von Veit, Leipzig (Sechste Vortrage, 1884). There is an English translation by J. Fitzgerald, in *The Popular Science Monthly*, New York, **V**, 17 (1874).

there are definite limits to its volume, and hence there is repulsion between atoms when sufficiently close. But then, how can we say forces are from a central point. Other problems, relating to a possible substratum in which the atoms are embedded, or to the difficulties of assuming continuous rather than discrete distribution of matter, are brought up in the lecture. Du Bois-Reymond says that no one who has given the question deep consideration has any question about the transcendental nature of the difficulties relating to the nature of matter. We are as helpless as were the ancient Ionian philosophers on these questions, and Laplace's supermind could do no better. Hence, we must recognize in this problem one of the limits on our knowledge.

The second place where du Bois-Reymond finds an inevitable limit to our understanding is in the problem of consciousness. He assumes that we may be able to gain the same kind of detailed knowledge of bodily processes associated with sensation as for astronomical phenomena. Thus, he says, we may come to learn which dance of hydrogen, oxygen, carbon, nitrogen, phosphorous, and other atoms gives happy musical sensations. Even so, what the conscious processes in themselves are would be as unknown as now. We cannot fashion a bridge into the domain of consciousness through the ordering of material particles in motion. There is no conceivable association that will explain how on one hand we have a given position and state of motion of a group of atoms, and on the other such fact-sentences as "I feel pain," "I see red," or "I exist," which are basic and can be explained no further. Not only are we unable to explain consciousness from its material conditions, but it is in the nature of things, the lecturer asserted, that it will never be explained from these conditions.

I need not recount the discussion that du Bois-Reymond gave of various philosophical attempts (Descartes, Clauberg, Malebranche, Geulincx, Leibnitz) to give an adequate resolution of the problem of consciousness. As with the understanding of force and matter, he finds that there has been no step forward in two thousand years, and that there never will be an advance. Because of the two absolute limits to natural knowledge, du Bois-Reymond finds that the universe is doubly incomprehensible. With respect to enigmas of the material world the scientist is accustomed to say, "We do not know" (*Ignoramus*). In looking back over the past successes of science, he can have quiet assurance that where he does not now know, under proper circumstances he can eventually know. But, the lecture concludes, as regards the questions, what are matter and force, and how are they held in mind, the scientist must resign himself to *Ignorabimus!*

Nearly a hundred years later, du Bois-Reymond's assertion of the impossibility of gaining further understanding of the atom seems ill-founded indeed. We have seen how the apparent paradoxes about the ultimate units of matter have been dissolved by the new knowledge that has come with the quantum physics of this century. Questions about the forces and fields associated with matter do remain, and are a prime target for physical investigation today; but there is no reason at all to consider these questions as beyond science. The limits that we have found in quantum physics are in their own way absolute, but they may be regarded not as limits of man's ignorance but as limits on the definability or structure of atomic-level entities themselves.

It would be rash to say that we have advanced in solving the problem of consciousness to the same degree that we have in the problem of atomic physics. But, there would be little disposition to say that we will never understand what consciousness is.[3] Probably we have not yet learned to ask the question properly, but at the least, we could today venture the opinion that a solution is not forthcoming along the lines that du Bois-Reymond asked it (in his own terms it would seem that he was right; atoms with only the classical-mechanical properties of mass, position, and motion can hardly be a basis for awareness).

Certainly we would not today be inclined to raise a question about what is "consciousness" as a self-existent entity, for, we would say that what we have is consciousness *of* something. There is response, of course, on all levels of organic and inorganic nature. Perhaps consciousness involves association of response with the notion of self, a notion that is built up by a human being, we know, only after accumulation of a store of memories and associations with its own physiological unit. It may be that memory, or projection into the future, is required to give the contrast, the awareness of self in relation to a given response, that seems to be involved in consciousness. These are crude suggestions, given only as indications that there are possibilities for comprehending the fact that there is consciousness.

I have already mentioned the proposal that the properties which we have now found for matter and radiation will perhaps give an opening for the understanding of the relation between psychic and physical properties of nature. Du Bois-Reymond, just before stating his conclusion, asks if the two limits may not be the same—that is, if we should ever comprehend the nature of matter and force, would we not also then understand how the basic substance can perceive, feel, desire, and think? That this is so, he says, is the simplest hypothesis to make, until there should be a refutation. But, he comments, it is in the nature of things that we come to no clarity on this point, and there is no gain in further discussion of it.

---

[3] Not all of du Bois-Reymond's scientific contemporaries shared his opinion. The physicist John Tyndall spoke as follows in an address given to the Mathematical and Physical section of the British Association for the Advancement of Science at Norwich, England, August 19, 1868: "The problem of the connection of body and soul is as insoluble in its modern form as it was in prescientific ages . . . . Perhaps the mystery may resolve itself into knowledge at some future day . . . . It is a long way from the Iguanadon and his contemporaries to the President and Members of the British Association. And whether we regard the improvement from the scientific or from the theological point of view, as the result of progressive development, or as the result of successive exhibition of creative energy, neither view entitles us to assume that man's present faculties end the series, —that the process of amelioration stops at him." [John Tyndall, essay on "Scientific Materialism," *Fragments of Science* (London, Longmans, 1871).]

The assertions that du Bois-Reymond made are of intrinsic interest for what they tell us of the outlook associated with the scientific materialism of the nineteenth century. We can also see in the lecture a warning that we should be extremely cautious in writing about limits or completeness in science. Clearly, it is hazardous to make absolute statements about future knowledge on the basis of a current state of science. Du Bois-Reymond is, of course, only one of many who have done this and then been proved wrong by their successors. Among the Greco-Roman natural philosophers, for example, there was a belief that the heat of the equatorial zone of the earth prevented man from crossing it. Accepting this limitation, Macrobius, writing at about 400 A.D., said it is reasonable to suppose that the Southern Temperate Zone is, like ours, inhabited, "but we never have had, and shall never have, the possibility of discovering by whom." [4]

In my treatment of the completeness of science I have tried to heed this warning, and to base my considerations on matters of logic and on established scientific knowledge. I have hoped to avoid drawing conclusions from defects in our knowledge or from present inability to see how those can be removed. It might be charged that in emphasizing the limitations on description and prediction that we find in quantum physics I have very strongly based an argument on a limit in current science. In a way this is clearly so, but I would answer that the basis is not something unknown in science, but rather, something that has been discovered. For, it is from the established principles of quantum theory themselves that we discern the boundaries of our microscopic natural knowledge. It is true that the principles could be found to be superseded; but, we recall that physics in its development has tended not so much towards declaring an already established truth to be wrong but rather towards incorporating that truth into a broader theory.

[4] Quoted by C. S. Lewis in his book *The Discarded Image* (New York, Cambridge University Press, 1964), p. 61.

14

The Noncognitive Completion of Science

1   PROJECTIONS TOWARD COMPLETENESS

ONE OF THE BEST KNOWN EFFORTS towards completeness in science is the Einstein unified field theory. During the last three decades of his life Professor Einstein worked on expanding the general relativity theory of gravitation into a theory of all the physical properties of nature. It was his hope that electrical–magnetic aspects of matter could be related to space–time structure, as apparently are the gravitational; and, further, he hoped to explain the fixed quantities of mass, charge, and spin of the elementary particles, and also the interaction forces between these particles, in terms of a single mathematical description of the structure of space–time.

The equations which Einstein developed are of high generality, and solutions of them must be given an interpretation before they can be considered as descriptive of physical phenomena. Some success has been achieved along these lines, notably by Vaclav Hlavaty. In general, however, the equations have not as yet been fruitful as a source of physical theory, and currently there is not very much interest in trying to work with them.

If the Einstein unified field theory had been successful, or should still prove to be so, we would have a theory which explains all of the observed physical properties of nature; explains, that is, in the sense of giving a "world formula" which shows how these properties are related to and derived from the nature of space–time. Further, we could reasonably expect that chemistry and biology could be developed from the basic theory, if it were entirely adequate for all physical properties (although probably with the additional description of natural factors that exist only with molecular structure or biological organization).

In view of what we have learned in quantum physics, most physicists are rather skeptical about the possibility of achieving a complete theory of the specific kind envisioned by Einstein. For, the inability to achieve a description of atomic phenomena in traditional space–time terms suggests that a theory based on a continuum of space–time variables may not be able to penetrate to the quantum level of nature. Also, the Einstein unified field theory is in the nineteenth century tradition of a scientist's describing a nature that is apart from himself. In contrast, the quantum theory with its emphasis on the interaction between observer and object of study seems rather more likely to point to a science that can include the scientist as a part of the nature he studies than does a theory which aims to describe nature throughout, with no role for the scientist who creates the theory. (At least, with no role in the first instance; perhaps the scientist and his place could eventually be constructed as an elaborate set of consequences of the theory.)

But let us put aside quantum-theoretic objections to a unified theory, and assume that in some form or other a theory with a "world formula" adequate for all physical phenomena could be achieved. In view of the tacit attitude that physicists have toward completeness, such a theory would to a considerable extent seem to constitute a realization of the goal of science. There is in physics, I believe, a strain of thought that may be regarded as a direct descendant of the Principle of Sufficient Reason of Leibniz. We recall that for Leibniz and other rationalists of his age, the giving of a reason constituted an explanation of any aspect of existence; and, primarily, a reason meant a necessary connection with some prior entity. One soon came to the prime question of the existence of the world itself. This existence was related to that of God. By a kind of mutual support, the world and God were each seen to be necessarily related to the other. An explanation for their being was thus achieved.[1] Somewhat similarly, in physics we accept that electromagnetic phenomena, for example, are explained by being described by Maxwell's equations. The fact that these equations and their consequences give a set of rational relations between descriptions of the phenomena means that there is a reason, in one context at least, for electromagnetic aspects of nature, and hence we can say that we understand them. If we had a unified theory which rationally related all aspects of nature, we might tend to feel that these were all understood. The theory itself would have a place as an elegant description of natural phenomena, and would somehow seem to be more than a set of concepts, since (if it were an altogether adequate theory) it would be completely confirmed by observations of the ways of nature.

And yet, just as electromagnetic theory rests on assumed principles and entities, the hypothetical unified theory would have its assumptions. There would be the form of the basic equations themselves, and the manifold (space–time, for example) to which they apply. Just as we can ask, "Why does a moving electron charge give rise to a magnetic field?" or "By what properties are electromagnetic waves propagated?" we could ask questions about the form and substance of the unified theory. It would be descriptive of the

---

[1] I am largely indebted for these comments on "sufficient reason" to Arthur O. Lovejoy's *The Great Chain of Being* (New York, Harper Torchbooks, Harper & Row, 1960). (First published by Harvard University Press, 1936.)

processes of the universe, and perhaps would even allow considerable extrapolation, backwards in time to earlier states of the universe. But the question of why the universe is as it is, or was at some time in the past, would remain.

Formally, the incompleteness of the kind of unified theory that we have projected lies of course in the necessity which we have frequently discussed, that a system of deduced consequences must begin with axioms and primitive terms. In the interests of considering possibilities for completeness, one might ask if this necessity could not be circumvented; if we might not achieve "closure" of a theory, in a manner such that it contains no underived (unexplained) elements. Might not the theory, somehow, have consequences that are themselves its basic ideas: the theory turning back, so to speak, and explaining its own underpinnings.

In a trivial sense, what we ask is true of any deductive theory. The axioms and terms of a theory are, obviously, immediately deducible from the theory itself, and in the sense of that deduction the theory is self-contained. But we want the axioms and terms to appear not as immediate consequences of their assertion, but as a requirement of the theory *in its application* to the natural world for which it was devised. For example, we might suppose that we have a unified theory whose primitive terms are directly associated with large-scale aspects of the universe. Deductions from the theory, we will assume, describe nature on the atomic level; and, further, consideration of these small-scale aspects, as required by the theory, leads to the necessity of the original large-scale aspects and to the initial form (axioms) of the theory. The passage back to the large-scale aspects, if the theory were not to be only trivially closed, would have to be through properties other than these by which the deduction from large-scale to small-scale aspects was made.

Ideas clustering around Mach's Principle suggest a partial illustration of the closure of theory that we are projecting. The Principle may be taken as requiring that the geometric structure of space–time is a consequence of the matter that exists in space–time. We might hope that a valid closed theory involving Mach's Principle could be developed somewhat as follows. (A) The kinematic behavior and other large-scale properties of matter are given by a theory which begins with an assumption of space–time and certain equations describing its properties. (B) Detailed theoretical study of matter, in accordance with the theory of A, leads to an adequate account of the quantum-level properties of matter and radiation. (C) The quantum-level aspects of nature are found directly to require (without the intermediate stage of macroscopic matter properties) the space–time properties that are described by the original equations of A.

We might symbolize our hypothetical closed theory in the following way. We assume the theory to be expressed as a set of equations,

$$\Phi^j(C_i{}^1),$$

where $C_i{}^1$ are a set of i constructs that constitute the primitive terms. They are related by the axiomatic equations, symbolized as Φ^j. The C_i^1 would presumably be of high generality and abstraction, but the $\Phi^j(C_i^1)$ would lead deductively to other equations, $f^s(C_i^1, C_i^2, \ldots, C_i^n)$, which define and relate constructs $C_i^2, C_i^3, \ldots, C_i^n$, using the initial set C_i^1. These derived constructs would be of successively lower degree of abstraction (closer to observed aspects of nature); each defining or relating equation, f^s, might contain some of the C's of the various levels, $1, 2, 3, \ldots, n$, and the classification of the constructs into C_i^2, C_i^3, etc. would perhaps be somewhat arbitrary. But, ultimately we would come to experienced aspects of nature which I signify as properties, $p_1, p_2, p_3 \ldots, p_k$. All of the constructs would at least indirectly be related to the p_k's; we indicate this relation by writing for each construct, $C^m(p_k)$, where (p_k) indicates a set of experienced aspects which determine a given C^m. If our theory is adequate, the derived relations between $C(p_k)$'s agree with observations constituted by the appropriate p_k's. That is, we find that derived "descriptive statements" f^s give the relations among C's that are in agreement with observed relations among the p_k's (for example, the observed relation "pointer tip in the meter opposite black line for 5.3").

We now express the proposed closure of the theory by stating that we will find among its consequences, as confirmed by experience, an approach which will lead us back to the original theory. What could such an approach mean? Either, (i) the initial constructs C_i^1 and relations Φ^j are among the p_k's or (ii), the relations f^s which have been confirmed by the p_k's will lead to C_i^1 and Φ^j. We reject the possibility i, since the p_k's are observations or experiences, and therefore simply are not entities of a deductive logical system. Possibility ii suggests first the previously mentioned trivial deduction that the various f^s contain the $\Phi^j(C_i^1)$; this kind of closure of a theory is merely tautological. We might next think of possibility ii as leading to closure, in that those f^s which are "descriptive statements" may be taken as empirical statements and the initial theory, $\Phi^j(C_i^1)$, built up from them. Such a procedure is, however, not deduction but induction. In practice, a theory is constructed and established by a combination of procedures of postulation, induction, and confirmation of deduced consequences. But certainly, a complete reconstruction of an established theory by inductive methods, using the relevant descriptive statements, would not constitute closure of the theory (even though it might be an instructive and convincing demonstration of the adequacy of the theory).

Finally, we might hope that possibility ii would lead to closure by the means of giving as further consequences from descriptive statements f^s, the initial equations and constructs. Such a deductive display of the consequences of the theory could certainly be of high interest in showing relations between constructs and principles of the theory. But it would not give closure in the sense of giving justification (explanation) of the theory independent of its own content and confirmation. Logically, a long chain of deductive consequences that led back eventually to one of the initial set of assumptions, $\Phi^j(C_i{}^1)$, is no different in its support of the assumption than would be its direct deduction simply as a consequence of its having been postulated (even though, to repeat, many interesting consequences of the assumptions may have appeared in a long chain of deductive reasoning). So, we again find that a deduction of the assumptions by use of the theory is trivial, rather than a closing of the theory such that no assumption is without explanation (derivation).

A quite different kind of hope for a complete, self-contained physical theory might come with an expectation that the properties of the natural world can be deduced entirely from the properties of certain general mathematical systems, for example, systems of integers and topological relations. We have briefly discussed, in Chapter 5, the efforts that A. S. Eddington made toward such a goal. It might be argued that if a physical theory were achieved essentially on the basis of logic alone, we could then understand the world as being necessary just because of certain simple logical relations, as the Principle of Noncontradiction.

I would like to suggest, however, that the derivation of relations that describe natural behavior, without the use of what we generally regard as physical assumptions, would mean that the logic or mathematics which was used had been shaped into a form consonant with the properties of the natural world. My suggestion rests on the widely accepted thesis, also discussed in Chapter 5, that statements of logic and of the empirical sciences cannot be sharply and completely separated, either with respect to their origin or their grounds of validity. If the logic that is used does implicitly contain "physical" statements, it would seem that questions about the "why" of these could be asked, just as they may be asked about the clearly stated assumptions of a conventional kind of physical theory. In any event, attempts so far to derive an adequate physical theory from considerations of logic alone have not met with success. If success were achieved, I suggest that we would find that the theory was not free of assumptions which themselves need to be explained.

2   THE INCOMPLETENESS OF SCIENCE

We must accept, I think, that there is an inherent limitation in the structure of science that prevents a scientific theory from ever giving us an adequate total explanation of the universe. Always, there is a base in nature (or, correspondingly, a set of assumptions in the theory) which cannot be explained by reference to some yet more fundamental property. This feature of science has been commented on by many writers in the philosophy of science; and, certainly the limitation is a point of difference between science and those religions or metaphysical systems in which there is an attempt to present a doctrine that gives answers for all ultimate questions. One of the continuing themes with respect to completeness in this book has been a philosophical analysis of the implications of the deductive aspects of scientific theory. The fact that the conclusion we reach is hardly a novel one need not concern us; for, to a considerable extent, philosophy is an adumbration of the obvious.

The incompleteness of scientific description for any natural domain is perhaps an even more primitive incompleteness than that which is concomitant with deductive scientific theory. Even though we may gain as much description as we judge desirable or practicable for a natural situation, we generally have in science only a minute fraction of the massive amount of potential factual data. Further, we describe only in the terms of the theory and the constructs that we have set up for nature, and these are not final and definitive at any given stage of science.

Most of our living is associated with an awareness that is directed by habit, and by various natural emotions, such as desire, hope, and fear, cast into a form by our past experience and learning. Only with training and maturity, and then not for all people, do we have moments of consciousness devoted to disciplined thinking of the kind associated with science. Our lives can be deeply affected throughout by those moments, but still, our scientific thinking is in a context of being and experience that largely is simply given to us. Somewhat similarly, the explicit structure of science must be regarded as a statement of a few abstracted aspects of the totality of nature: aspects that have universality, and are of importance to us, but do not constitute the entirety of experience.

In a word, science is a very, very partial account. A few hundred years ago only some studies of the gross mechanical aspects of nature and some salient items about the behavior of light rays had been put into a deductive scientific form. Mankind lived tolerably well, nonetheless, with its accumulation of descriptive knowledge and working theories of nature (some of which must have been on an instinctive level). Today, the domains encompassed by science have been widened. With chemistry, nuclear physics, biology, psychology, and the social sciences, far more of nature and of man's behavior is described by science than they were with Newtonian macroscopic physics. But, there are many activities of man—those, among others, which are described by the words politics, literature, art, religion—which still lie to a considerable degree outside of the circle of established scientific description and theory.

It was a doctrine of nineteenth century scientific materialism–determinism that science could eventually encompass all of the natural world; that any event of nature or act of man could come to be understood in the terms of a deductive science. The developments in physics of this century have removed the supports for such a prospect, even though there actually has been an immense broadening of our knowledge of nature. We have come to atomic aspects of nature that do not individually fit into a rational, predictive scheme, and we are faced in science with problems of how man's interaction with nature gives rise to awareness of it. How far natural science as a predictive description of man is thereby going to be limited is a question that we cannot at present answer. We can confidently hope that striking advances are yet to be made in biology and psychology, and that much more of our ways of behaving and of experiencing the broad nature about us will come into the purview of science. One might expect, though, that limitations of science which are peculiar to biology and to psychology will eventually be discovered, just as we have found limits in atomic physics on the use of modes of description that are appropriate for larger-scale aspects of nature.

We must see science as unable, *in itself*, to achieve a complete outlook: as unable to give understanding and guidance with respect to all aspects of the world and our living in it. Fragmentation of nature is an element in scientific procedures. We do our science for a selected domain of nature, and use what we learn only for activities with respect to that domain. The scope of science, the span of natural domains it describes, is increasing, but still, today at least, much of what is closest and most important to man's interests is outside of science. Even if the descriptive limits on the scientific study of man's thought and behavior should prove to be trivial, and even if unification should eventually be achieved for all the specialties and sub-specialties of science, there would remain the limit on complete explanation that comes with any deductive theory. The unifying master theory would itself rest on an axiomatic base, to be taken as given rather than as itself explained and understood.

3   THE AUTHORITY OF SCIENCE

And yet, among most of those who are the leaders of mankind today, science appears to have won out over other ways of interpreting the universe. Regardless of what its limitations may be, the word of science is looked to as being a final authority. Indeed, *in an effective way, science is for many the religion of our age.* We look to science for the solution of our problems of living, both social and individual. We respect the scientist as the person who tells us what the universe is, independently of the traditions and myths of particular cultures. Our sense of security in life, and our source of support in time of puzzlement or fear, are in large measure in the firmness of the findings of natural science. In all these ways we regard science much as we once regarded the church and its ministers; and if these are accepted at all by the intellectually alert of today, they must share the role of providing answers for philosophical questions and a center for social amelioration.

The strength of the day-by-day role of science in our living is apparent in our use of science in engineering and in manufacturing technology. We also see our obvious reliance upon science in the great advances that have been made in the medical arts. The use by political and military leaders of sophisticated applications of scientific knowledge is all too clear in the threats of catastrophic war with which we now live. And, the role of science as a primary guide in our lives, in contrast with former reliance on religions or other traditional doctrines, is impressive in decisions with respect to social behavior. The social scientist has become an intrinsic part of the machinery of social affairs: the economist advising on the financial policy of national governments, the planning expert helping to determine future water and transportation needs of an area, the sociologist called upon to assist a community in its delinquency and disorder problems. Education is guided by elaborate scientific studies. Business has its marketing and consumer research specialists. In all, our society is regarded as a structure which is to be understood (and controlled) by means of scientific studies of it in a context of knowledge of man as one of the natural species. Most assuredly, we do not see human society as, say, an expression of God's plan for mankind on earth.

In the guidance of personal behavior we likewise find many indications that science has to a large extent usurped the role of custom and religion, at least in Western culture. The psychiatrist as a replacement for the priest, in time of conflict or despair, is an instance that comes to mind at once. In a more general way many of our precepts for living are now based on studies in human physiology and psychology, rather than on the authority of an accepted religion. We find a striking example in the rearing of children. Parents now actively look to child psychologists for specific instructions about training and discipline: the standards of a child's behavior often come from science, not from authority accepted on other grounds as final.

Science is today the essential element in man's intellectual and spiritual response to the universe. It is his way of finding order among the manifold of experiences of the universe, and his way of coping with the nature of the world and himself. In brief, he finds understanding through science and, as far as he can, he employs science to shape nature for the needs of his own living. Science has become man's mediation, we might say, against despair and helplessness in the universe.

It has not always been so. Magic, religious belief and ceremony, elaboration of the pleasures of daily living, perhaps the violence of war and pillage (an alternative not yet gone from us), have in times past served as the essential mode in man's response to the opportunities of life. But the dominance of science in our culture is now strongly manifest in its educational and ideal-seeking activities. The attention to science in our universities has for some decades tended to overshadow regard for the humanistic fields. And, although there are some notable countermovements, expansion more and more seems to be in science and technology. In the United States, and perhaps elsewhere too, science study is now beginning to be a significant part of education even in the primary schools. All over the world, societies in which scientific activity has been little developed are grateful for assistance in establishing opportunities for scientific and technological education.

Every nation that possibly can support it seems eager to have an atomic energy program, even though economic and material benefits may not be apparent. The space-exploration program has been enthusiastically accepted by the practical leaders of the United States and of the Soviet Union, and a considerable fraction of the productive capacities of these countries is currently devoted to the gaining of detailed information about the extraterrestrial solar system. The fact that these efforts are motivated to a large degree by a race for prestige, rather than by a desire for natural knowledge, shows emphatically the place of science: the worth of achieving an expansion of scientific knowledge is unquestioned. Likewise, in the United States, in Western Europe, and in Russia, governments have been willing in recent years to give large sums, hundreds of millions of dollars, to the building of particle accelerators, accepting the word of physicists that the expense is justified by what may be learned in studying high-energy physical processes.

The resources that our society gives to scientific activities of all kinds are rapidly increasing: over the past few hundred years the increase in number of scientists and amount of scientific research has been roughly exponential, with a doubling about every twenty years.[2] Obviously, such an increase cannot continue indefinitely, and a saturation level must eventually put a limit on the increase in people and resources devoted to science. This level may change, of course, with the structure and resources of a given society; but, in the future that is evident today, we can see science as overwhelmingly mankind's major intellectual activity (perhaps even today one could say this), and scientists as the controlling group in virtually all aspects of our culture and our society.

The benefits of science are so obvious, and the results of science so reliable in contrast with those from other attempts to understand nature, that the generality of mankind is now rushing to accept the presuppositions and methods of science, happily leaving their nonscientific beliefs and ways to die away. For some centuries it seemed that only an inspired few would be devotees of science in any one day; for, a curiosity that goes beyond matters of immediate personal concern, and a certain setting aside of accepted ways of looking at the world, were required of the scientist in the pioneer days of the establishing of natural science. But that time passed some decades ago in the industrial societies, and today science is interwoven in the fabric of our culture. We see a good measure of its acceptance in the fact that for a young man or woman the path of science is now an obvious one to the broadest kind of success.

[2] Derek J. Price, *Little Science, Big Science* (New York, Columbia University Press, 1963); see also his *Science Since Babylon* (New Haven, Connecticut, Yale University Press, 1961).

4   THE MEDIAEVAL COMMITMENT

The present era of science is for Western culture a development from an age in which Christianity was the essential factor in man's response to the universe. One can today look back and separate out various intermediate periods: the Renaissance, with man's increased interest in the things of nature around him; the new emphasis on logic and science alone in the Age of Reason; the intrinsic value given to self-expression in the attitudes of Romanticism. Throughout these movements, modern science was growing, steadily increasing in the number of scientists, in rate of discovery, and in influence. But at the beginning of the change to the present age of science we find a European culture in which a Christian doctrine and unity of belief reigned supreme. This was the civilization of the high mediaeval period in Western Europe, a period extending, say, for the four hundred years from 1000 to 1400 A.D.

Mediaeval society was almost completely prescientific in its intellectual life (although certainly not prelogical, and not without significant technological accomplishments). It was a society that was suffused in all its activities by its Christian religion. The ideal of living with continual awareness of God and obedience to what were regarded as His dictates was an essential factor in practical as well as artistic and intellectual aspects of life. Man understood the universe, and sensed it, in terms of his Christianity, whereas today our comprehension and feeling for the world are in the terms of natural science.

To us, as to mediaeval man, the dominating symbol of his culture was the cathedral. The great structures which we can still visit in Europe give us visible evidence of the force that religion can have in society. One feels that for the inhabitants of a mediaeval city the building of a cathedral gave a barrier against despair and bewilderment and at least some partial comprehension of the world. Christianity was the primary source of meaning and order in life, and the church building a literal expression of Christian belief and doctrine.

The breadth of the role of religion in mediaeval society is indicated too by the fact that, in addition to its religious, artistic, and philosophical significance, the church or cathedral was an enormous economic effort, and a focus for rivalry for prestige among communities. The parallel with current scientific efforts in space exploration, for example, is a striking one. One can indeed, see other analogies between the place of science in our contemporary culture and that of Christianity in mediaeval society. The daily cathedral service, for example, came to be presented not as an event of worship for those lay people living nearby (who in some cases were not even admitted), but as an offering to God, of intrinsic merit beyond whatever value it had to participants or observers. The scientific paper is today an expression of the value we put upon an effort to describe or understand through science some aspect of nature. It is hardly an academic secret that a published paper is considered an achievement, simply by virtue of its having been done, without regard to its content (as long as respectable enough to have been given editorial approval) or to its number of readers after publication (which may well be zero). The paper, with its data and its arguments, is a votive offering in support of our conviction that by the combination of theory construction and appropriate observation we achieve valid understanding. Of course, some of the papers that are published do have a contribution to make, and will be studied by many readers. Likewise, we could say, in the context of Christian belief, that many liturgical offerings are presented to appreciative congregations and are religiously effective.

Henry Adams, in his *Mont-Saint Michel and Chartres,* has given us a vivid discussion of the interplay between the conceptualized Christian divinities, in particular the Virgin Mary, and the life and art of the mediaeval period. His accounts of architecture, literature, and historical events convey to us how thoroughly the mediaeval European saw the world from a firm, unquestioned base in Christianity. His commitment was such that both the affairs of life and the phenomena of nature could all be manifest evidence of the presence and dominance of the Christian God, throughout the realm of existence. Adams saw the cathedral as an expression of mediaeval man's attempt to understand the world through Christianity. He writes: ". . . Chartres expressed, besides whatever else it meant, an emotion, the deepest man ever felt—the struggle of his own littleness to grasp the infinite. . . . In act, all men's work ends there;—mathematics, physics, chemistry, dynamics, optics, every sort of machinery science may invent—to this favour come at last, as religion and philosophy did before science was born. All that the centuries can do is to express the idea differently: a miracle or a dynamo; a dome or a coalpit; a cathedral or a world's fair; and sometimes to confuse the two expressions together." [3]

Henry Adams is telling us, in effect, that man may use different ways of making peace with his hopes and fears about living, and his curiosity about the universe. The mediaeval elaboration of a religious order, based on expectations for afterlife and on ideals of love and renunciation, was one such way. Gradually, however, that attitude toward ourselves and our world was eroded away, and now the new way of science has come into dominance: a way based on discerning of constructs and theories that will order and predict the phenomena of nature. Clearly, the way a man behaves and the awareness of that way by a supposed God are no longer central in the mediation between man and the universe. Rather, the natural world itself has become the firm and dominant aspect of existence.

To say of man's attempt to grasp the universe, as Adams does, that "all

---

[3] *Mont-Saint Michel and Chartres,* opening paragraph, Chapter VII.

that the centuries can do is to express the idea differently," is to imply a skepticism with respect to the validity, or, at least, the completeness, of the actually accepted philosophy of any one period. We find change in form and content, he seems to be saying, but no essential advance or improvement. Without wishing altogether to dismiss his assertion, we can nevertheless point out that it is hardly a fair account with respect to natural science. The rationalism of mediaeval thought played a major role in the birth of modern science, but it was not in itself a fruitful path to natural knowledge. We do not have again to fight the battle between science and scholastic philosophy, the outcome of which was decisively settled several centuries ago. The reliability of science in application is alone an obvious support for its validity as a system of knowledge of nature, and we need not dilate upon its superiority in this respect to notions about the universe that are accepted on religious authority.

A supporter could justifiably say, however, that the successful effort in science in our age does not disprove Henry Adams' point of view. The people of the mediaeval period were not primarily concerned with science, and they made their achievements in quite a different way. We must regard the period as one in which the cultivation of the heart and spirit, with respect to man and to the divine personages of Christianity, was far more a matter of daily life than in our natural-world oriented culture. It is hardly possible for us, today, to reconstruct the sense and feeling of a mediaeval man, but the texts that we read can tell us that he of course could gain fruition and stability in his life, in a context of belief and purpose very different from ours.

It is clear, too, that the mediaeval period left a heritage of nonscientific civilization that was of major significance in the societies that developed in later centuries. The mediaeval emphasis on nonbodily aspects of life, which seems extreme and unwise to our more naturalistic age, may have been an idealistic corrective response in an age that was cruel and barbaric in many ways. The Christian doctrines of love and brotherhood did bring European society a long way toward a unified civilization that gradually achieved some degree of unselfishness and kindness among its members. This achievement was based, we emphasize, on a commitment to Christian ideals that had its own intrinsic strength and appeal, and, in the broadest kind of way, made sense in terms of what men felt and thought about their fellow men and their world.

The commitment was not impregnably supported by the experience of life, and in time a large share of thoughtful men have come to see science as giving a better way to deal with the universe. But the commitment to science likewise rests on a broad assent of thought and feeling. One must want to know about nature in the theoretical, exact way that science tells us of it, if one is to do science: there is no necessary, absolute reason that requires such a response to the natural world. And indeed even today there are many people who find the scientist's way of thinking to be uncongenial.

The fact that science has been concerned with nature generally, and only incidentally with man, has meant that the commitment to it tended to leave a gap in the effective philosophy of our age. There is no overwhelming, unquestioned acceptance of ideals with respect to what life should be or how our fellow men may be treated, to run parallel with the iron-tight commitment of our age to the presuppositions of science. It seems to be a consequence that the great inhumanities of war and genocide in twentieth-century Western society could occur, and that patterns of life which are empty and unfulfilled can proliferate in our industrial culture.

There were, of course, cruelty and horror aplenty in mediaeval times, and we do not mean to look back to a golden period of human behavior. In any case, comparative questions of more or less are not the issue. Rather, we are concerned with the sense in which the emphasis on belief in science has seemed to carry with it a lack of completeness. In the period of culture from which our scientific age grew there was an emphasis, in belief, on ideals of behavior regarded as absolutes. There went along with that emphasis, to be sure, much that was shockingly superstitious and shallow. We have lost the myth and superstition of mediaeval culture, and gained the solid achievements of modern science. But, in our commitment to that achievement we have not found a comparable new strength in guidance of human behavior. We go along with what we have inherited in the religion and philosophy of mediaeval and other periods. And, it is a question whether this inheritance is enough to guide mankind successfully, given the capabilities with which science now equips him. The mediaeval culture with its commitment to a Christian ethics did bring forth a civilization from the societies of the preceding Dark Ages. The age of science, for all its great superiority in many respects to the mediaeval culture, has not shown a commitment to beliefs that bring a comparable advance in the elements of humane living.

5   THE NONCOGNITIVE COMPLETION OF SCIENCE

In our preceding discussion we have seen evidence of the fact that the emphasis of science, at least in its present stage of development, does lie largely outside the realm of ethical decisions by man. We may regard the lack of engagement between science and ultimate religious and ethical beliefs as a factor of incompleteness of science, in addition to those we have already considered. We live in a day in which science is for many at the core of our explicit philosophical presuppositions. And yet, because science is not complete our acquaintance with the world and the direction of our thought and activity are in large measure a result of what I shall term noncognitive agents.

Knowledge or doctrine which is held on a basis of deduction from accepted premises may be regarded as being cognitive. But, in addition we shall consider knowledge which is *explicitly formulated* on the basis of observation

or other experience as cognitive. This latter inclusion is not without ambiguity. Scientific description, as well as everyday statements of fact, would
normally be included; also, statements which result from a combination
of deduction and construction of inferred entities, with substantial empirical
confirmation, would be considered as cognitive. A problem does arise with
statements which are based on rather tenuous experience, as, for example, an
assertion by a person on the basis of what he felt in a certain eerie location
that a ghostlike presence does exist there. But, we will take it that common
consent can resolve whether or not a given statement is cognitive, in the sense
of having an adequate base in experience. In general, then, knowledge which
comes neither within an accepted deductive system nor as a formulated
verifiable statement that is primarily empirical will be regarded as noncognitive. We may now set forth the ways in which science, in consequence
of its incompleteness, is complemented by other, nonscientific (noncognitive)
ways to knowledge or belief.

(*i*) *Experience and Description.* Because scientific description is partial
and selective, it does not contain all that nature can present with respect
to a set of experiences. Direct sensory perception brings an intensity of actual *being* which scientific description cannot convey. I may describe a
block of wood, but the written description needs to be supplemented by direct
experience of the block before completeness of description is achieved. The
block is a construct, and as such it may be exhaustively described within the
confines of its verbal definition. But, that description may be indefinitely
extended, to include new properties, by virtue of the richness of property and
relation of natural entities. Hence, experience (based on physical interaction
in any possible way between block and observer) is the ground for complete
knowing, and the explicit description of science is cognitive knowledge that
is only partial with respect to all that may be experienced about the block.
The experience by which additional information may be obtained is not, of
course, limited to the simple, unaided use of senses such as sight and touch
(although these senses do give an immediate sensation that is unattainable by
any scientific description). The devices of science immensely enrich the
available experience: the use of electron diffraction, for example, will bring
information about the crystalline structure of the block, information that is
completely out of the range of our direct sensory perception.

Scientific description is created, then, out of a context, or milieu, of
direct, noncognitive experience. It is this experience, available or potentially
available, that constitutes man's widest possible acquaintanceship with nature.
But, the direct noncognitive knowledge of any one person is partial and fragmentary with respect to the total of human experiences, just as is any one
person's scientific knowledge. One of the prime characteristics of scientific
description is that it can be communicated. Attempts are also made to convey
noncognitive perceptions from one person to others; the photograph, for

example, brings to those who look at it some part of the perception that a human observer would have of the objects photographed.

The artist may also attempt to put his sensory experience into his work of art, and thereby bring the experience to others. It has been suggested that art is superior to science in conveying experiences of what exists, and in some respects this seems clearly to be so. The painting of a bird, for example, can bring its vivid appearance far better than can a carefully written description, or perhaps even better than can a photograph. But in art too there is selection and even pronounced distortion, in the artist's emphasis on those aspects that he feels do best carry the "reality" of the object. There is too, of course, a further important dimension of art—one which does not have to do with depiction of what is to be experienced. We shall presently return to a discussion of art in this respect. It suffices here to note that descriptive science and art do have a common ground in the noncognitive experience of nature; but they differ in that science attempts to tell of the experience by use of language that is associated with cognition, whereas in art the attempted communication remains in the noncognitive realm, by use of the medium of the work of art.

(*ii*) *Acceptance of Assumption.* A second way in which science is supplemented by a noncognitive process is in its acceptance of terms and postulates of a deductive system. Every system, we have seen, is ultimately taken as an expression of how or what nature is, with no further explanatory deduction.

The scientist's position may often be that once we have found a theory which adequately describes a domain of nature, it is then our proper scientific attitude simply to accept the entities and regularities which that theory postulates. Even if we should ever achieve a unified master theory, we could do no more than stop with the fundamental aspects of the universe as described by this theory. Current philosophical positivism tends to support this point of view: we must ultimately simply accept the world, and to ask "Why is nature as it is?" when science can give no further answer would be to ask a meaningless question.[4]

But if we wish to consider how a complete view of the universe may be formed with all due cognizance of science, it is interesting to explore the possibilities by which the axiomatic end-point of a deductive system in science might be supported with the introduction of noncognitive elements.

In the first section of this chapter we discussed the possibility of obtaining closure (or "self-support") of a theory through the device of finding the

[4] In his recent study, *The Mystery of Existence: An Essay in Philosophical Cosmology* (New York, Appleton-Century-Crofts, 1965), Milton K. Munitz has concluded that it is meaningful to consider the question of whether or not there is a reason for the existence of the world, but with the proviso that a unique meaning for "reason" is required; further, he concludes that no rational method which might lead to an answer to the question is available.

basic assumptions of the theory $\Phi^j(C_i^1)$, as deduced consequences. We saw, however, that there was no way that we could expect to carry out such a deduction which would not be essentially both tautological and trivial. A first possibility, which we considered and discarded, involved not deduction, but an appeal to the elements of experience, p_k, which are the empirical base of the theory. The constructs $C^m(p_k)$ are formed from the experienced elements, p_k, and cognitive, descriptive statements are made up of C^m's. Observed relations among the C^m's are compared with relations f^s between the $C^m(p_k)$'s which are deductive statements of the theory. Our first suggestion, however, was that perhaps the p_k's could themselves include the initial postulates and constructs, $\Phi^j(C_i^1)$, and hence give a direct support in experience for them. But we dismissed this possibility, for the valid reason that the p_k's are items of experience or perceptions, that is, are raw, unverbalized data, and noncognitive. The postulates, Φ^j, in contrast, are verbal, cognitive propositions, and hence cannot be among the p_k's. (The constructs, C_i^1, are formed ultimately by reference to noncognitive elements of experience, and have the dual properties of existing in nature and of being subject to verbal formulation, as discussed in Chapter 2; hence, for them the objection is not compelling.)

We now drop the requirement, however, that we must stay within the cognitive structure of science, and ask if possibly the p_k's *could* contain the postulates Φ^j, and thereby in some manner give a direct explanation for the theoretical structure based on the postulates. It should be appreciated that this is a peculiar suggestion indeed, and only excusable because we are now considering a noncognitive completion of science. Suppose, to give a simple example, that one of our $\Phi^j(C_i^1)$ is Newton's second law of motion, $F = ma$ (force equals mass times acceleration). Force, mass, and acceleration are all constructs, C_i^1. The law may be tested by making observations, p_k, which can be compared with the requirements on them as given by the deduced relations f^s among the C_i^n's. (The constructs are ultimately defined in terms of p_k's.) But our novel suggestion is that the *law itself*, $F = ma$ (not its consequences or predictions f^s for experience), may be sensed and explained as a p_k, thereby receiving support beyond that gained by its usual scientific confirmation. Experience would then directly give explanation about *why* it is that we have the law, $F = ma$.

Such a mixing of formal, linguistic assumption and experience obviously does require a noncognitive process. Indeed, one may well ask if the proposal in any way makes sense. In the illustration given, it hardly seems to. But we can see (and now the reader must be prepared to be very speculative) a paradigm for a direct noncognitive explanation of axiom in a hypothetical religious kind of construction. Suppose that a successful scientific theory, of high generality, did require a Being, C_1^1, and a statement of relation, Φ^1, between C_1^1 and other physical constructs. Let us suppose that from the basic axiom, Φ^1, it was found possible mathematically to derive all observed natural phenomena, and that the properties postulated for C_1^1 were also confirmed in observation. The theory would be, then, an achieved master theory; but the question would arise as to why $\Phi^1(C_1^1, C_i^n)$ and why C_1^1? But let us further suppose that among the items of experience p_k there was some direct experience or intuition about the existence of C_1^1 and the relation Φ^1, and that this experience in a noncognitive way did justify or explain the Being and its relations to other constructs. A situation like that sometimes expressed in religious experiences comes to mind: that there are direct intuitions of God which carry a sense of understanding about His creation of the world and of Himself. I do not mean, however, to specify a religious intuition only, but to use that as an example of a perception which can answer a basic "why" question in a noncognitive manner. Our illustration would require, of course, not a God that is in an undetermined manner the creator of the universe; rather, the postulated $\Phi^1(C_1^1, C_i^n)$ would be the axiomatic basis of a proper scientific theory.

We may give as a further illustration a more prosaic kind of perception which, to some extent, seems actually to operate today as a noncognitive completion of science. We have spoken of "accepting the universe as it is." It happens that people sometimes find among their p_k's a sense of "rightness with the world"; there can be an intuitive feeling that the world is good in its being, and the joy of participating in it points to the justification for existence. It is to be granted that these data of experience do not obviously add, in an explanatory sense, to our present structure of science, and that they arise more as a sign of good health and fortune than as a completion of science. But we wish only to indicate a kind of possibility for transcending the unsatisfactoriness of having explanation stop completely with the axiomatic base of science. The existence of anything is noncognitive (it is not commensurate with the linguistic structure of science) and we might therefore expect that ultimate explanation is to be found in that which exists in our direct, noncognitive experience. We can present this expectation, however, only as a hope and possibility, to be realized with continued refinement both of man's understanding of nature and subtlety of perception.

One intriguing suggestion that is sometimes made is that the artist can convey perceptions which do go closer to the heart of reality than do the constructions of science. In the terms we have been using this would be to say that artists can perceive and communicate p_k's which in a significant way illuminate constructs and relations, C's and Φ's, that are fundamental in the universe. We might, on this suggestion, expect it to be in art that we would find the p_k that explained an axiom Φ^1 previously established as basic for scientific theory.

It is surely the case that art is concerned with more than depicting selected aspects of common experience (although that does sometimes seem to be its chief concern, as in representational painting). Thus, the suggestion of patterns which do not exist in the ordinary structures of nature is an element in much of art. In music, for example, simple representation of experiences in the natural world has a minor role. But more than the kind of imaginative construction exemplified in the music of, say, a string quartet is proposed for art: it can give a profound insight into the nature of things. There is then the requirement that the artist feel, and convey to his audience, something that escapes the common run of men, and also is not caught by the nets of cognition that the scientist weaves from experience.

Art does indeed contain in many instances a large element that is an expression of thought and feeling of the artist (and we now refer to art as including literature, sculpture and painting, music, architecture, and many aspects of the practical arts). This element can never vanish entirely, for the very selection of what is presented requires a choice by the artist. The artist can point up that which is particularly appealing, for reasons of its sensual beauty, or for a host of other reasons: sentiment, familiarity, geometric design, fear, aspiration, to name a few. The scent of a rose, the curve of a street in the shadow, a momentous public event in one's lifetime—these can all mean more for artists' having written or sung about them. But also, the artist can bring to us feeling and perception that has been a part of him. Our awareness of the world can hence be enlarged through art, and we may gain vision not otherwise vouchsafed to us.

But, granted the role of art in enriching our lives, often in ways that are intrinsically satisfying in themselves, does art also bring to us truths about man and his universe that are beyond science and rational philosophy? Do we learn answers to questions about first principles of the kind that science strives for but has not given us? An indication of a positive answer is given by the poet Wallace Stevens, who wrote: ". . . do we not begin to think of the possibility that poetry is only reality, after all, and that poetic truth is a factual truth, seen, it may be, by those whose range in the perception of fact —that is, whose sensibility—is greater than our own?"[5] The artist is indeed often a person of high sensitivity over the entire range of human response, and it is my opinion that he sometimes may lead the scientist, though in a fragmentary and highly imperfect way.

The scientist in his work is himself frequently guided by intuition rather than analysis, and likewise the artist may have insights that are communicated in art, and that are hints or first perceptions of truths that science has not found. Artists were very likely telling man of natural order in the universe before science displayed that order. Perhaps, in the century or two past when science was carrying that order too far, into a strict determinism, art told us of the creativity of indeterminism in the universe. Certainly it seems true that art has been ahead of social science in telling us of the validity and the importance of love and mutual respect in the universe. The somewhat chaotic, experimental art of the twentieth century seems not to be un-

---

[5] Wallace Stevens, *The Necessary Angel* (London, Faber, 1960), p. 59.

related to the change in physics from a relatively clear mechanical philosophy to the complexities of contemporary theory, and possibly here too art has been a little bit in the lead.

But with respect to specific noncognitive explanation by art of basic scientific axioms I think it is best to reserve judgment. Obviously, the physicist of today will scarcely expect to gain from an item p_k in the artist's manifold of experience an immediate feeling for why, say, the electromagnetic field must be described by a tensor with the antisymmetry property. Perhaps, though, in a science that is less fragmentary and more inclusive than that of today, the sensitivity of the artist could be of importance in bringing the perceptions that might effect a noncognitive completion of the explanatory processes of science. The possibility is one that has the attraction of fitting together the two approaches, so often disjoint in our culture, of intellectual construction and the direct appeals of the nonrational, nonverbal property of existence itself.

(iii) *Science and the Humanities.* The third major aspect of incompleteness which we have designated for science is its lack of development for many of man's most important kinds of thought and activity. We here refer to personal, social, and political behavior of man; to his attitudes and standards with respect to such behavior; to his beliefs about what is and what is not desirable, or beautiful; and to his religious and metaphysical concepts. Academically, what we refer to are the aspects of man that are generally within the province of the humanities, although, also, they are to some extent part of the concerns of the social sciences. In some of these human activities science has, as we have already indicated, achieved significant knowledge, with corresponding effect throughout the science-oriented societies. But in much of man's guiding philosophy science is still not a major factor. And, even where it is, it must rest on assumptions that are themselves without further rational explication.

We may say, then, that if we are to have a set of ideas that will serve as a guide to basic questions in all areas of action and thought, there must be a wide supplementing of science with nonscientific elements. To call these elements noncognitive is in a way incorrect, because there are significant uses of logical reasoning, and also of appeal to experience for confirmation or negation, in the development of ideas with respect to humanistic activities. But because there generally is a greater emphasis on acceptance for its own apparent merit, as compared with what is done in scientifically establishing an idea, we shall in considering the entire nonscientific element of total philosophy or outlook also apply the term "noncognitive completion."

We saw earlier in this chapter, in the discussion of mediaeval European culture, that the commitment of a society could be very dominantly to a religious doctrine, with little intermixture of the cognitive processes of empirical science; and yet also, that the people of mediaeval culture achieved much that we can admire, and transmitted a precious heritage of civilization. Today, our scientific culture shows many signs of not having a concern with the noncognitive aspects of civilization, comparable with the thought and effort that we give to scientific activities. The work of the humanist seems particularly to be needed. The discussion of how we should act and what we should want; the humanizing of our policies and institutions with respect to war; acceptance of population control and preparation for man's ability to control genetic inheritance; the amelioration of physical and psychological blight in urban living; the enriching of life by the various roles of art; a continual emphasis on the importance of simple person-to-person good feeling—one could extend the list, but these suffice to indicate the kind of humanistic activities that must supplement the accumulation of scientific knowledge about man and nature.

I do not believe that the level of nonscientific human activities is necessarily to be described as being inferior today to what it has been at times in the past. But science has given man new powers, and also has put strains on formerly satisfactory modes of living. As a result, the challenge and need of guidance for human activities does seem to be greater than ever before. But how is this to be achieved? We must, it seems, as much as possible emphasize and encourage the humanist's approach and see it as not in the least "antiscientific," but as the proper and only approach we have in many of the most important of human activities. The study of past human responses in literature and art, the awareness of man's history, discussion of ethical and religious questions, the application of principles to public issues of the day: by the encouragement of activities such as these in schools and community centers we can work toward more concern with the questions that are not in the purview of science. The church can be, of course, a natural focus for these activities.

The acceptance of ideals of conduct, or standards of art, or of an ultimate metaphysics, is much more by intuitive assent than in the case of scientific knowledge. The process of testing of assumption with something of a critical, tentative attitude toward any theory is contrary, in a large measure at least, to the absolute conviction which often characterizes the less scientific beliefs. But it would be a mistake to think that empirical evidence is not relevant to these beliefs; it is just that the method of using experience is less formal and less rigorous than in scientific work. The doctrine, "Honesty is the best policy," for example, does have empirical support (as well as justification in principle) : if it were regularly found that honesty seemed to fail as a guide for behavior, people would not hold to it as a virtue. In general the acceptance of a nonscientific belief seems to result from many factors, some analytic and some emotional or intuitive. The insight by which one sees the belief as compelling and valid may be analogous to the intuition of scientific discovery, by which different elements of theory and observation are suddenly seen to fit together.

The noncognitive belief does rest ultimately, of course, on a conviction which has no further explanation, just as does the ultimate scientific assumption. The difference lies in the fact that the scientific belief has the warrant of the procedures which were carried out to establish it scientifically, while the less cognitive belief has a vaguely defined mixture of experience and cognitive argument which supports it (but generally without rigorously requiring it, logically or empirically). I think it is also the case, however, that the basic nonscientific belief is more likely to have immediate noncognitive justification than is the root scientific assumption: more likely to have an immediate warrant in an item p_k of experience, to use our previously introduced terminology. The assumption, for example, that space–time is curved in association with matter has been established by empirical confirmation of a meaningful mathematical statement of the assumption; but there is little in direct experience to give a noncognitive explanation for the assumption (that is, there is little that gives a noncognitive completion of this basic idea of physical science). In contrast, for example, the ethical doctrine, "human life is sacred," has not been established as a truth of science, but many can give immediate noncognitive assent to it, as meaning that each person's life should be protected and encouraged whenever possible—an assent that seems to have a warrant in our and the world's own best properties.

To the scientist, the manner in which nonscientific attitudes and convictions become established has a haphazard, unpredictable quality. We have become accustomed, in science, to widespread, conscious attacks on a problem, either through a formal project or a consensus that a certain problem is important and amenable to investigation. But one does not see a clear progression of events in, for example, changes of ethical attitudes toward behavior: the actual causative factors are probably extremely complex combinations of various aspects of individual and social life. We can to some extent, to be sure, associate changes with key human beings and their influence. The prime example that comes to the Western mind is the person of Jesus Christ, whose ethical assertions have been accepted, in various forms, for almost two thousand years over much of the world. Or, to come to comparatively much smaller effects, think of the influence a popular writer can have in his own day. Ernest Hemingway, for example, after writing for a few devoted years in Paris, not only changed styles of writing in his generation, but also affected the way people looked at some of the prominent non-intellectual aspects of life: sports, sex, war, alchohol. We can prepare a reception for new insights in the nonscientific problems of man by encouraging thought and activity with respect to them. But it would seem that we must simply look to the native genius of our species for enriching intuitions and their convincing statement. It is in their own way, obviously, that the humanists can give us, we trust, the guidance that will prevent man from being overwhelmed by the uses of a science.

Florence Moog, in the words quoted in Chapter 1, speaks of science as "a planet that has been circumnavigated," and asserts that not through it will men "come to live in peace and dignity . . . ." The comments we have been making on the third way in which science by itself is incomplete do give, if they are valid, ample support to that assertion, particularly for the present situation of the world and the present content of science. But, if we think not just of what science is today, but of what it may yet become, then in view of its increasing scope it does not seem correct to say that there is no more to be expected from science with respect to the problems of man. As scientists study new aspects of human behavior, we can expect that their findings will continue to supplant, or at least to supplement, that which was previously held on the basis of intuition or commonsense. There is sometimes an expression of resentment that this process should occur, but I think there are no sound grounds for such an attitude. Scientific knowledge can generally improve the attaining of human ends, and it is only when the proper ends are themselves lost or subverted (and this is not generally a question for science as such) that there is a loss to human living.

The preparation of fine foods, for example, is properly regarded as an important art, even if not of high cultural significance. Some complain that "old-fashioned" cooking, without benefit of the technology of food prepara-tion, was superior to contemporary methods. And yet, it is doubtful if there is any loss for the best cooks, and certainly there is immense gain to the whole population as a result of the scientific knowledge we now have, both of food preservation and of human nutrition. Or, for an example with a more ethical implication, we can consider the change of attitude towards delin-quency of all kinds that has come with scientific studies of offenders. As a result we now know more about why people are delinquent than we once did. It is still necessary to implant standards of good behavior, and in some cases to ask what these standards should be; but it hardly seems that we are less able to do this as a result of such firm scientific information as we have about human behavior.

The point has been made too, and I think it is a valid one, that science does influence our nonscientifically accepted principles, just because of the kind of human activity that it does itself bring into society. In all, I believe, this influence is clearly salutary, by reason of the virtues that are present in good science. E. F. H. Caldin, in a work that is largely concerned with a discussion of the role of science in ethical and religious aspects of contem-porary society, gives a reasonable statement[6] of science as a general ethical factor: "The major crisis of our time is the decline in our conception of man, in respect for truth and justice and other values of Western culture . . . [Science is] concerned in solving this problem, not as a material panacea nor as the only valid method of gaining knowledge, but in so far as it is one version of rational method, and so favors respect for truth and for the

[6] E. F. H. Caldin, *The Power and Limits of Science: a philosophical study* (London, Chapman and Hall, 1949), p. 169.

human person and represents rational standards. By itself it cannot help us; but in association with other forms of knowledge it could play a useful part."

The further achievement of scientific knowledge about human behavior should not mean a progression towards a state in which man is considered only as a "machine," without the distinctive human qualities that we prize. Rather, by gaining understanding of ourselves as a part of the natural world, we should better be able to foster and use our lives. If the nineteenth century mechanism–materialism had been correct, and man's spirit something adjunct to a rigorously determined machine, there might have been reason to expect conflict between the scientific and humanistic study of man. We have seen, however, how much the older mechanistic point of view has been discredited. Hence, we can say that the conception of man as a creature with freedom, and possibility for novel, unpredictable behavior, is not at all contradicted by what we have learned of the natural world. We can rather think that what we learn of human nature, scientifically, can be an instrument to assist us in carrying out the noncognitive living that is also a part of our natural being.

CONCLUDING REMARKS

Our discussion of the nonscientific ways in which we gain awareness of the universe emphasizes how much more nature is than that which we present in our science. At the same time, however, we must not forget that science is the central activity in our extension of our natural knowledge, and that it is a corrective to error based on less rigorous, nonscientific approaches to knowledge. The limits that we have found on its completeness do mean (as should be obvious in any case) that science is not a surrogate for reality, and also, that science alone cannot be a complete philosophy. There must, so to speak, be a set of noncognitive beliefs in which our science is embedded. But even though it has these limitations, and in part perhaps because it has them, science is a remarkably effective procedure for man's learning of his world. Science has given us so much of what even philosophers seek, has so liberated mankind, and offers so much promise, that no dimming of its honor should follow from an awareness of its limits.

And indeed, for a person who wishes realistically to understand the universe, a philosophy of naturalism is probably the best to follow: by such a philosophy I mean one that does not postulate a reality comparable to that of the natural world for any process or being not a part of nature. There is, however, a danger in a naturalistic philosophy, in that naturalism tends to encourage a tendency to define nature only as science sees it. But because of the limitations that do exist on the completeness of science, it is desirable to be aware of subtle, perhaps inchoate aspects of experience which are not explicitly described by science. We have pointed out that everyday living actually provides a vast amount of such experience; the advance of science itself is, of course, dependent on awareness of nature beyond that defined by science, and we have spoken of the role of noncognitive awareness for artist, theologian, and philosopher. We want to further science for its truth and help, for science can discern the structure of the natural world, even in certain respects, we have seen, to their end and limit. Also, though, it is a sign of wisdom to realize that science alone now brings us only an incomplete measure of guidance and understanding. We require an effort toward balance, short of our gaining a happy day when the voices of science and of life everywhere are one.

Index